Fundamentals of the Finite Element Method for Heat and Fluid Flow

Fundamentals of the Finite Element Method for Heat and Fluid Flow

Roland W. Lewis
University of Wales Swansea, UK

Perumal Nithiarasu
University of Wales Swansea, UK

Kankanhalli N. Seetharamu
Universiti Sains Malaysia, Malaysia

John Wiley & Sons, Ltd

Other Wiley Editorial Offices

John Wiley & Sons Inc., 111 River Street, Hoboken, NJ 07030, USA

Jossey-Bass, 989 Market Street, San Francisco, CA 94103-1741, USA

Wiley-VCH Verlag GmbH, Boschstr. 12, D-69469 Weinheim, Germany

John Wiley & Sons Australia Ltd, 33 Park Road, Milton, Queensland 4064, Australia

John Wiley & Sons (Asia) Pte Ltd, 2 Clementi Loop #02-01, Jin Xing Distripark, Singapore 129809

John Wiley & Sons Canada Ltd, 22 Worcester Road, Etobicoke, Ontario, Canada M9W 1L1

Wiley also publishes its books in a variety of electronic formats. Some content that appears
in print may not be available in electronic books.

Library of Congress Cataloging-in-Publication Data

Lewis, R. W. (Roland Wynne)
    Fundamentals of the finite element method for heat and fluid flow / Roland W. Lewis,
Perumal Nithiarasu, Kankanhalli N. Seetharamu.
        p. cm.
    Includes bibliographical references and index.
    ISBN 0-470-84788-3 (alk. paper)—ISBN 0-470-84789-1 (pbk. : alk. paper)
      1. Finite element method. 2. Heat equation. 3. Heat–Transmission. 4. Fluid dynamics. I.
Nithiarasu, Perumal. II. Seetharamu, K. N. III. Title.

    QC20.7.F56L49 2004
    530.15'5353–dc22

                                                                        2004040767

British Library Cataloguing in Publication Data

A catalogue record for this book is available from the British Library

ISBN 0-470-84788-3 (HB)
      0-470-84789-1 (PB)

Produced from LaTeX files supplied by the author, typeset by Laserwords Private Limited, Chennai, India
Printed and bound in Great Britain by Antony Rowe Ltd, Chippenham, Wiltshire
This book is printed on acid-free paper responsibly manufactured from sustainable forestry
in which at least two trees are planted for each one used for paper production.

To

Celia
Sujatha
and Uma

Contents

Preface   **xiii**

1 Introduction   **1**
   1.1 Importance of Heat Transfer   1
   1.2 Heat Transfer Modes   2
   1.3 The Laws of Heat Transfer   3
   1.4 Formulation of Heat Transfer Problems   5
        1.4.1 Heat transfer from a plate exposed to solar heat flux   5
        1.4.2 Incandescent lamp   7
        1.4.3 Systems with a relative motion and internal heat generation   8
   1.5 Heat Conduction Equation   10
   1.6 Boundary and Initial Conditions   13
   1.7 Solution Methodology   14
   1.8 Summary   15
   1.9 Exercise   15
   Bibliography   17

2 Some Basic Discrete Systems   **18**
   2.1 Introduction   18
   2.2 Steady State Problems   19
        2.2.1 Heat flow in a composite slab   19
        2.2.2 Fluid flow network   22
        2.2.3 Heat transfer in heat sinks (combined conduction–convection) . . .   25
        2.2.4 Analysis of a heat exchanger   27
   2.3 Transient Heat Transfer Problem (Propagation Problem)   29
   2.4 Summary   31
   2.5 Exercise   31
   Bibliography   37

3 The Finite Element Method   **38**
   3.1 Introduction   38
   3.2 Elements and Shape Functions   41
        3.2.1 One-dimensional linear element   42
        3.2.2 One-dimensional quadratic element   45

      3.2.3   Two-dimensional linear triangular elements 48

      3.2.4   Area coordinates 52

      3.2.5   Quadratic triangular elements 54

      3.2.6   Two-dimensional quadrilateral elements 57

      3.2.7   Isoparametric elements 62

      3.2.8   Three-dimensional elements 70

  3.3   Formulation (Element Characteristics) 75

      3.3.1   Ritz method (Heat balance integral method—Goodman's method) . 76

      3.3.2   Rayleigh–Ritz method (Variational method) 78

      3.3.3   The method of weighted residuals 80

      3.3.4   Galerkin finite element method 85

  3.4   Formulation for the Heat Conduction Equation 87

      3.4.1   Variational approach 88

      3.4.2   The Galerkin method 91

  3.5   Requirements for Interpolation Functions 92

  3.6   Summary 98

  3.7   Exercise 98

  Bibliography 100

4 Steady State Heat Conduction in One Dimension   **102**

  4.1   Introduction 102

  4.2   Plane Walls 102

      4.2.1   Homogeneous wall 102

      4.2.2   Composite wall 103

      4.2.3   Finite element discretization 105

      4.2.4   Wall with varying cross-sectional area 107

      4.2.5   Plane wall with a heat source: solution by linear elements 108

      4.2.6   Plane wall with a heat source: solution by quadratic elements 112

      4.2.7   Plane wall with a heat source: solution by modified quadratic
              equations (static condensation) 114

  4.3   Radial Heat Flow in a Cylinder 115

      4.3.1   Cylinder with heat source 117

  4.4   Conduction–Convection Systems 120

  4.5   Summary 123

  4.6   Exercise 123

  Bibliography 125

5 Steady State Heat Conduction in Multi-dimensions   **126**

  5.1   Introduction 126

  5.2   Two-dimensional Plane Problems 127

      5.2.1   Triangular elements 127

  5.3   Rectangular Elements 136

  5.4   Plate with Variable Thickness 139

5.5   Three-dimensional Problems 141
5.6   Axisymmetric Problems 142
      5.6.1   Galerkin's method for linear triangular axisymmetric elements . . . 145
5.7   Summary 147
5.8   Exercise 147
Bibliography 149

6 Transient Heat Conduction Analysis   **150**
6.1   Introduction 150
6.2   Lumped Heat Capacity System 150
6.3   Numerical Solution 152
      6.3.1   Transient governing equations and boundary and initial conditions . 152
      6.3.2   The Galerkin method 153
6.4   One-dimensional Transient State Problem 154
      6.4.1   Time discretization using the Finite Difference Method (FDM) . . . 156
      6.4.2   Time discretization using the Finite Element Method (FEM) 160
6.5   Stability 161
6.6   Multi-dimensional Transient Heat Conduction 162
6.7   Phase Change Problems—Solidification and Melting 164
      6.7.1   The governing equations 164
      6.7.2   Enthalpy formulation 165
6.8   Inverse Heat Conduction Problems 168
      6.8.1   One-dimensional heat conduction 168
6.9   Summary 170
6.10 Exercise 170
Bibliography 172

7 Convection Heat Transfer   **173**
7.1   Introduction 173
      7.1.1   Types of fluid-motion-assisted heat transport 174
7.2   Navier–Stokes Equations 175
      7.2.1   Conservation of mass or continuity equation 175
      7.2.2   Conservation of momentum 177
      7.2.3   Energy equation 181
7.3   Non-dimensional Form of the Governing Equations 183
      7.3.1   Forced convection 184
      7.3.2   Natural convection (Buoyancy-driven convection) 185
      7.3.3   Mixed convection 187
7.4   The Transient Convection–diffusion Problem 187
      7.4.1   Finite element solution to convection–diffusion equation 188
      7.4.2   Extension to multi-dimensions 195
7.5   Stability Conditions 200
7.6   Characteristic-based Split (CBS) Scheme 201
      7.6.1   Spatial discretization 206

7.6.2   Time-step calculation 210
7.6.3   Boundary and initial conditions 211
7.6.4   Steady and transient solution methods 212
7.7   Artificial Compressibility Scheme 213
7.8   Nusselt Number, Drag and Stream Function 213
7.8.1   Nusselt number 214
7.8.2   Drag calculation 215
7.8.3   Stream function 216
7.9   Mesh Convergence 217
7.10   Laminar Isothermal Flow 218
7.10.1   Geometry, boundary and initial conditions 218
7.10.2   Solution 219
7.11   Laminar Non-isothermal Flow 220
7.11.1   Forced convection heat transfer 220
7.11.2   Buoyancy-driven convection heat transfer 223
7.11.3   Mixed convection heat transfer 227
7.12   Introduction to Turbulent Flow 230
7.12.1   Solution procedure and result 233
7.13   Extension to Axisymmetric Problems 234
7.14   Summary 235
7.15   Exercise 236
Bibliography 236

8   Convection in Porous Media   240
8.1   Introduction 240
8.2   Generalized Porous Medium Flow Approach 243
8.2.1   Non-dimensional scales 245
8.2.2   Limiting cases 247
8.3   Discretization Procedure 247
8.3.1   Temporal discretization 247
8.3.2   Spatial discretization 249
8.3.3   Semi- and quasi-implicit forms 252
8.4   Non-isothermal Flows 254
8.5   Forced Convection 255
8.6   Natural Convection 256
8.6.1   Constant porosity medium 258
8.7   Summary 262
8.8   Exercise 262
Bibliography 262

9   Some Examples of Fluid Flow and Heat Transfer Problems   265
9.1   Introduction 265
9.2   Isothermal Flow Problems 265
9.2.1   Steady state problems 265
9.2.2   Transient flow 277

    9.3   Non-isothermal Benchmark Flow Problem 280
          9.3.1 Backward-facing step 281
    9.4   Thermal Conduction in an Electronic Package 283
    9.5   Forced Convection Heat Transfer From Heat Sources 286
    9.6   Summary 294
    9.7   Exercise 294
    Bibliography 296

10 Implementation of Computer Code   **299**
    10.1 Introduction 299
    10.2 Preprocessing 300
          10.2.1 Mesh generation 300
          10.2.2 Linear triangular element data 302
          10.2.3 Element size calculation 303
          10.2.4 Shape functions and their derivatives 304
          10.2.5 Boundary normal calculation 305
          10.2.6 Mass matrix and mass lumping 306
          10.2.7 Implicit pressure or heat conduction matrix 307
    10.3 Main Unit 309
          10.3.1 Time-step calculation 310
          10.3.2 Element loop and assembly 313
          10.3.3 Updating solution 314
          10.3.4 Boundary conditions 315
          10.3.5 Monitoring steady state 316
    10.4 Postprocessing 317
          10.4.1 Interpolation of data 317
    10.5 Summary 317
    Bibliography 317

A Green's Lemma   **319**

B Integration Formulae   **321**
    B.1   Linear Triangles 321
    B.2   Linear Tetrahedron 321

C Finite Element Assembly Procedure   **323**

D Simplified Form of the Navier–Stokes Equations   **326**

Index   **329**

Preface

In this text, we provide the readers with the fundamentals of the finite element method for heat and fluid flow problems. Most of the other available texts concentrate either on conduction heat transfer or the fluid flow aspects of heat transfer. We have combined the two to provide a comprehensive text for heat transfer engineers and scientists who would like to pursue a finite element–based heat transfer analysis. This text is suitable for senior undergraduate students, postgraduate students, engineers and scientists.

The first three chapters of the book deal with the essential fundamentals of both the heat conduction and the finite element method. The first chapter deals with the fundamentals of energy balance and the standard derivation of the relevant equations for a heat conduction analysis. Chapter 2 deals with basic discrete systems, which are the fundamentals for the finite element method. The discrete system analysis is supported with a variety of simple heat transfer and fluid flow problems. The third chapter gives a complete account of the finite element method and its relevant history. Several examples and exercises included in Chapter 3 give the reader a full account of the theory and practice associated with the finite element method.

The application of the finite element method to heat conduction problems are discussed in detail in Chapters 4, 5 and 6. The conduction analysis starts with a simple one-dimensional steady state heat conduction in Chapter 4 and is extended to multi-dimensions in Chapter 5. Chapter 6 gives the transient solution procedures for heat conduction problems.

Chapters 7 and 8 deal with heat transfer by convection. In Chapter 7, heat transfer, aided by the movement of a single-phase fluid, is discussed in detail. All the relevant differential equations are derived from first principles. All the three types of convection modes, forced, mixed and natural convection, are discussed in detail. Examples and comparisons are provided to support the accuracy and flexibility of the finite element method. In Chapter 8, convection heat transfer is extended to flow in porous media. Some examples and comparisons provide the readers an opportunity to access the accuracy of the methods employed.

In Chapter 9, we have provided the readers with several examples, both benchmark and application problems of heat transfer and fluid flow. The systematic approach of problem solving is discussed in detail. Finally, Chapter 10 briefly introduces the topic of computer implementation. The readers will be able to download the two-dimensional source codes from the authors' web sites. They will also be able to analyse both two-dimensional heat conduction and heat convection studies on unstructured meshes using the downloaded programs.

Many people helped either directly or indirectly during the preparation of this text. In particular, the authors wish to thank Professors N.P. Weatherill, K. Morgan and O. Hassan of the University of Wales Swansea for allowing us to use the 3-D mesh generator in some of the examples provided in this book. Dr Nithiarasu also acknowledges Dr N. Massarotti of the University of Cassino, Italy, and Dr J.S. Mathur of the National Aeronautical Laboratories, India, for their help in producing some of the 3-D results presented in this text. Professor Seetharamu acknowledges Professor Ahmed Yusoff Hassan, Associate Professor Zainal Alimuddin and Dr Zaidi Md Ripin of the School of Mechanical Engineering, Universiti Sains Malaysia for their moral support.

R.W. Lewis
P. Nithiarasu
K.N. Seetharamu

1

Introduction

1.1 Importance of Heat Transfer

The subject of heat transfer is of fundamental importance in many branches of engineering. A *mechanical engineer* may be interested in knowing the mechanisms of heat transfer involved in the operation of equipment, for example boilers, condensers, air pre-heaters, economizers, and so on, in a thermal power plant in order to improve their performance. Nuclear power plants require precise information on heat transfer, as safe operation is an important factor in their design. Refrigeration and air-conditioning systems also involve heat-exchanging devices, which need careful design. *Electrical engineers* are keen to avoid material damage due to hot spots, developed by improper heat transfer design, in electric motors, generators and transformers. An *electronic engineer* is interested in knowing the efficient methods of heat dissipation from chips and semiconductor devices so that they can operate within safe operating temperatures. A *computer hardware engineer* is interested in knowing the cooling requirements of circuit boards, as the miniaturization of computing devices is advancing at a rapid rate. *Chemical engineers* are interested in heat transfer processes in various chemical reactions. A *metallurgical engineer* would be interested in knowing the rate of heat transfer required for a particular heat treatment process, for example, the rate of cooling in a casting process has a profound influence on the quality of the final product. *Aeronautical engineers* are interested in knowing the heat transfer rate in rocket nozzles and in heat shields used in re-entry vehicles. An *agricultural engineer* would be interested in the drying of food grains, food processing and preservation. A *civil engineer* would need to be aware of the thermal stresses developed in quick-setting concrete, the effect of heat and mass transfer on building and building materials and also the effect of heat on nuclear containment, and so on. An *environmental engineer* is concerned with the effect of heat on the dispersion of pollutants in air, diffusion of pollutants in soils, thermal pollution in lakes and seas and their impact on life. The global, thermal changes and associated problems caused by *El Nino* are very well known phenomena, in which energy transfer in the form of heat exists.

Fundamentals of the Finite Element Method for Heat and Fluid Flow   R. W. Lewis, P. Nithiarasu and K. N. Seetharamu
© 2004 John Wiley & Sons, Ltd   ISBNs: 0-470-84788-3 (HB); 0-470-84789-1 (PB)

The previously-mentioned examples are only a sample of heat transfer applications to name but a few. The solar system and the associated energy transfer are the principal factors for existence of life on earth. It is not untrue to say that it is extremely difficult, often impossible, to avoid some form of heat transfer in any process on earth.

The study of heat transfer provides economical and efficient solutions for critical problems encountered in many engineering items of equipment. For example, we can consider the development of heat pipes that can transport heat at a much greater rate than copper or silver rods of the same dimensions, even at almost isothermal conditions. The development of present day gas turbine blades, in which the gas temperature exceeds the melting point of the material of the blade, is possible by providing efficient cooling systems and is another example of the success of heat transfer design methods. The design of computer chips, which encounter heat flux of the order occurring in re-entry vehicles, especially when the surface temperature of the chips is limited to less than 100 °C, is again a success story for heat transfer analysis.

Although there are many successful heat transfer designs, further developments are still necessary in order to increase the life span and efficiency of the many devices discussed previously, which can lead to many more new inventions. Also, if we are to protect our environment, it is essential to understand the many heat transfer processes involved and, if necessary, to take appropriate action.

1.2   Heat Transfer Modes

Heat transfer is that section of engineering science that studies the energy transport between material bodies due to a temperature difference (Bejan 1993; Holman 1989; Incropera and Dewitt 1990; Sukhatme 1992). The three modes of heat transfer are

1. Conduction

2. Convection

3. Radiation.

The conduction mode of heat transport occurs either because of an exchange of energy from one molecule to another, without the actual motion of the molecules, or because of the motion of the free electrons if they are present. Therefore, this form of heat transport depends heavily on the properties of the medium and takes place in solids, liquids and gases if a difference in temperature exists.

Molecules present in liquids and gases have freedom of motion, and by moving from a hot to a cold region, they carry energy with them. The transfer of heat from one region to another, due to such macroscopic motion in a liquid or gas, added to the energy transfer by conduction within the fluid, is called *heat transfer* by convection. Convection may be free, forced or mixed. When fluid motion occurs because of a density variation caused by temperature differences, the situation is said to be a free, or natural, convection. When the fluid motion is caused by an external force, such as pumping or blowing, the state is defined as being one of forced convection. A mixed convection state is one in which both natural and forced convections are present. Convection heat transfer also occurs in boiling and condensation processes.

All bodies emit thermal radiation at all temperatures. This is the only mode that does not require a material medium for heat transfer to occur. The nature of thermal radiation is such that a propagation of energy, carried by *electromagnetic waves*, is emitted from the surface of the body. When these electromagnetic waves strike other body surfaces, a part is reflected, a part is transmitted and the remaining part is absorbed.

All modes of heat transfer are generally present in varying degrees in a real physical problem. The important aspects in solving heat transfer problems are identifying the significant modes and deciding whether the heat transferred by other modes can be neglected.

1.3 The Laws of Heat Transfer

It is important to quantify the amount of energy being transferred per unit time and for that we require the use of rate equations.

For heat conduction, the rate equation is known as *Fourier's law*, which is expressed for one dimension as

$$q_x = -k \frac{dT}{dx} \tag{1.1}$$

where q_x is the heat flux in the x direction (W/m^2); k is the thermal conductivity (W/mK, a property of material, see Table 1.1)and dT/dx is the temperature gradient (K/m).

For convective heat transfer, the rate equation is given by *Newton's law of cooling* as

$$q = h(T_w - T_a) \tag{1.2}$$

where q is the convective heat flux; (W/m^2); $(T_w - T_a)$ is the temperature difference between the wall and the fluid and h is the convection heat transfer coefficient, (W/m^{2}K) (film coefficient, see Table 1.2).

The convection heat transfer coefficient frequently appears as a boundary condition in the solution of heat conduction through solids. We assume h to be known in many such problems. In the analysis of thermal systems, one can again assume an appropriate h if not available (e.g., heat exchangers, combustion chambers, etc.). However, if required, h can be determined via suitable experiments, although this is a difficult option.

The maximum flux that can be emitted by radiation from a black surface is given by the *Stefan–Boltzmann Law*, that is,

$$q = \sigma T_w^4 \tag{1.3}$$

where q is the radiative heat flux, (W/m^2); σ is the Stefan–Boltzmann constant (5.669 × 10^{-8}), in W/m^{2}K^4 and T_w is the surface temperature, (K).

The heat flux emitted by a real surface is less than that of a black surface and is given by

$$q = \epsilon \sigma T_w^4 \tag{1.4}$$

Table 1.1   Typical values of thermal conductivity of some materials
in W/mK at 20 °C

Material	Thermal conductivity
Metals:	
Pure silver	410
Pure copper	385
Pure aluminium	200
Pure iron	73
Alloys:	
Stainless steel (18% Cr, 8% Ni)	16
Aluminium alloy (4.5% Cr)	168
Non metals:	
Plastics	0.6
Wood	0.2
Liquid:	
Water	0.6
Gases:	
Dry air	0.025 (at atmospheric pressure)

Table 1.2   Typical values of heat
transfer coefficient in W/m^{2}K

Gases (stagnant)	15
Gases (flowing)	15–250
Liquids (stagnant)	100
Liquids (flowing)	100–2000
Boiling liquids	2000–35,000
Condensing vapours	2000–25,000

where ϵ is the radiative property of the surface and is referred to as the *emissivity*. The net radiant energy exchange between any two surfaces 1 and 2 is given by

$$Q = F_\epsilon F_G \sigma A_1 (T_1^4 - T_2^4) \qquad (1.5)$$

where F_ϵ is a factor that takes into account the nature of the two radiating surfaces; F_G is a factor that takes into account the geometric orientation of the two radiating surfaces and A_1 is the area of surface 1.

When a heat transfer surface, at temperature T_1, is completely enclosed by a much larger surface at temperature T_2, the net radiant exchange can be calculated by

$$Q = qA_1 = \epsilon_1 \sigma A_1 (T_1^4 - T_2^4) \qquad (1.6)$$

With respect to the laws of thermodynamics, only the first law is of interest in heat transfer problems. The increase of energy in a system is equal to the difference between the energy transfer by heat to the system and the energy transfer by work done on the surroundings by the system, that is,

$$dE = dQ - dW \qquad (1.7)$$

where Q is the total heat entering the system and W is the work done on the surroundings. Since we are interested in the rate of energy transfer in heat transfer processes, we can restate the first law of thermodynamics as

'The rate of increase of the energy of the system is equal to the difference between the rate at which energy enters the system and the rate at which the system does work on the surroundings', that is,

$$\frac{dE}{dt} = \frac{dQ}{dt} - \frac{dW}{dt} \qquad (1.8)$$

where t is the time.

1.4 Formulation of Heat Transfer Problems

In analysing a thermal system, the engineer should be able to identify the relevant heat transfer processes and only then can the system behaviour be properly quantified. In this section, some typical heat transfer problems are formulated by identifying appropriate heat transfer mechanisms.

1.4.1 Heat transfer from a plate exposed to solar heat flux

Consider a plate of size $L \times B \times d$ exposed to a solar flux of intensity q_s, as shown in Figure 1.1. In many solar applications such as a solar water heater, solar cooker and so on, the temperature of the plate is a function of time. The plate loses heat by convection and radiation to the ambient air, which is at a temperature T_a. Some heat flows through the plate and is convected to the bottom side. We shall apply the law of conservation of energy to derive an equation, the solution of which gives the temperature distribution of the plate with respect to time.

Heat entering the top surface of the plate:

$$q_s A_T \qquad (1.9)$$

Heat loss from the plate to surroundings:

Top surface:

$$h A_T (T - T_a) + \epsilon \sigma A_T (T^4 - T_a^4) \qquad (1.10)$$

Side surface:

$$h A_S (T - T_a) + \epsilon \sigma A_S (T^4 - T_a^4) \qquad (1.11)$$

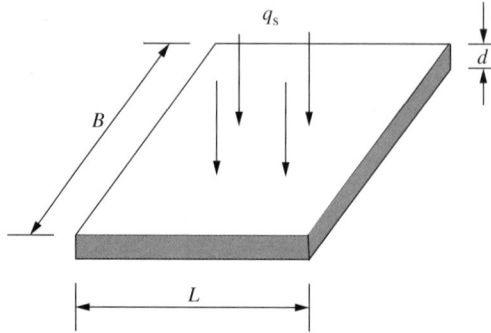

Figure 1.1   Heat transfer from a plate subjected to solar heat flux

Bottom surface:

$$hA_B(T - T_a) + \epsilon\sigma A_B(T^4 - T_a^4) \tag{1.12}$$

where the subscripts T, S and B are respectively the top, side and bottom surfaces. The subject of radiation exchange between a gas and a solid surface is not simple. Readers are referred to other appropriate texts for further details (Holman 1989; Siegel and Howell 1992). Under steady state conditions, the heat received by the plate is lost to the surroundings, thus

$$q_s A_T = hA_T(T - T_a) + \epsilon\sigma A_T(T^4 - T_a^4) + hA_S(T - T_a)$$
$$+ \epsilon\sigma A_S(T^4 - T_a^4) + hA_B(T - T_a) + \epsilon\sigma A_B(T^4 - T_a^4) \tag{1.13}$$

This is a nonlinear algebraic equation (because of the presence of the T^4 term). The solution of this equation gives the steady state temperature of the plate. If we want to calculate the temperature of the plate as a function of time, t, we have to consider the rate of rise in the internal energy of the plate, which is

$$\text{(Volume) } \rho c_p \frac{dT}{dt} = (LBd)\rho c_p \frac{dT}{dt} \tag{1.14}$$

where ρ is the density and c_p is the specific heat of the plate. Thus, at any instant of time, the difference between the heat received and lost by the plate will be equal to the heat stored (Equation 1.14). Thus,

$$(LBd)\rho c_p \frac{dT}{dt} = q_s A_T - [hA_T(T - T_a) + \epsilon\sigma A_T(T^4 - T_a^4) + hA_S(T - T_a)$$
$$+ \epsilon\sigma A_S(T^4 - T_a^4) + hA_B(T - T_a) + \epsilon\sigma A_B(T^4 - T_a^4)] \tag{1.15}$$

This is a first-order nonlinear differential equation, which requires an initial condition, namely,

$$t = 0, \quad T = T_a \tag{1.16}$$

The solution is determined iteratively because of the nonlinearity of the problem. Equation 1.15 can be simplified by substituting relations for the surface areas. It should be noted, however, that this is a general equation that can be used for similar systems.

It is important to note that the spatial variation of temperature within the plate is neglected here. However, this variation can be included via Fourier's law of heat conduction, that is, Equation 1.1. Such a variation is necessary if the plate is not thin enough to reach equilibrium instantly.

1.4.2   Incandescent lamp

Figure 1.2 shows an idealized incandescent lamp. The filament is heated to a temperature of T_f by an electric current. Heat is convected to the surrounding gas and is radiated to the wall, which also receives heat from the gas by convection. The wall in turn convects and radiates heat to the ambient at T_a. A formulation of equations, based on energy balance, is necessary in order to determine the temperature of the gas and the wall with respect to time.

Gas:

Rise in internal energy of gas:

$$m_g c_{pg} \frac{dT_g}{dt} \tag{1.17}$$

Convection from filament to gas:

$$h_f A_f (T_f - T_g) \tag{1.18}$$

Convection from gas to wall:

$$h_g A_g (T_g - T_w) \tag{1.19}$$

Radiation from filament to gas:

$$\epsilon_f A_f \sigma (T_f^4 - T_g^4) \tag{1.20}$$

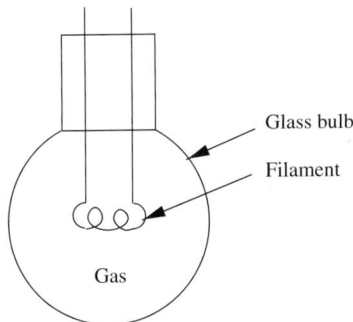

Figure 1.2   Energy balance in an incandescent light source

Now, the energy balance for gas gives

$$m_g c_{pg} \frac{dT_g}{dt} = h_f A_g (T_f - T_g) - h_g A_g (T_g - T_w) + \epsilon_f A_f \sigma (T_f^4 - T_g^4) \qquad (1.21)$$

Wall:

Rise in internal energy of wall:

$$m_w c_{pw} \frac{dT_w}{dt} \qquad (1.22)$$

Radiation from filament to wall:

$$\epsilon_f \sigma A_f (T_f^4 - T_w^4) \qquad (1.23)$$

Convection from wall to ambient:

$$h_w A_w (T_w - T_a) \qquad (1.24)$$

Radiation from wall to ambient:

$$\epsilon_w \sigma A_w (T_w^4 - T_a^4) \qquad (1.25)$$

Energy balance for wall gives

$$m_w c_{pw} \frac{dT_w}{dt} = h_g A_g (T_g - T_w) + \epsilon_f \sigma A_f (T_f^4 - T_w^4) - h_w A_w (T_w - T_a) - \epsilon_w \sigma A_w (T_w^4 - T_a^4)$$
$$(1.26)$$

where m_g is the mass of the gas in the bulb; c_{pg}, the specific heat of the gas; m_w, the mass of the wall of the bulb; c_{pw}, the specific heat of the wall; h_f, the heat transfer coefficient between the filament and the gas; h_g, the heat transfer coefficient between the gas and wall; h_w, the heat transfer coefficient between the wall and ambient and ϵ is the emissivity. The subscripts f, w, g and a respectively indicate filament, wall, gas and ambient.

Equations 1.21 and 1.26 are first-order nonlinear differential equations. The initial conditions required are as follows:

At $t = 0$,

$$T_g = T_a \text{ and } T_w = T_a \qquad (1.27)$$

The simultaneous solution of Equations 1.21 and 1.26, along with the above initial condition results in the temperatures of the gas and wall as a function of time.

1.4.3   Systems with a relative motion and internal heat generation

The extrusion of plastics, drawing of wires and artificial fibres (optical fibre), suspended electrical conductors of various shapes, continuous casting etc. can be treated alike.

In order to derive an energy balance for such a system, we consider a small differential control volume of length, Δx, as shown in Figure 1.3. In this problem, the heat lost to

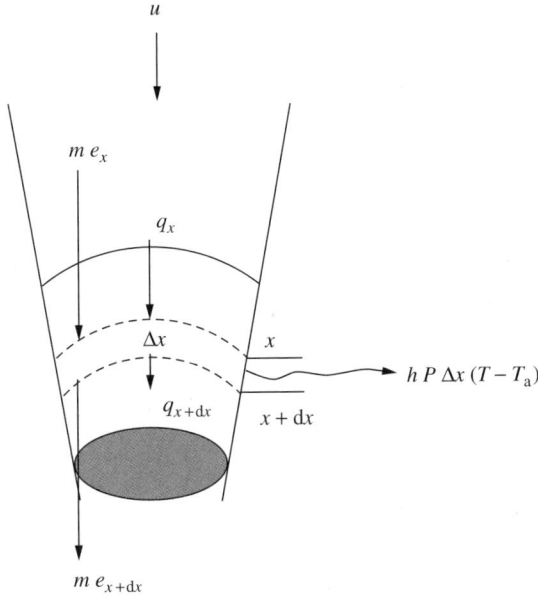

Figure 1.3   Conservation of energy in a moving body

the environment by radiation is assumed to be negligibly small. The energy is conducted, convected and transported with the material in motion. With reference to Figure 1.3, we can write the following equations of conservation of energy, that is,

$$q_x + me_x + GA\Delta x = q_{x+dx} + me_{x+dx} + hP\Delta x(T - T_a) \tag{1.28}$$

where m is the mass flow, ρAu which is assumed to be constant; ρ, the density of the material; A, the cross-sectional area; P, the perimeter of the control volume; G, the heat generation per unit volume and u, the velocity at which the material is moving. Using a Taylor series expansion, we obtain

$$m(e_x - e_{x+dx}) = -m\frac{de_x}{dx}\Delta x = -mc_p\frac{dT}{dx}\Delta x \tag{1.29}$$

Note that $de_x = c_p dT$ at constant pressure. Similarly, using Fourier's law (Equation 1.1),

$$q_x - q_{x+dx} = \frac{d}{dx}\left[kA\frac{dT}{dx}\right] \tag{1.30}$$

Substituting Equations 1.29 and 1.30 into Equation 1.28, we obtain the following conservation equation:

$$\frac{d}{dx}\left[kA\frac{dT}{dx}\right] - hP(T - T_a) - \rho c_p Au\frac{dT}{dx} + GA = 0 \tag{1.31}$$

In the above equation, the first term is derived from the heat diffusion (conduction) within the material, the second term is due to convection from the material surface to ambient, the third term represents the heat transport due to the motion of the material and finally the last term is added to account for heat generation within the body.

1.5 Heat Conduction Equation

The determination of temperature distribution in a medium (solid, liquid, gas or combination of phases) is the main objective of a conduction analysis, that is, to know the temperature in the medium as a function of space at steady state and as a function of time during the transient state. Once this temperature distribution is known, the heat flux at any point within the medium, or on its surface, may be computed from Fourier's law, Equation 1.1. A knowledge of the temperature distribution within a solid can be used to determine the structural integrity via a determination of the thermal stresses and distortion. The optimization of the thickness of an insulating material and the compatibility of any special coatings or adhesives used on the material can be studied by knowing the temperature distribution and the appropriate heat transfer characteristics.

We shall now derive the conduction equation in Cartesian coordinates by applying the energy conservation law to a differential control volume as shown in Figure 1.4. The solution of the resulting differential equation, with prescribed boundary conditions, gives the temperature distribution in the medium.

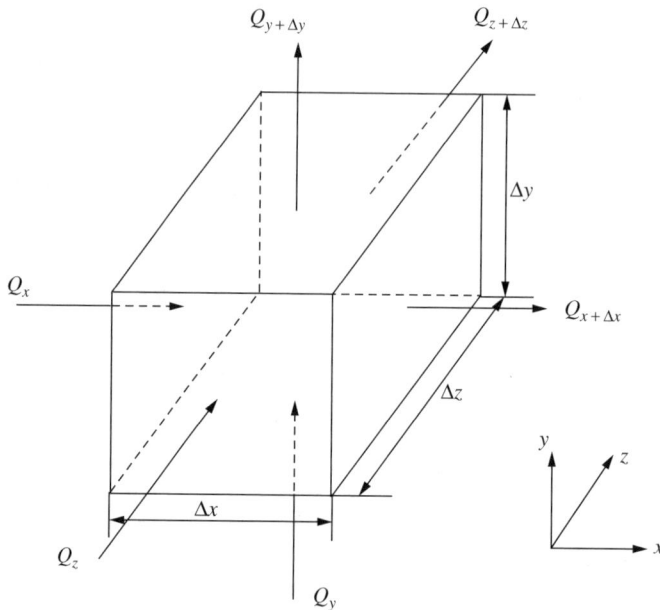

Figure 1.4   A differential control volume for heat conduction analysis

A Taylor series expansion results in

$$Q_{x+dx} = Q_x + \frac{\partial Q_x}{\partial x}\Delta x$$

$$Q_{y+dy} = Q_y + \frac{\partial Q_y}{\partial y}\Delta y$$

$$Q_{z+dz} = Q_z + \frac{\partial Q_z}{\partial z}\Delta z \qquad (1.32)$$

Note that the second- and higher-order terms are neglected in the above equation. The heat generated in the control volume is $G\Delta x\Delta y\Delta z$ and the rate of change in energy storage is given as

$$\rho\Delta x\Delta y\Delta z c_{\mathrm{p}}\frac{\partial T}{\partial t} \qquad (1.33)$$

Now, with reference to Figure 1.4, we can write the energy balance as

```
inlet energy + energy generated = energy stored + exit energy
```

that is,

$$G\Delta x\Delta y\Delta z + Q_x + Q_y + Q_z = \rho\Delta x\Delta y\Delta z\frac{\partial T}{\partial t} + Q_{x+dx} + Q_{y+dy} + Q_{z+dz} \qquad (1.34)$$

Substituting Equation 1.32 into the above equation and rearranging results in

$$-\frac{\partial Q_x}{\partial x}\Delta x - \frac{\partial Q_y}{\partial y}\Delta y - \frac{\partial Q_z}{\partial z}\Delta z + G\Delta x\Delta y\Delta z = \rho c_{\mathrm{p}}\Delta x\Delta y\Delta z\frac{\partial T}{\partial t} \qquad (1.35)$$

The total heat transfer Q in each direction can be expressed as

$$Q_x = \Delta y\Delta z q_x = -k_x\Delta y\Delta z\frac{\partial T}{\partial x}$$

$$Q_y = \Delta x\Delta z q_y = -k_y\Delta x\Delta z\frac{\partial T}{\partial y}$$

$$Q_z = \Delta x\Delta y q_z = -k_z\Delta x\Delta y\frac{\partial T}{\partial z} \qquad (1.36)$$

Substituting Equation 1.36 into Equation 1.35 and dividing by the volume, $\Delta x\Delta y\Delta z$, we get

$$\frac{\partial}{\partial x}\left[k_x\frac{\partial T}{\partial x}\right] + \frac{\partial}{\partial y}\left[k_y\frac{\partial T}{\partial y}\right] + \frac{\partial}{\partial z}\left[k_z\frac{\partial T}{\partial y}\right] + G = \rho c_{\mathrm{p}}\frac{\partial T}{\partial t} \qquad (1.37)$$

Equation 1.37 is the transient heat conduction equation for a stationary system expressed in Cartesian coordinates. The thermal conductivity, k, in the above equation is a vector. In its most general form, the thermal conductivity can be expressed as a tensor, that is,

$$\mathbf{k} = \begin{bmatrix} k_{xx} & k_{xy} & k_{xz} \\ k_{yx} & k_{yy} & k_{yz} \\ k_{zx} & k_{zy} & k_{zz} \end{bmatrix} \qquad (1.38)$$

The preceding equations, that is, 1.37 and 1.38 are valid for solving heat conduction problems in anisotropic materials with a directional variation in the thermal conductivities. In many situations, however, the thermal conductivity can be taken as a non-directional property, that is, isotropic. In such materials, the heat conduction equation is written as (constant thermal conductivity)

$$\frac{\partial^2 T}{\partial x^2} + \frac{\partial^2 T}{\partial y^2} + \frac{\partial^2 T}{\partial z^2} + \frac{G}{k} = \frac{1}{\alpha} \frac{\partial T}{\partial t} \tag{1.39}$$

where $\alpha = k/\rho c_p$ is the *thermal diffusivity*, which is an important parameter in transient heat conduction analysis.

If the analysis is restricted only to steady state heat conduction with no heat generation, the equation is reduced to

$$\frac{\partial^2 T}{\partial x^2} + \frac{\partial^2 T}{\partial y^2} + \frac{\partial^2 T}{\partial z^2} = 0 \tag{1.40}$$

For a one-dimensional case, the steady state heat conduction equation is further reduced to

$$\frac{d}{dx} \left(k \frac{dT}{dx} \right) = 0 \tag{1.41}$$

The heat conduction equation for a cylindrical coordinate system is given by

$$\frac{1}{r} \frac{\partial}{\partial r} \left[k_r r \frac{\partial T}{\partial r} \right] + \frac{1}{r^2} \frac{\partial}{\partial \phi} \left[k_\phi \frac{\partial T}{\partial \phi} \right] + \frac{\partial}{\partial z} \left[k_z \frac{\partial T}{\partial z} \right] + G = \rho c_p \frac{\partial T}{\partial t} \tag{1.42}$$

where the heat fluxes can be expressed as

$$q_r = -k_r \frac{\partial T}{\partial r}$$

$$q_\phi = -\frac{k_\phi}{r} \frac{\partial T}{\partial \phi}$$

$$q_z = -k_z \frac{\partial T}{\partial z} \tag{1.43}$$

The heat conduction equation for a spherical coordinate system is given by

$$\frac{1}{r^2} \frac{\partial}{\partial r} \left[k_r r^2 \frac{\partial T}{\partial r} \right] + \frac{1}{r^2 \sin^2 \theta} \frac{\partial}{\partial \phi} \left[k_\phi \frac{\partial T}{\partial \phi} \right] + \frac{1}{r^2 \sin \theta} \frac{\partial}{\partial \theta} \left[k_\theta \sin \theta \frac{\partial T}{\partial \theta} \right] + G = \rho c_p \frac{\partial T}{\partial t} \tag{1.44}$$

where the heat fluxes can be expressed as

$$q_r = -k_r \frac{\partial T}{\partial r}$$

$$q_\phi = -\frac{k_\phi}{r \sin \theta} \frac{\partial T}{\partial \phi}$$

$$q_\theta = -\frac{k_\theta}{r} \frac{\partial T}{\partial \theta} \tag{1.45}$$

It should be noted that for both cylindrical and spherical coordinate systems, Equations 1.42 and 1.44 can be derived in a similar fashion as for Cartesian coordinates by considering the appropriate differential control volumes.

1.6   Boundary and Initial Conditions

The heat conduction equations, discussed in Section 1.5, will be complete for any problem only if the appropriate boundary and initial conditions are stated. With the necessary boundary and initial conditions, a solution to the heat conduction equations is possible. The boundary conditions for the conduction equation can be of two types or a combination of these—the *Dirichlet* condition, in which the temperature on the boundaries is known and/or the *Neumann* condition, in which the heat flux is imposed (see Figure 1.5):

Dirichlet condition

$$T = T_0 \text{ on } \Gamma_T \tag{1.46}$$

Neumann condition

$$q = -k\frac{\partial T}{\partial n} = C \text{ on } \Gamma_{qf} \tag{1.47}$$

In Equations 1.46 and 1.47, T_0 is the prescribed temperature; Γ the boundary surface; n is the outward direction normal to the surface and C is the constant flux given. The insulated, or adiabatic, condition can be obtained by substituting $C = 0$. The convective heat transfer boundary condition also falls into the *Neumann* category and can be expressed as

$$-k\frac{\partial T}{\partial n} = h(T_w - T_a) \text{ on } \Gamma_{qc} \tag{1.48}$$

It should be observed that the heat conduction equation has second-order terms and hence requires two boundary conditions. Since time appears as a first-order term, only one initial value (i.e., at some instant of time all temperatures must be known) needs to be specified for the entire body, that is,

$$T = T_0 \text{ all over the domain } \Omega \text{ at } t = t_0 \tag{1.49}$$

where t_0 is a reference time.

The constant, or variable temperature, conditions are generally easy to implement as temperature is a scalar. However, the implementation of surface fluxes is not as straight-

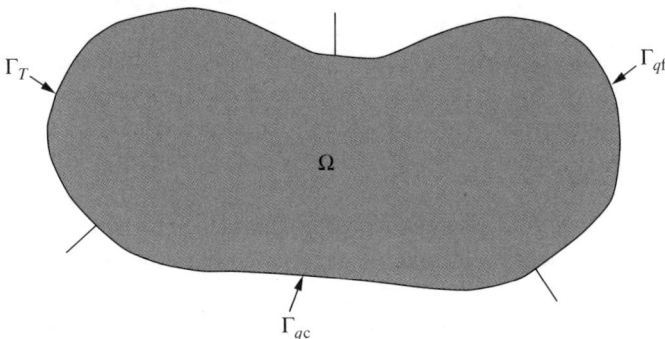

Figure 1.5   Boundary conditions

forward. Equation 1.47 can be rewritten with the direction cosines of the outward normals as

$$k_x \frac{\partial T}{\partial x} \tilde{l} + k_y \frac{\partial T}{\partial y} \tilde{m} + k_z \frac{\partial T}{\partial z} \tilde{n} = C \text{ on } \Gamma_{qf} \tag{1.50}$$

Similarly, Equation 1.48 can be rewritten as

$$k_x \frac{\partial T}{\partial x} \tilde{l} + k_y \frac{\partial T}{\partial y} \tilde{m} + k_z \frac{\partial T}{\partial z} \tilde{n} = h(T - T_a) \text{ on } \Gamma_{qc} \tag{1.51}$$

where $\tilde{l}$, $\tilde{m}$ and $\tilde{n}$ are the direction cosines of the appropriate outward surface normals.

In many industrial applications, for example, wire drawing, crystal growth, continuous casting, and so on, the material will have a motion in space, and this motion may be restricted to one direction, as in the example (Section 1.4.3) cited previously. The general energy equation for heat conduction, taking into account the spatial motion of the body is given by

$$\frac{\partial}{\partial x}\left(k_x \frac{\partial T}{\partial x} \right) + \frac{\partial}{\partial y}\left(k_y \frac{\partial T}{\partial y} \right) + \frac{\partial}{\partial z}\left(k_z \frac{\partial T}{\partial z} \right) + G = \rho c_p \left(\frac{\partial T}{\partial t} + u\frac{\partial T}{\partial x} + v\frac{\partial T}{\partial y} + w\frac{\partial T}{\partial z} \right)$$

$$\tag{1.52}$$

where u, v and w are the components of the velocity in the three directions, x, y and z respectively.

The governing equations for convection heat transfer are very similar to the above and will be discussed in Chapter 7.

1.7 Solution Methodology

Although a number of analytical solutions for conduction heat transfer problems are available (Carslaw and Jaeger 1959; Ozisik 1968), in many practical situations, the geometry and the boundary conditions are so complex that an analytical solution is not possible. Even if one could develop analytical relations for such complicated cases, these will invariably involve complex series solutions and would thus be practically difficult to implement. In such situations, conduction heat transfer problems do need a numerical solution. Some commonly employed numerical methods are the Finite Difference (Ozisik and Czisik 1994), Finite Volume (Patankar 1980), Finite Element and Boundary Elements (Ibanez and Power 2002) techniques. This text will address the issues related to the Finite Element Method (FEM) only (Comini *et al.* 1994; Huang and Usmani 1994; Lewis *et al.* 1996; Reddy and Gartling 2000).

In contrast to an analytical solution that allows for the temperature determination at any point in the medium, a numerical solution enables the determination of temperature only at discrete points. The first step in any numerical analysis must therefore be to select these points. This is done by dividing the region of interest into a number of smaller regions. These regions are bounded by points. These reference points are termed *nodal points* and their assembly results in a *grid* or *mesh*. It is important to note that each node represents a certain region surrounding it, and its temperature is a measure of the temperature distribution in that region. The numerical accuracy of these calculations depends strongly on the number of designated nodal points, which control the number of elements generated. The accuracy approaches an exact value as the mesh size (region size) approaches zero.

Further details on the numerical methods, for example, accuracy and error will be discussed in later chapters.

1.8 Summary

In this chapter, the subject of heat transfer was introduced and various modes of heat transport were discussed. The fundamentals of energy conservation principles and the application of such principles to some selected problems were also presented. Finally, the general heat conduction equations in multi-dimensions were derived and the appropriate boundary and initial conditions were given. Although brief, we trust that this chapter gives the reader the essential fundamental concepts involved in heat transfer in general and some detailed understanding of conduction heat transfer in particular.

1.9 Exercise

Exercise 1.9.1 *Extend the problem formulation of the plate subjected to a solar heat flux in Section 1.4.1 for a square plate. Assume the bottom surface of the plate is insulated.*

Exercise 1.9.2 *Repeat the incandescent lamp problem of Section 1.4.2 but now assume that the light source is within an enclosure (room). Assume that the enclosure is also participating in conserving energy.*

Exercise 1.9.3 *Derive the energy balance equations for a rectangular fin of variable cross section as shown in Figure 1.6. The fin is stationary and is attached to a hot heat source. (Hint: This is similar to the problem given in Section (1.4.3), but without relative motion).*

Exercise 1.9.4 *Consider the respective control volumes in both cylindrical and spherical coordinates and derive the respective heat conduction equations. Verify these against Equations 1.42 and 1.44.*

Exercise 1.9.5 *The inner body temperature of a healthy person remains constant at $37\,^\circ C$, while the temperature and humidity of the environment change. Explain, via heat transfer mechanisms between the human body and the environment, how the human body keeps itself cool in summer and warm in winter.*

Exercise 1.9.6 *Discuss the modes of heat transfer that determine the equilibrium temperature of a space shuttle when it is in orbit. What happens when it re-enters the earth's atmosphere?*

Exercise 1.9.7 *A closed plastic container, used to serve coffee in a seminar room, is made of two layers with an air gap placed between them. List all heat transfer processes associated*

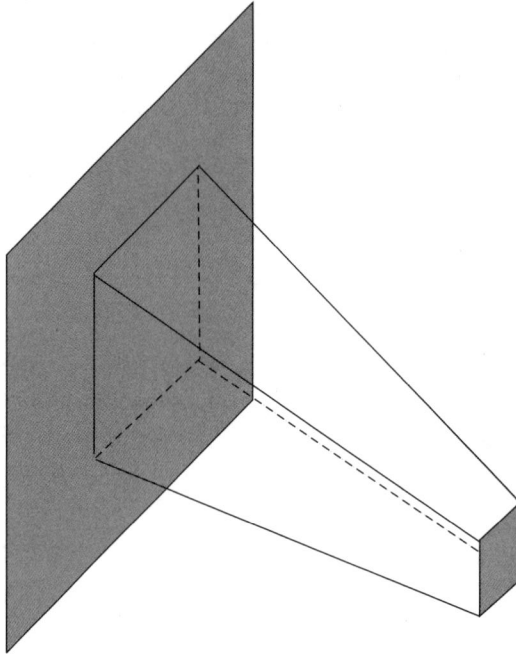

Figure 1.6   Rectangular fin

with the cooling of the coffee in the inner plastic vessel. What steps do you consider necessary for a better container design so as to reduce the heat loss to ambient.

Exercise 1.9.8 *A square chip of size 8 mm is mounted on a substrate with the top surface being exposed to a coolant flow at 20 °C. All other surfaces of the chip are insulated. The chip temperature must not exceed 80 °C in order for the chip to function properly. Determine the maximum allowable power that can be applied to the chip if the coolant is air with a heat transfer coefficient of 250 W/m²K. If the coolant is a dielectric liquid with a heat transfer coefficient of 2500 W/m²K, how much additional power can be dissipated as compared to air cooling?*

Exercise 1.9.9 *Consider a person standing in a room that is at a temperature of 21 °C. Determine the total heat rate from this person if the exposed surface area of the person is 1.6 m² and the average outer surface temperature of the person is 30 °C. The convection coefficient from the surface of the person is 5 W/m² °C. What is the effect of radiation if the emissivity of the surface of the person is 0.90?*

Exercise 1.9.10 *A thin metal plate has one large insulated surface and another large surface exposed to solar radiation at a rate of 600 W/m². The surrounding air temperature is 20 °C. Determine the equilibrium surface temperature of the plate if the convection heat transfer coefficient from the plate surface is 20 W/m²K and the emissivity of the top surface of the plate is 0.8.*

Exercise 1.9.11 *A long, thin copper wire of radius r and length L has an electrical resistance of ρ per unit length. The wire is initially kept at a room temperature of T_a and subjected to an electric current flow of I. The heat generation due to the current flow is simultaneously lost to the ambient by convection. Set up an equation to determine the temperature of the wire as a function of time. Mention the assumptions made in the derivation of the equation.*

Exercise 1.9.12 *In a continuous casting machine, the billet moves at a rate of u m/s. The hot billet is exposed to an ambient temperature of T_a. Set up an equation to find the temperature of the billet as a function of time in terms of the pertinent parameters. Assume that radiation also plays a role in the dissipation of heat to ambient.*

Exercise 1.9.13 *In a double-pipe heat exchanger, hot fluid (mass flow M kg/s and specific heat c kJ/kg °C) flows inside a pipe and cold fluid (mass flow m kg/s and specific heat c kJ/kg °C) flows outside in the annular space. The hot fluid enters the heat exchanger at T_{h1} and leaves at T_{h2}, whereas the cold fluid enters at T_{c1} and leaves at T_{c2}. Set up the differential equation to determine the temperature variation (along the heat exchanger) for hot and cold fluids.*

Bibliography

Bejan A 1993 *Heat Transfer*, John Wiley & Sons, New York.

Carslaw HS and Jaeger JC 1959 *Conduction of Heat in Solids*, Second Edition, Oxford University Press, Fairlawn, NJ.

Comini GS and Nonino C 1994 *Finite Element Analysis in Heat Transfer Basic Formulation and Linear Problems Series in Computational and Physical Processes in Mechanics and Thermal Sciences*, Taylor & Francis, Bristol, PA.

Holman JP 1989 *Heat Transfer*, McGraw-Hill.

Huang H-C and Usmani AS 1994 *Finite Element Analysis for Heat Transfer*, Springer-Verlag, London.

Ibanez MT and Power H 2002 *Advanced Boundary Elements for Heat Transfer (Topics in Engineering)*, WIT Press.

Incropera FP and Dewitt DP 1990 *Fundamentals of Heat and Mass Transfer*, John Wiley & Sons, New York.

Lewis RW, Morgan K, Thomas HR and Seetharamu KN 1996 *Finite Element Methods in Heat Transfer Analysis*, John Wiley & Sons.

Ozisik MN 1968 *Boundary Value Problems of Heat Conduction*, International Text Book Company, Scranton, PA.

Ozisik MN and Czisik MN 1994 *Finite Difference Methods in Heat Transfer*, CRC Press.

Patankar SV 1980 *Numerical Heat Transfer and Fluid Flow*, Hemisphere Publishers.

Reddy JN and Gartling GK 2000 *The Finite Element Method in Heat Transfer and Fluid Dynamics*, Second Edition, CRC Press.

Siegel R and Howell JR 1992 *Thermal Radiation Heat Transfer*, Third Edition, Hemisphere Publishing Corporation.

Sukhatme SP 1992 *A Text Book on Heat Transfer*, Third Edition, Orient Longman Publishers.

2

Some Basic Discrete Systems

2.1 Introduction

Many engineering systems may be simplified by subdividing them into components or elements. These elements can readily be analysed from first principles, and by assembling these together, the analysis of a full original system can be reconstructed. We refer to such systems as *discrete systems*. In a large number of situations, a reasonably adequate model can be obtained using a finite number of well-defined components. This chapter discusses the application of such techniques for the formulation of certain heat and fluid flow problems. The problems presented here provide a valuable basis for the discussion of the finite element method (Bathe 1982; Huebner and Thornton 1982; Hughes 2000; Reddy 1993; Segerlind 1984; Zienkiewicz and Taylor 2000), which is presented in subsequent chapters.

In the analysis of a discrete system, the actual system response is described directly by the solution of a finite number of unknowns. However, a continuous system is one in which a continuum is described by complex differential equations. In other words, the system response is described by an infinite number of unknowns. It is often difficult to obtain an exact solution for a continuum problem and therefore standard numerical methods are required.

If the characteristics of a problem can be represented by relatively simplified equations, it can be analysed employing a finite number of components and simple matrices as shown in the following sections of this chapter. Such procedures reduce the continuous system to an idealization that can be analysed as a discrete physical system. In reality, an important preliminary study to be made by the engineer is whether an engineering system can be treated as discrete or continuous.

If a system is to be analysed using complex governing differential equations, then one has to make a decision on how these equations can be discretized by an appropriate numerical method. Such a system is a refined version of discrete systems, and the accuracy of the solution can be controlled by changing the number of unknowns and elements. The

Fundamentals of the Finite Element Method for Heat and Fluid Flow   R. W. Lewis, P. Nithiarasu and K. N. Seetharamu
© 2004 John Wiley & Sons, Ltd   ISBNs: 0-470-84788-3 (HB); 0-470-84789-1 (PB)

importance of the finite element method finds a place here, that is, finite element techniques, in conjunction with the digital computer, have enabled the numerical idealization and solution of continuous systems in a systematic manner. This in effect has made possible the practical extension and application of classical procedures to very complex engineering systems.

We deal here with some basic discrete, or lumped-parameter systems, that is, systems with a finite number of degrees of freedom. The steps in the analysis of a discrete system are as follows:

Step 1: Idealization of system: System is idealized as an assembly of elements
Step 2: Element characteristics: The characteristics of each element, or component, is found in terms of the primitive variables
Step 3: Assembly: A set of simultaneous equations is formed via assembly of element characteristics for the unknown state variables
Step 4: Solution of equations: The simultaneous equations are solved to determine all the primitive variables on a selected number of points.

We consider in the following sections some heat transfer and fluid flow problems. The same procedure can be extended to structural, electrical and other problems, and the interested reader is referred to other finite element books listed at the end of this chapter.

2.2 Steady State Problems

2.2.1 Heat flow in a composite slab

Consider the heat flow through a composite slab under steady state conditions as shown in Figure 2.1. The problem is similar to that of a roof slab subjected to solar flux on the left-hand face. This is subjected to a constant flux q W/m^2 and the right-hand face is subjected to a convection environment. We are interested in determining the temperatures T_1, T_2 and T_3 at nodes 1, 2 and 3 respectively.

The steady state heat conduction equation for a one-dimensional slab with a constant thermal conductivity is given by Equation 1.41, that is,

$$\frac{d^2 T}{dx^2} = 0 \qquad (2.1)$$

Integration of the above equation yields the following temperature gradient and temperature distribution:

$$\frac{dT}{dx} = a \qquad (2.2)$$

and

$$T = ax + b \qquad (2.3)$$

Consider a homogeneous slab of thickness L with the following boundary conditions (in one dimension):

$$\text{At} \quad x = 0, T = T_1 \quad \text{and} \quad \text{At} \quad x = L, T = T_2 \qquad (2.4)$$

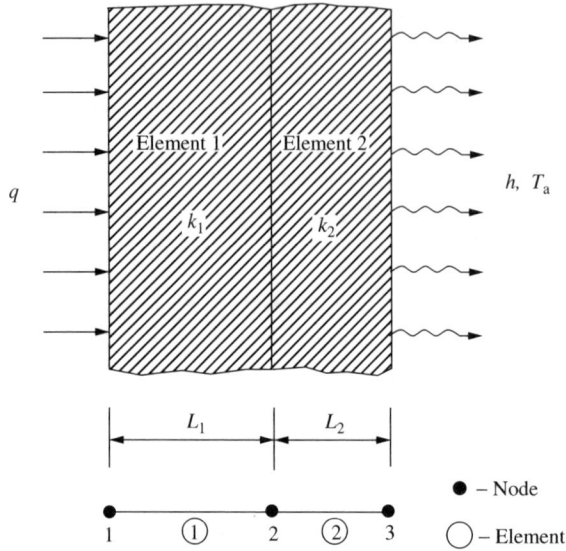

Figure 2.1   Heat transfer through a composite slab

Substitution of the boundary conditions, Equation 2.4, gives

$$c = T_1 \quad \text{and} \quad a = \frac{T_2 - T_1}{L} \tag{2.5}$$

The heat flux can be calculated from Equation 2.3 as

$$q = -k\frac{dT}{dx} = -k\frac{T_2 - T_1}{L} \tag{2.6}$$

or, the total heat flow is expressed as

$$Q = qA = -kA\frac{T_2 - T_1}{L} \tag{2.7}$$

where A is the area perpendicular to the direction of heat flow.

The total heat flow will be constant at any section perpendicular to the heat flow direction (conservation of energy) if the height and breadth are infinitely long (i.e., one-dimensional heat flow). Applying the above principle to the composite slab shown in Figure 2.1 results in the following heat balance equations at different nodes:

at node 1

$$qA = k_1 A\frac{T_1 - T_2}{L_1} \tag{2.8}$$

at node 2

$$k_1 A\frac{T_1 - T_2}{L_1} = k_2 A\frac{T_2 - T_3}{L_2} \tag{2.9}$$

at node 3

$$k_2 A\frac{T_2 - T_3}{L_2} = hA(T_3 - T_a) \tag{2.10}$$

where h is the heat transfer coefficient and T_a is the ambient temperature. We can rearrange the previous three equations as follows:

$$\frac{k_1 A}{L_1} T_1 - \frac{k_1 A}{L_1} T_2 = q A$$

$$-\frac{k_1 A}{L_1} T_1 + \left[\frac{k_1 A}{L_1} + \frac{k_2 A}{L_2} \right] T_2 - \frac{k_2 A}{L_2} T_3 = 0$$

$$-\frac{k_2 A}{L_2} T_2 + \left[\frac{k_2 A}{L_2} + hA \right] T_3 = hAT_a \tag{2.11}$$

The above equation can be rewritten in matrix form as

$$\begin{bmatrix} \dfrac{k_1 A}{L_1} & \dfrac{-k_1 A}{L_1} & 0 \\[2mm] \dfrac{-k_1 A}{L_1} & \left[\dfrac{k_1 A}{L_1} + \dfrac{k_2 A}{L_2} \right] & \dfrac{-k_2 A}{L_2} \\[2mm] 0 & \dfrac{-k_2 A}{L_2} & \left[\dfrac{k_2 A}{L_2} + hA \right] \end{bmatrix} \begin{Bmatrix} T_1 \\ T_2 \\ T_3 \end{Bmatrix} = \begin{Bmatrix} qA \\ 0 \\ hAT_a \end{Bmatrix} \tag{2.12}$$

or

$$[\mathbf{K}]\{\mathbf{T}\} = \{\mathbf{f}\} \tag{2.13}$$

The solution of Equation 2.13 gives the unknown temperatures T_1, T_2 and T_3. In the case of heat conduction, there is only one degree of freedom at each node as temperature is a scalar. The following important features of Equation 2.13 should be observed.

- The characteristics of each layer of the slab for heat conduction can be written as

$$\frac{kA}{L} \begin{bmatrix} 1 & -1 \\ -1 & 1 \end{bmatrix} \begin{Bmatrix} T_i \\ T_j \end{Bmatrix} = \begin{Bmatrix} Q \\ -Q \end{Bmatrix} \tag{2.14}$$

- where Q is the total heat flow and is constant.

- The global stiffness matrix $[\mathbf{K}]$ can be obtained by assembling the stiffness matrices of each layer and the result is a symmetric and positive definite matrix.

- The effect of the heat flux boundary condition appears only in the loading terms $\{\mathbf{f}\}$.

- The convective heat transfer effect appears both in the stiffness matrix and the loading vector.

- The thermal force vector consists of known values. The method of assembly can be extended to more than two layers of insulation.

- The effect of natural boundary conditions (flux boundary conditions) is evident at the formulation stage.

In summary, if $[\mathbf{K}]$ and $\{\mathbf{f}\}$ can be formed, then the temperature distribution can be determined by any standard matrix solution procedure.

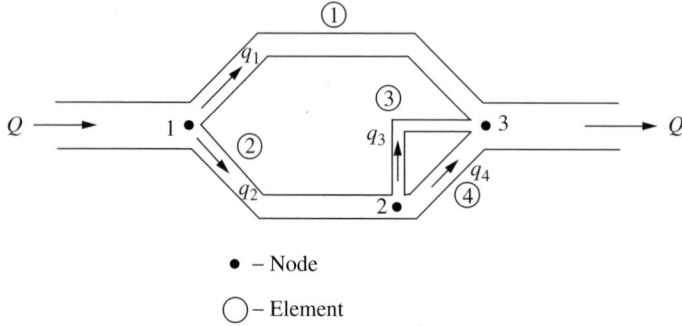

• – Node

◯ – Element

Figure 2.2   Fluid flow network

2.2.2   Fluid flow network

Many practical problems require a knowledge of flow in various circuits, for example water distribution systems, ventilation ducts in electrical machines (including transformers), electronic cooling systems, internal passages in gas turbine blades, and so on. In the cooling of electrical machines and electronic components, it is necessary to determine the heat transfer coefficients of the cooling surfaces, which are dependent on the mass flow of air on those surfaces. In order to illustrate the flow calculations in each circuit, laminar incompressible flow is considered in the network of circular pipes [1] as shown in Figure 2.2. If a quantity Q m^3/s of fluid enters and leaves the pipe network, it is necessary to compute the fluid nodal pressures and the volume flow rate in each pipe. We shall make use of a four-element and three-node model as shown in Figure 2.2.

The fluid resistance for an element is written as (Poiseuille flow (Shames 1982))

$$R_k = \frac{128L\mu}{\pi D^4} \tag{2.15}$$

where L is the length of the pipe section; D, the diameter of the pipe section and μ, the dynamic viscosity of the fluid and the subscript k, indicates the element number. The mass flux rate entering and leaving an element can be written as

$$q_i = \frac{1}{R_k}(p_i - p_j) \quad \text{and} \quad q_j = \frac{1}{R_k}(p_j - p_i) \tag{2.16}$$

where p is the pressure, q is the mass flux rate and the subscripts i and j indicate the two nodes of an element.

The characteristics of the element, thus, can be written as

$$\frac{1}{R_k}\begin{bmatrix} 1 & -1 \\ -1 & 1 \end{bmatrix}\begin{Bmatrix} p_i \\ p_j \end{Bmatrix} = \begin{Bmatrix} q_i \\ q_j \end{Bmatrix} \tag{2.17}$$

Similarly, we can construct the characteristics of each element in Figure 2.2 as

---

[1] It should be noted that we use the notation Q for both total heat flow and fluid flow rate

Element 1

$$\frac{1}{R_1}\begin{bmatrix} 1 & -1 \\ -1 & 1 \end{bmatrix}\begin{Bmatrix} p_1 \\ p_3 \end{Bmatrix} = \begin{Bmatrix} q_1 \\ -q_1 \end{Bmatrix} \tag{2.18}$$

Note that the mass flux rate entering an element is positive and leaving an element is negative.

Element 2

$$\frac{1}{R_2}\begin{bmatrix} 1 & -1 \\ -1 & 1 \end{bmatrix}\begin{Bmatrix} p_1 \\ p_2 \end{Bmatrix} = \begin{Bmatrix} q_2 \\ -q_2 \end{Bmatrix} \tag{2.19}$$

Element 3

$$\frac{1}{R_3}\begin{bmatrix} 1 & -1 \\ -1 & 1 \end{bmatrix}\begin{Bmatrix} p_2 \\ p_3 \end{Bmatrix} = \begin{Bmatrix} q_3 \\ -q_3 \end{Bmatrix} \tag{2.20}$$

Element 4

$$\frac{1}{R_4}\begin{bmatrix} 1 & -1 \\ -1 & 1 \end{bmatrix}\begin{Bmatrix} p_2 \\ p_3 \end{Bmatrix} = \begin{Bmatrix} q_4 \\ -q_4 \end{Bmatrix} \tag{2.21}$$

From the above element equations, it is possible to write the following nodal equations:

$$\left[\frac{1}{R_1} + \frac{1}{R_2}\right]p_1 - \frac{1}{R_2}p_2 - \frac{1}{R_1}p_3 = q_1 + q_2 = Q$$

$$-\frac{1}{R_2}p_1 + \left[\frac{1}{R_2} + \frac{1}{R_3} + \frac{1}{R_4}\right]p_2 - \left[\frac{1}{R_3} + \frac{1}{R_4}\right]p_3 = q_3 + q_4 - q_2 = 0$$

$$-\frac{1}{R_1}p_1 - \left[\frac{1}{R_3} + \frac{1}{R_4}\right]p_2 + \left[\frac{1}{R_1} + \frac{1}{R_3} + \frac{1}{R_4}\right]p_3 = -q_1 - q_3 - q_4 = -Q \tag{2.22}$$

Now, the following matrix form can be written from the above equations:

$$\begin{bmatrix} \left[\dfrac{1}{R_1} + \dfrac{1}{R_2}\right] & -\dfrac{1}{R_2} & -\dfrac{1}{R_1} \\ -\dfrac{1}{R_2} & \left[\dfrac{1}{R_2} + \dfrac{1}{R_3} + \dfrac{1}{R_4}\right] & -\left[\dfrac{1}{R_3} + \dfrac{1}{R_4}\right] \\ -\dfrac{1}{R_1} & -\left[\dfrac{1}{R_3} + \dfrac{1}{R_4}\right] & \left[\dfrac{1}{R_1} + \dfrac{1}{R_3} + \dfrac{1}{R_4}\right] \end{bmatrix}\begin{Bmatrix} p_1 \\ p_2 \\ p_3 \end{Bmatrix} =$$

$$\begin{Bmatrix} q_1 + q_2 \\ -q_2 + q_3 + q_4 \\ -q_1 - q_3 - q_4 \end{Bmatrix} = \begin{Bmatrix} Q \\ 0 \\ -Q \end{Bmatrix} \tag{2.23}$$

Note that $q_1 + q_2 = Q$ and $q_2 = q_3 + q_4$

In this fashion, we can solve problems such as electric networks, radiation networks, and so on. Equations 2.18 to 2.21 are also valid and may be used to determine the pressures if q_1, q_2, q_3 and q_4 are known *a priori*. Let us consider a numerical example to illustrate the above.

Table 2.1 Details of pipe network

Component Number	Diameter, cm	Length, m
1	2.50	30.00
2	2.00	20.00
3	2.00	25.00
4	1.25	20.00

Example 2.2.1 *In a pipe network as shown in Figure 2.2, water enters the network at a rate of 0.1 m³/s with a viscosity of 0.96 × 10⁻³ Ns/m². The component details are given in Table 2.1. Determine the pressure values at all nodes.*

On substitution of the various values, we get the following resistances in Ns/m⁵ from Equation 2.15

$R_1 = 0.3 \times 10^7$

$R_2 = 0.5 \times 10^7$

$R_3 = 0.6 \times 10^7$

$R_4 = 3.2 \times 10^7$

Now Equation 2.23 can be formulated as

$$10^{-7} \begin{bmatrix} 5.33 & -2.00 & -3.33 \\ -2.00 & 3.98 & -1.98 \\ -3.33 & -1.98 & 5.31 \end{bmatrix} \begin{Bmatrix} p_1 \\ p_2 \\ p_3 \end{Bmatrix} = \begin{Bmatrix} 0.1 \\ 0.0 \\ -1.0 \end{Bmatrix} \tag{2.24}$$

The solution of the above simultaneous system of equations with $p_3 = 0.0$ (assumed as reference pressure) gives

$p_1 = 0.231 \times 10^6 \ N/m^2$

$p_2 = 0.116 \times 10^6 \ N/m^2$

From Equations 2.18, 2.19, 2.20 and 2.21, we can calculate the flow quantities as

$$q_1 = \frac{p_1 - p_3}{R_1} = 0.0769 \ m^3/s$$

$$q_2 = \frac{p_1 - p_2}{R_2} = 0.0231 \ m^3/s$$

$$q_3 = \frac{p_2 - p_3}{R_3} = 0.0193 \ m^3/s$$

$$q_4 = \frac{p_2 - p_3}{R_4} = 0.0036 \ m^3/s \tag{2.25}$$

It is possible to take into account the entrance loss, exit loss, bend loss, and so on, in the calculation of nodal pressures and flows in each circuit. If the fluid flow in the network is turbulent, it is still possible to define an element, but the element equations are no longer linear as can be seen from an empirical relation governing fully developed turbulent pipe flow (Darcy-Weisbach formula (Shames 1982))

$$p_1 - p_2 = \frac{8fLQ^2\rho}{\pi D^5} \tag{2.26}$$

where 'f' is the Moody friction factor, which is a function of the Reynolds number and the pipe roughness. The fluidity matrix will contain known functions of the flow rate 'Q' instead of constants. Hence, the problem becomes nonlinear.

2.2.3 Heat transfer in heat sinks (combined conduction–convection)

In order to increase the heat dissipation by convection from a given primary surface, additional surfaces may be added. The additional material added is referred to either as an 'Extended Surface' or a 'Fin'. A familiar example is in motorcycles, in which fins extend from the outer surface of the engine to dissipate more heat by convection. A schematic diagram of such a fin array is shown in Figure 2.3. This is a good example of a heat sink.

We shall assume for simplicity that there is no variation in temperature in the thickness and width of fins. We will also assume that the temperature varies only in the length direction of the fin and the height direction of the hot body to which the fin is attached. We can then derive a simplified model as shown in Figure 2.4. A typical element in the fin array is shown in Figure 2.5.

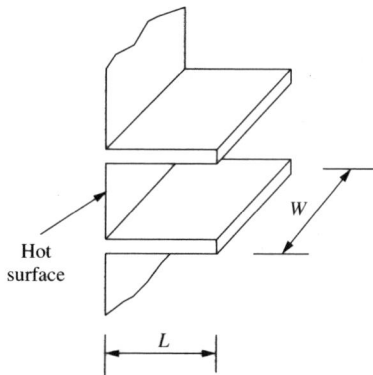

Figure 2.3   Array of thin rectangular fins

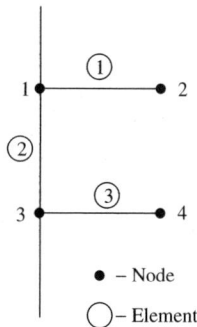

Figure 2.4   A simplified model of the rectangular fins of Figure 2.3

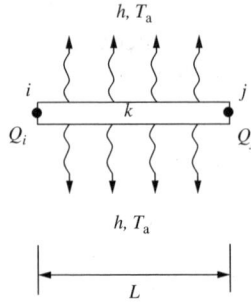

Figure 2.5 A typical element from the rectangular fin arrangement and conduc-
tive–convective heat transfer mechanism

We could write the heat balance equations at nodes i and j as follows:
At node i

$$Q_i - \frac{kA}{L}(T_i - T_j) - \frac{hPL}{2}\left(\frac{T_i + T_j}{2} - T_a\right) = 0 \qquad (2.27)$$

and at node j

$$-Q_j + \frac{kA}{L}(T_i - T_j) - \frac{hPL}{2}\left(\frac{T_i + T_j}{2} - T_a\right) = 0 \qquad (2.28)$$

On simplification we get, for the node i

$$\left(\frac{kA}{L} + \frac{hPL}{4}\right)T_i + \left(-\frac{kA}{L} + \frac{hPL}{4}\right)T_j = Q_i + \frac{hPL}{2}T_a \qquad (2.29)$$

and for the node j

$$\left(-\frac{kA}{L} + \frac{hPL}{4}\right)T_i + \left(\frac{kA}{L} + \frac{hPL}{4}\right)T_j = -Q_j + \frac{hPL}{2}T_a \qquad (2.30)$$

It is now possible to write the above two equations in matrix form as

$$\begin{bmatrix} \dfrac{kA}{L} + \dfrac{hPL}{4} & -\dfrac{kA}{L} + \dfrac{hPL}{4} \\ -\dfrac{kA}{L} + \dfrac{hPL}{4} & \dfrac{kA}{L} + \dfrac{hPL}{4} \end{bmatrix} \begin{Bmatrix} T_i \\ T_j \end{Bmatrix} = \begin{Bmatrix} Q_i + \dfrac{hPL}{2}T_a \\ -Q_j + \dfrac{hPL}{2}T_a \end{Bmatrix} \qquad (2.31)$$

In the above equation, either Q_j or T_i is often known and quantities such as T_a, h,
k, L and P are also generally known a priori. The above problem is therefore reduced to
finding three unknowns Q_i or T_i, T_j and Q_j. In addition to the above two equations, an
additional equation relating Q_i and Q_j may be used, that is,

$$Q_i = Q_j + hPL\left(\frac{T_i + T_j}{2} - T_a\right) \qquad (2.32)$$

It is now possible to solve the system to find the unknowns. If there is more than one
element, then an assembly procedure is necessary as discussed in the previous section.

Equation 2.31 reduces to Equation 2.14 in the absence of convection from the surface. Also, if the terms $(T_i + T_j)/2$ in Equation 2.31 are replaced by $(2T_i + T_j)/3$, then we obtain the standard Galerkin weighted residual form discussed in Example 3.5.1.

2.2.4   Analysis of a heat exchanger

The performance of a heat exchanger can be calculated in terms of its effectiveness for a given condition (Holman 1989; Incropera and Dewitt 1990). In order to determine the effectiveness of a heat exchanger, we have to calculate the outlet temperatures of both the hot fluid and the cold fluid for the given inlet temperatures. The overall heat transfer coefficient may be a constant or could vary along the heat exchanger.

For the purpose of illustration, let us consider a shell and tube heat exchanger as shown in Figure 2.6 (Ravikumaur *et al.* 1984). In this type of heat exchanger, the hot fluid flows through the tube and the tube is passed through the shell. The cooling fluid is pumped into the shell and thus the hot fluid in the tube is cooled.

Let us divide the given heat exchanger into eight cells as shown in Figure 2.7. It is assumed that both the hot and cold fluids will travel through the cell at least once. Let the overall heat transfer coefficient be U and the surface area of the tubes be 'A'. These are assumed to be constant throughout the heat exchanger within each element. Let us assume that the hot and cold fluid temperatures vary linearly along the flow.

Now, the heat leaving node 1 and entering element 1 (Figure 2.7b) is

$$Q_1 = W_1 T_1 \tag{2.33}$$

where W_1 is ρc_p times the volume flow rate. The heat leaving element 1 and entering node 2 is (the energy balance is considered with respect to the element where the heat entering is taken as being positive and that leaving the element is taken as being negative)

$$Q_2 = W_1 T_1 - U A (T_{1,2} - T_{11,12}) \tag{2.34}$$

where

$$T_{1,2} = \frac{T_1 + T_2}{2} \quad \text{and} \quad T_{11,12} = \frac{T_{11} + T_{12}}{2} \tag{2.35}$$

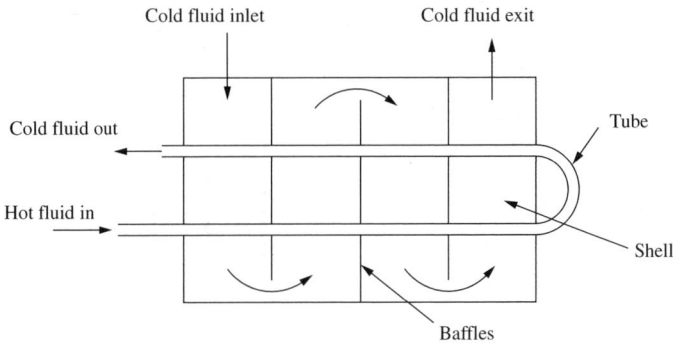

Figure 2.6   Schematic diagram of a shell and tube heat exchanger

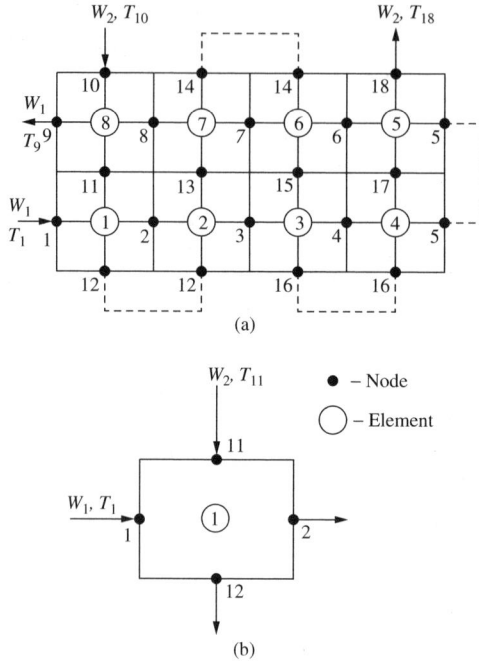

Figure 2.7   (a) Simplified model of a heat exchanger, (b) Element

Similarly, the heat leaving node 11 and entering element 1 is

$$Q_{11} = W_2 T_{11} \tag{2.36}$$

and the heat leaving element 1 and entering node 12 is

$$Q_{12} = W_2 T_{11} - UA(T_{11,12} - T_{1,2}) \tag{2.37}$$

In this example, the heat transfer between the fluids is given by $UA(T_{11,12} - T_{1,2})$, whereas some other models use $UA(T_{12} - T_2)$. The assumption in the present model is more logical in view of the continuous variation (linear in our case) of the temperature difference between the hot and cold fluids.

Equations 2.33, 2.34, 2.36 and 2.37 can be combined and recast in matrix form to give the element characteristics, that is,

$$
\begin{bmatrix}
W_1 & 0.0 & 0.0 & 0.0 \\
W_1 - C & -C & C & C \\
0.0 & 0.0 & W_2 & 0.0 \\
C & C & W_2 - C & -C
\end{bmatrix}
\begin{Bmatrix}
T_1 \\
T_2 \\
T_{11} \\
T_{12}
\end{Bmatrix}
=
\begin{Bmatrix}
Q_1 \\
Q_2 \\
Q_{11} \\
Q_{12}
\end{Bmatrix}
\tag{2.38}
$$

where $C = \frac{UA}{2}$.

Assembly of the element characteristics for elements 1 to 8 will result in the global stiffness matrix in which Q_1, and Q_{10} are known (in other words T_1, and T_{10} are known). The solution of the remaining equations will give the temperature distribution for both the fluids, that is, $T_2, T_3, T_4, T_5, T_6, T_7, T_8$ and T_9 for the incoming hot fluid and $T_{11}, T_{12}, T_{13}, T_{14}, T_{15}, T_{16}, T_{17}$ and T_{18} for the coolant.

With the calculated exit temperatures T_9 and T_{18}, the effectiveness of the heat exchanger can be calculated.

2.3 Transient Heat Transfer Problem (Propagation Problem)

In a transient, or propagation, problem, the response of a system changes with time. The same methodology used in the analysis of a steady state problem is employed here, but the temperature and element equilibrium relations depend on time. The objective of the transient analysis is to calculate the temperatures with respect to time.

Figure 2.8 shows an idealized case of a heat treatment chamber. A metallic part is heated to an initial temperature, T_p, and is placed in a heat treatment chamber in which an inert gas such as nitrogen is present. Heat is transferred from the metallic part to the gas by convection. The gas in turn loses heat to the enclosure wall by convection. The wall also receives heat by radiation from the metallic part directly as the gas is assumed to be transparent. The wall loses heat to the atmosphere by radiation and convection.

The unknown variables in the present analysis are the temperature of the metallic part T_p, the temperature of the gas T_g, and the temperature of the enclosure wall T_w.

For simplicity, we are using a lumped-parameter approach, that is, the temperature variation within the metal, gas and wall is ignored.

Let c_p, c_g and c_w be the heat capacities of the metallic part, the gas and the wall respectively. The heat balance equations with respect to time can be derived as follows:

For the metallic part,

$$c_p \frac{dT_p}{dt} = -\left\{ hA_p(T_p - T_g) + \epsilon_p \sigma A_p(T_p^4 - T_w^4) \right\} \tag{2.39}$$

For the gaseous part,

$$c_g \frac{dT_g}{dt} = h_p A_p(T_p - T_g) - h_g A_g(T_g - T_w) \tag{2.40}$$

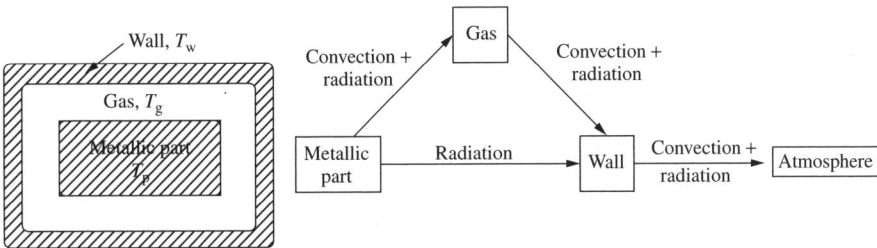

Figure 2.8   Heat treatment chamber and associated heat transfer processes

For the furnace wall,

$$c_w \frac{dT_w}{dt} = \epsilon_p \sigma A_p (T_p^4 - T_w^4) + h_g A_g (T_g - T_w)$$

$$- h_w A_w (T_w - T_a) - \epsilon_w \sigma A_w (T_w^4 - T_a^4) \qquad (2.41)$$

The above three equations can be recast in matrix form as

$$[C]\left\{\dot{T}\right\} + [K]\{T\} = \{f\} \qquad (2.42)$$

where

$$[C] = \begin{bmatrix} c_p & 0.0 & 0.0 \\ 0.0 & c_g & 0.0 \\ 0.0 & 0.0 & c_w \end{bmatrix} \qquad (2.43)$$

$$\left\{\dot{T}\right\} = \left\{ \begin{array}{c} \dfrac{dT_p}{dt} \\[2mm] \dfrac{dT_g}{dt} \\[2mm] \dfrac{dT_w}{dt} \end{array} \right\} \qquad (2.44)$$

$$\{T\} = \left\{ \begin{array}{c} T_p \\ T_g \\ T_w \end{array} \right\} \qquad (2.45)$$

$$[K] = \begin{bmatrix} h_p A_p & -h_p A_p & 0.0 \\ -h_p A_p & h_p A_p + h_g A_g & -h_g A_g \\ 0.0 & -h_g A_g & h_g A_g + h_w A_w \end{bmatrix} \qquad (2.46)$$

and

$$\{f\} = \left\{ \begin{array}{c} 0.0 \\ 0.0 \\ h_w A_w T_a + \epsilon_p \sigma A_p (T_p^4 - T_w^4) - \epsilon_w \sigma A_w (T_w^4 - T_a^4) \end{array} \right\} \qquad (2.47)$$

where h_p is the heat transfer coefficient from the metallic part to the gas; A_p, the surface area of the metallic part in contact with the gas; h_g, the heat transfer coefficient of the gas to the wall; A_g, the surface area of the gas in contact with the wall; h_w, the heat transfer coefficient from the wall to the atmosphere; A_w, the wall area in contact with the atmosphere; ϵ_p and ϵ_w, the emissivity values of the metallic part and the wall respectively and σ the Stefan–Boltzmann constant (Chapter 1).

Although we follow the SI system of units, it is essential to reiterate here that the temperatures T_p, T_g, T_w and T_a should be in K (Kelvin) as radiation heat transfer is involved in the given problem. In view of the radiation terms appearing in the governing equations (i.e., temperature to the power of 4), the problem is highly nonlinear and an iterative procedure is necessary. An initial guess of the unknown temperature values is also essential to start any iterative procedure.

In this example, if the time terms are neglected, we can recover the steady state formulation. However, the time-dependent load terms are necessary to carry out any form of transient analysis. In practice, the reduction of an appropriate discrete system that contains all the important characteristics of the actual physical system is usually not straightforward. In general, a different discrete model should be chosen for a transient response prediction than that chosen for a steady state analysis.

The time-derivative terms used in the above formulation have to be approximated in order to obtain a temperature distribution. As discussed in later chapters, approximations such as backward Euler, central difference, and so on, may well be employed.

2.4   Summary

In this chapter, we have discussed some basic discrete system analyses. It is important to reiterate here that this chapter gives only a brief discussion of the system analysis. We believe that the material provided in this chapter is sufficient to give the reader a starting point. It should be noted that the system analysis is straightforward and works for many simple heat transfer problems. However, for complex continuum problems, a standard discretization of the governing equations and solution methodology is essential. We will discuss these problems in detail in the following chapters.

2.5   Exercise

Exercise 2.5.1 *Use the system analysis procedure described in this chapter and construct the discrete system for heat conduction through the composite wall shown in Figure 2.9. Also, from the following data, calculate the temperature distribution in the composite wall.*
   Areas: $A_1 = 2.0\,m^2$, $A_2 = 1.0\,m^2$ and $A_3 = 1.0\,m^2$.
   Thermal conductivity: $k_1 = 2.00\,W/mK$, $k_2 = 2.5\,W/mK$ and $k_3 = 1.5\,W/mK$.
   Heat transfer coefficient: $h = 0.1\,W/m^2\,K$
   Atmospheric temperature: $T_a = 30\,^\circ C$
   Temperature at the left face of wall: $T_1 = 75.0\,^\circ C$.

Exercise 2.5.2 *The cross section of an insulated pipe carrying a hot fluid is shown in Figure 2.10. The inner and outer radii of the pipe are r_1 and r_2 respectively. The thickness of the insulating material is $r_2 - r_3$. Assume appropriate conditions and form the discrete system equations.*

Exercise 2.5.3 *The pipe network used to circulate hot water in a domestic central heating arrangement is shown in Figure 2.11. The flow rate at the entrance is Qm^3/s. Neglecting any loss of mass, construct a system of simultaneous equations to calculate the pressure distribution at selected points using a discrete system analysis. Assume laminar flow occurs in the system.*

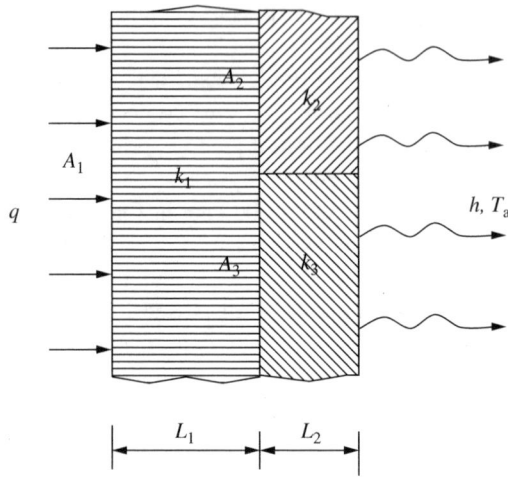

Figure 2.9   Heat transfer in a composite wall

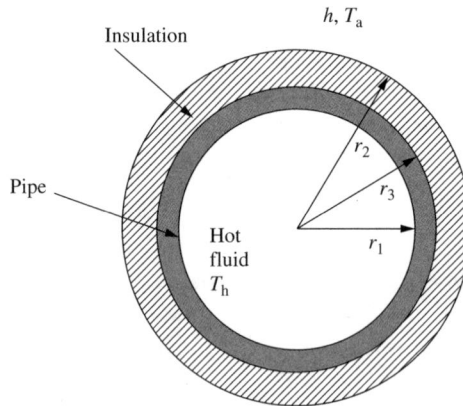

Figure 2.10   Heat transfer through an insulating material

Exercise 2.5.4 *A schematic diagram of a counterflow heat exchanger is shown in Figure 2.12. The hot fluid enters the central, circular pipe from the left and exits at the right. The cooling fluid is circulated around the inner tube to cool the hot fluid. Using the principles of heat exchanger system discussed in this chapter, construct a discrete system to determine the temperature distribution.*

Exercise 2.5.5 *A transient analysis is very important in the casting industry. In Figure 2.13, a simplified casting arrangement is shown (without a runner or raiser). The molten metal is poured into the mould and the metal loses heat to the mould and solidifies. It is often possible to have a small air gap between the metal and the mould. The figure shows an idealized system that has a uniform gap all around the metal. Assume that heat is transferred from the*

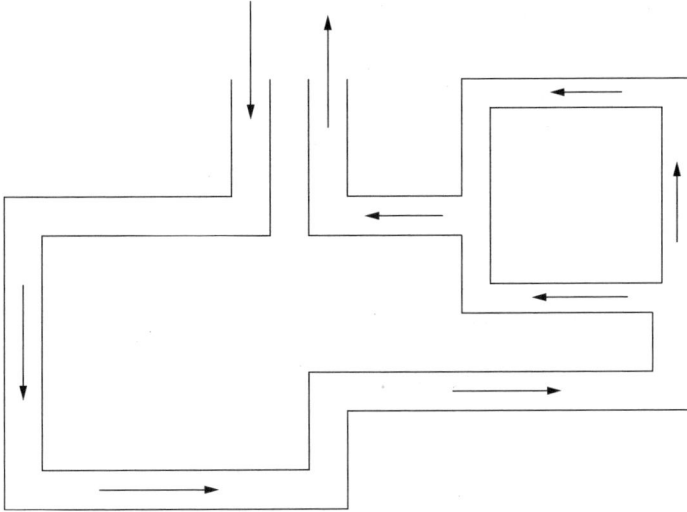

Figure 2.11 Pipe network for central heating

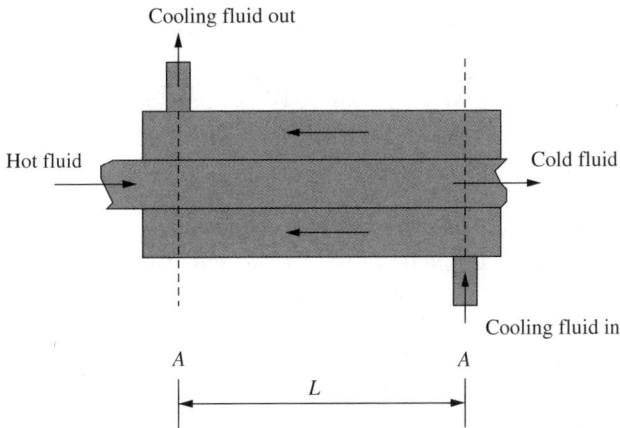

Figure 2.12 Counterflow heat exchanger

metal to the mould via radiation and conduction. Then heat is conducted through the mould and convected to the atmosphere. Stating all assumptions, derive a system of equations to carry out a transient analysis.

Exercise 2.5.6 *Consider a 0.6-m high and 2-m wide double-glazed window consisting of two 4 mm thick layers of glass (k = 0.80 W/m °C) separated by an 8-mm wide stagnant air space (k = 0.025 W/m °C). Determine the steady state heat transfer through the window and the temperature of the inner surface for a day when the outside air temperature is −15 °C and the room temperature is 20 °C. The heat transfer coefficient on the inner and outer*

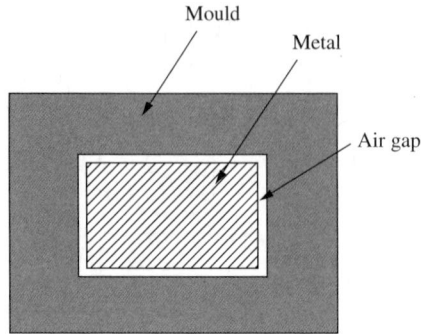

Figure 2.13   Casting and mould arrangement

Table 2.2   Details of the composite wall

Material	Thermal conductivity (W/m °C)	Thickness (cm)
Aluminium	200	5
Copper	400	15
Steel	50	20

surface of the window are 10 W/m² °C and 40 W/m² °C respectively. Note that these heat transfer coefficients include the effect of radiation. If the air gap is not provided, what is the temperature of the glass inside the room?

Exercise 2.5.7 *A simplified model can be applied to describe the steady state temperature distribution through the core region, muscle region and skin region of the human body. The core region temperature T_c, is the mean operating temperature of the internal organs. The muscle temperature, T_m, is the operating temperature of the muscle layer of the human body. Muscle is a shell tissue, and can be either resting or actively working. The skin temperature, T_s, is the operating temperature of the surface region of the body consisting of a subcutaneous fat layer, the dermal layer and finally the epidermal layer. If the metabolic heat rate of a common man is 45 W/m² and the skin temperature is 32.6 °C, calculate the core region temperature if the thermal conductivity of the core, muscle and skin are 0.48 W/m °C and the thickness of the layers are 4 cm, 2 cm and 1 cm respectively. Also calculate the muscle temperature.*

Exercise 2.5.8 *A composite wall consists of layers of aluminium, copper and steel. The steel external surface is 350 °C, and the external surface of the aluminium is exposed to an ambient of 25 °C with a heat transfer coefficient of 5 W/m² °C. Calculate the heat loss and the interfacial temperature using a three-element model using the data given in Table 2.2.*

Exercise 2.5.9 *An incompressible fluid flows through a pipe network of circular pipes as shown in Figure 2.14. If 0.1 m³/s of fluid enters and leaves the pipe network, using a 4-node*

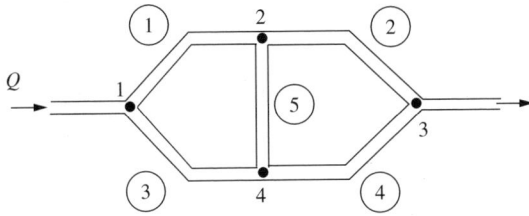

Figure 2.14   Incompressible flow through a pipe network

Table 2.3   Pipe network element details

Element number	Nodes	Diameter, D (cm)	Length, L (m)
1	1,2	5	25
2	2,3	5	25
2	1,4	5	25
4	4,3	5	25
5	2,4	10	90

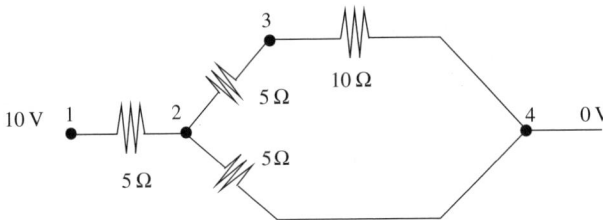

Figure 2.15   A direct current circuit

5-element model, calculate the nodal pressure and the volume flow in each pipe. If nodes 1 and 3 are directly connected, in addition to the existing arrangement, what change takes place in the nodal pressure and volume fluid in each pipe? The viscosity of the fluid is $1 \times 10^{-2} \, N \, s/m^2$. For laminar flow, the resistance for the flow is given by $128 \, \mu L / \pi D^4$. The details of the elements are given in Table 2.3.

Exercise 2.5.10 *Figure 2.15 shows a direct current circuit. The voltage at the output terminals are also shown in Figure 2.15. Calculate the voltage at each node and the current in each of the branches using the discrete system analysis.*

Exercise 2.5.11 *A cross section of a heat sink used in electronic cooling is shown in Figure 2.16. All the fins are of same size. Calculate the heat dissipating capacity of the heat sink per unit length of the heat sink.*

Exercise 2.5.12 *The details of a double pipe heat exchanger are given as (a) cold fluid heat capacity rate $C_1 = 1100 \, W/kg \,°C$; (b) hot fluid heat capacity rate $C_2 = 734 \, W/kg \,°C$;*

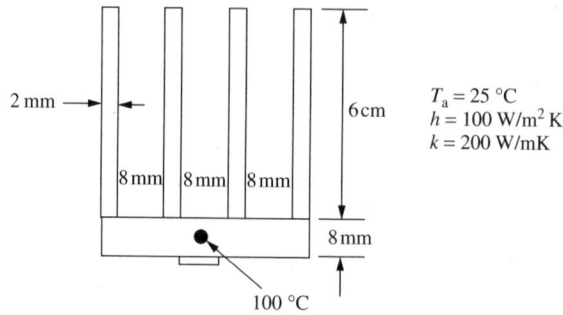

Figure 2.16 A heat sink

(c) overall heat transfer coefficient $U = 600 \, W/m^2 \, °C$ (d) heat exchanger area $A = 4 \, m^2$ (e) cold fluid entry temperature $T_{ci} = 20 \, °C$ (f) hot fluid entry temperature $T_{hi} = 80 \, °C$. Set up the stiffness matrix and hence solve for the outlet temperature and the effectiveness of the heat exchanger by using 1 element, 2 elements and 4 elements for the heat exchanger. Also determine the minimum number of elements required for converged solution.

Exercise 2.5.13 *Figure 2.17 shows an arrangement for cooling of an electronic equipment consisting of a number of printed circuit boards (PCBs) enclosed in a box. Air is forced through the box by a fan. Select a typical element and write down the stiffness matrix and show that this method can take care of non-uniform flow (by using the methodology similar to that in Exercise 2.5.9, the non-uniform flow in each channel can be determined) and non-uniform heat generation in individual PCB.*

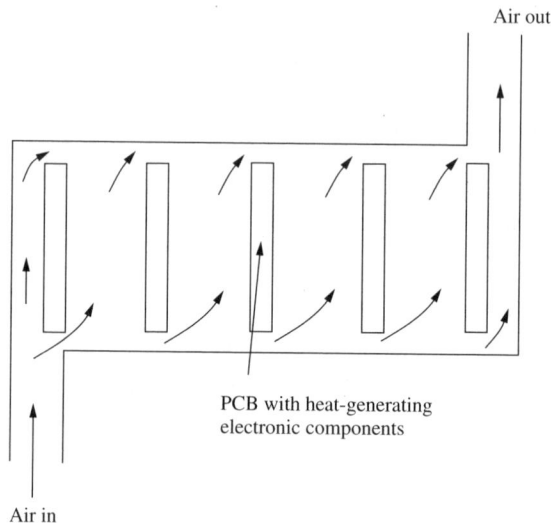

Figure 2.17 Assembly of printed circuit boards

Bibliography

Bathe KJ 1982 *Finite Element Procedures in Engineering Analysis*, Prentice Hill, Englewood Cliffs, NJ.

Holman JP 1989 *Heat Transfer*, McGraw-Hill, Singapore.

Huebner K and Thornton EA 1982 *The Finite Element Method for Engineers*, Second Edition, John Wiley & Sons.

Hughes TJR 2000 *The Finite Element Method: Linear Static and Dynamic Finite Element Analysis*, Dover Publications, New York.

Incropera, FP and Dewitt, DP 1990 *Fundamentals of Heat and Mass Transfer*, John Wiley & Sons, New York.

Ravikumaur SG, Seetharamu KN and Aswatha Narayana PA 1986 Applications of finite elements in heat exchangers, *Communications in Applied Numerical Methods*, **2**, 229–234.

Reddy JN 1993 *An Introduction to Finite Element Method*, Second Edition, McGraw-Hill Book Company, New York.

Segerlind LJ 1984 *Applied Finite Element Analysis*, Second Edition, John Wiley & Sons, New York.

Shames IH 1982 *Mechanics of Fluids*, McGraw-Hill, Singapore.

Zienkiewicz OC and Taylor RL 2000 *The Finite Element Method, Vol. 1, The Basis*, Fifth Edition, Butterworth and Heinemann, London.

3

The Finite Element Method

3.1 Introduction

The finite element method is a numerical tool for determining approximate solutions to a large class of engineering problems. The method was originally developed to study the stresses in complex air-frame structures (Clough 1960) and was later extended to the general field of continuum mechanics (Zienkiewicz and Cheung 1965). There have been many articles on the history of finite elements written by numerous authors with conflicting opinions on the origins of the technique (Gupta and Meek 1996; Oden 1996; Zienkiewicz 1996). The finite element method is receiving considerable attention in engineering education and in industry because of its diversity and flexibility as an analysis tool. It is often necessary to obtain approximate numerical solutions for complex industrial problems, in which exact closed-form solutions are difficult to obtain. An example of such a complex situation can be found in the cooling of electronic equipment (or chips). Also, the dispersion of pollutants during non-uniform atmospheric conditions, metal wall temperatures in the case of gas turbine blades in which the inlet gas temperatures exceed the melting point of the material of the blade, cooling problems in electrical motors, various phase-change problems, and so on, are a few examples of such complex problems. Although it is possible to derive the governing equations and boundary conditions from first principles, it is difficult to obtain any form of analytical solution to such problems. The complexity is due to the fact that either the geometry, or some other feature of the problem, is irregular or arbitrary. Analytical solutions rarely exist; yet these are the kinds of problems that engineers and scientists solve on a day-to-day basis.

Among the various numerical methods that have evolved over the years, the most commonly used techniques are the finite difference, finite volume and finite element methods. The finite difference is a well-established and conceptually simple method that requires a point-wise approximation to the governing equations. The model, formed by writing the difference equations for an array of grid points, can be improved by increasing the number of points. Although many heat transfer problems may be solved using the finite difference

Fundamentals of the Finite Element Method for Heat and Fluid Flow R. W. Lewis, P. Nithiarasu and K. N. Seetharamu
© 2004 John Wiley & Sons, Ltd ISBNs: 0-470-84788-3 (HB); 0-470-84789-1 (PB)

methods (Ozisik and Czisik 1994), as soon as irregular geometries or an unusual speci-fication of boundary conditions are encountered, the finite difference technique becomes difficult to use.

The finite volume method is a further refined version of the finite difference method and has become popular in computational fluid dynamics (Patankar 1980). The vertex-centred finite volume technique is very similar to the linear finite element method (Malan *et al.* 2002).

The finite element method (Baker 1985; Bathe 1982; Chandrupatla and Belegundu 1991; Huebner and Thornton 1982; Hughes 2000; Lewis *et al.* 1996; Rao 1989; Reddy 1993; Segerlind 1984; Zienkiewicz and Morgan 1983; Zienkiewicz and Taylor 2000) considers that the solution region comprises many small, interconnected, sub-regions or elements and gives a piece-wise approximation to the governing equations, that is, the complex partial differential equations are reduced to either linear or nonlinear simultaneous equations. Thus, the finite element discretization (i.e., dividing the region into a number of smaller regions) procedure reduces the continuum problem, which has an infinite number of unknowns, to one with a finite number of unknowns at specified points referred to as *nodes*. Since the finite element method allows us to form the elements, or sub-regions, in an arbitrary sense, a close representation of the boundaries of complicated domains is possible.

Most of the finite difference schemes used in fluid dynamics and heat transfer problems can be viewed as special cases within a weighted residual framework. For weighted residual procedures, the error in the approximate solution of the conservation equations is not set to zero, but instead its integral, with respect to selected 'weights', is required to vanish. Within this family, the collocation method reproduces the classical finite difference equations, whereas the finite volume algorithm is obtained by using constant weights.

For engineers whose expertise lies in fluid dynamics and heat transfer, the finite element approaches introduced by mathematicians or structural analysts, may be difficult to follow. Therefore, in this book we intend to present a step-by-step procedure of the finite element method as applied to heat transfer problems. In doing so, we intend to present the topic in as simplified a form as possible so that both students and practising engineers can benefit.

A numerical model for a heat transfer problem starts with the physical model of the problem, an example of which is shown in Figure 3.1. As can be seen, one part of the model deals with the discretization of the domain and the other carries out the discrete approxima-tion of the partial differential equations. Finally, by combining both, the numerical solution to the problem is achieved.

The solution of a continuum problem by the finite element method is approximated by the following step-by-step process[1].

1. *Discretize the continuum*

Divide the solution region into non-overlapping elements or sub-regions. The finite element discretization allows a variety of element shapes, for example, triangles, quadrilat-erals. Each element is formed by the connection of a certain number of nodes (Figure 3.2).

---

[1]It should be noted that on first reading, these steps may not be very obvious to beginners. However, these steps will be clear as we go through the details in the following sections

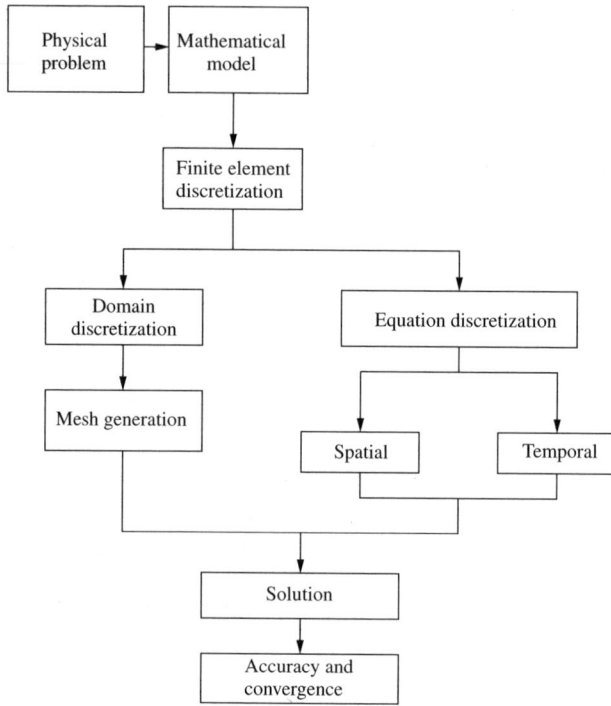

Figure 3.1   Numerical model for heat transfer calculations

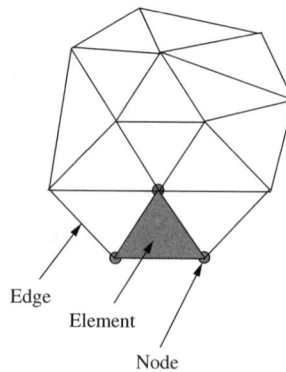

Figure 3.2   Typical finite element mesh. Elements, nodes and edges

The number of nodes employed to form an element depends on the type of element (or interpolation function).

2. *Select interpolation or shape functions*

   The next step is to choose the type of interpolation function that represents the variation of the field variable over an element. The number of nodes form an element; the nature and number of unknowns at each node decide the variation of a field variable within the element.

3. *Form element equations (Formulation)*

Next, we have to determine the matrix equations that express the properties of the individual elements by forming an element Left Hand Side (LHS) matrix and load vector. For example, a typical LHS matrix and a load vector can be written as

$$[\mathbf{K}]_e = \frac{Ak}{l} \begin{bmatrix} 1 & -1 \\ -1 & 1 \end{bmatrix} \tag{3.1}$$

$$\{\mathbf{f}\}_e = \begin{Bmatrix} Q_i \\ Q_j \end{Bmatrix} \tag{3.2}$$

where the subscript e represents an element; Q is the total heat transferred; k is the thermal conductivity; l is the length of a one-dimensional linear element and i and j represent the nodes forming an element. The unknowns are the temperature values on the nodes.

4. *Assemble the element equations to obtain a system of simultaneous equations*

To find the properties of the overall system, we must assemble all the individual element equations, that is, to combine the matrix equations of each element in an appropriate way such that the resulting matrix represents the behaviour of the entire solution region of the problem. The boundary conditions must be incorporated after the assemblage of the individual element contributions (see Appendix C), that is,

$$[\mathbf{K}]\{\mathbf{T}\} = \{\mathbf{f}\} \tag{3.3}$$

where $[\mathbf{K}]$ is the global LHS matrix, which is the assemblage of the individual element LHS matrices, as given in Equation 3.1, $\{\mathbf{f}\}$ is the global load vector, which is the assemblage of the individual element load vectors the Equation 3.2, and $\{\mathbf{T}\}$ is the global unknown vector.

5. *Solve the system of equations*

The resulting set of algebraic equations, Equation 3.3, may now be solved to obtain the nodal values of the field variable, for example, temperature.

6. *Calculate the secondary quantities*

From the nodal values of the field variable, for example, temperatures, we can then calculate the secondary quantities, for example, space heat fluxes.

3.2   Elements and Shape Functions

As shown in Figure 3.1, the finite element method involves the discretization of both the domain and the governing equations. In this process, the variables are represented in a piece-wise manner over the domain. By dividing the solution region into a number of small regions, called *elements*, and approximating the solution over these regions by a suitable known function, a relation between the differential equations and the elements is established. The functions employed to represent the nature of the solution within each element are called shape functions, or interpolating functions, or basis functions. They are called *interpolating functions* as they are used to determine the value of the field variable within an element by interpolating the nodal values. They are also known as *basis functions* as they form the basis of the discretization method. Polynomial type functions have been

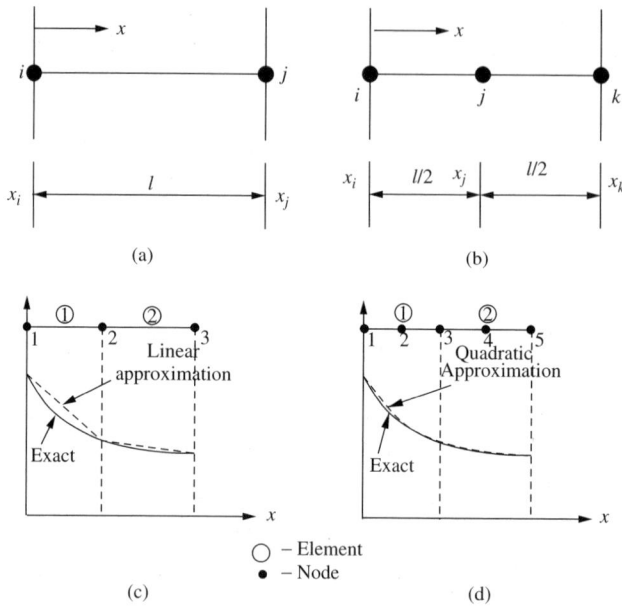

Figure 3.3   One-dimensional finite elements. (a) A linear element, (b) a quadratic element, (c) linear and (d) quadratic variation of temperature over an element

most widely used as they can be integrated, or differentiated, easily and the accuracy of the results can be improved by increasing the order of the polynomial as shown in Figure 3.3(c) and (d).

3.2.1   One-dimensional linear element

Many industrial and environmental problems may be approximated using a one-dimensional finite element model. For instance, pipe flow, river flow, heat transfer through a fin with a uniform cross section, and so on, can be resolved approximately using a one-dimensional assumption. Figure 3.3 shows the temperature profile in an element as represented by linear and quadratic polynomials.

Let us consider a typical linear element with end nodes 'i' and 'j' with the corresponding temperature being denoted by T_i and T_j respectively.

The linear temperature variation in the element is represented by

$$T(x) = \alpha_1 + \alpha_2 x \tag{3.4}$$

where T is the temperature at any location x and the parameters α_1, and α_2 are constants. Since there are two arbitrary constants in the linear representation, it requires only two nodes to determine the values of α_1, and α_2, namely,

$$T_i = \alpha_1 + \alpha_2 x_i$$

$$T_j = \alpha_1 + \alpha_2 x_j \tag{3.5}$$

From the above equations, we get

$$\alpha_1 = \frac{T_i x_j - T_j x_i}{x_j - x_i}$$

$$\alpha_2 = \frac{T_j - T_i}{x_j - x_i} \tag{3.6}$$

On substituting the values of α_1, and α_2 into Equation 3.4 we get

$$T = T_i \left[\frac{x_j - x}{x_j - x_i} \right] + T_j \left[\frac{x - x_i}{x_j - x_i} \right] \tag{3.7}$$

or

$$T = N_i T_i + N_j T_j = \begin{bmatrix} N_i & N_j \end{bmatrix} \begin{Bmatrix} T_i \\ T_j \end{Bmatrix} \tag{3.8}$$

where N_i and N_j are called *Shape functions* or *Interpolation functions* or *Basis functions*.

$$N_i = \left[\frac{x_j - x}{x_j - x_i} \right]$$

$$N_j = \left[\frac{x - x_i}{x_j - x_i} \right] \tag{3.9}$$

Equation 3.8 can be rewritten as

$$T = [\mathbf{N}]\{\mathbf{T}\} \tag{3.10}$$

where

$$[\mathbf{N}] = \begin{bmatrix} N_i & N_j \end{bmatrix} \tag{3.11}$$

is the shape function matrix and

$$\{\mathbf{T}\} = \begin{Bmatrix} T_i \\ T_j \end{Bmatrix} \tag{3.12}$$

is the vector of unknown temperatures.

Equation 3.8 shows that the temperature T at any location x can be calculated using the shape functions N_i and N_j evaluated at x. The shape functions at different locations within an element are tabulated in Table 3.1.

Table 3.1 Properties of linear shape functions

Item	Node, i	Node, j	Arbitrary x
N_i	1	0	between 0 and 1
N_j	0	1	between 0 and 1
$N_i + N_j$	1	1	1

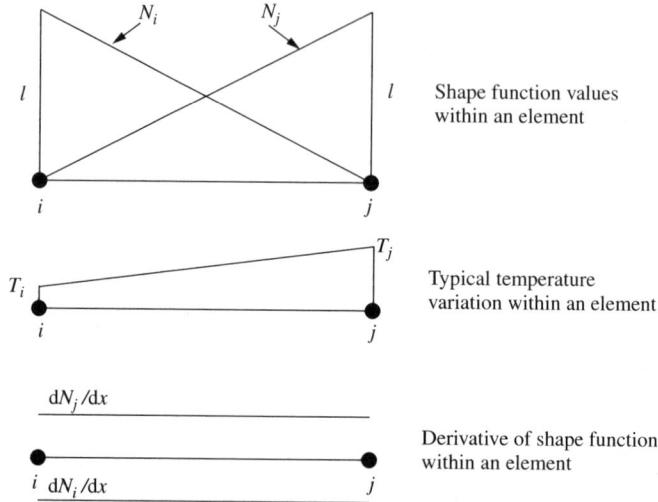

Figure 3.4   Variation of shape functions, temperature and derivatives within a linear element

The shape function assumes a value of unity at the designated node and zero at all other nodes. We also see that the sum of all the shape functions in an element is equal to unity anywhere within the element including the boundaries. These are the two essential requirements of the properties of the shape functions of any element in one, two or three dimensions. Figure 3.4 shows the variation of the shape functions and their derivatives within a linear element. A typical linear variation of temperature is also shown in this figure. As seen, the derivatives of the shape functions are constant within an element.

From Equation 3.8, the temperature gradient is calculated as

$$\frac{dT}{dx} = \frac{dN_i}{dx}T_i + \frac{dN_j}{dx}T_j = -\frac{1}{x_j - x_i}T_i + \frac{1}{x_j - x_i}T_j \tag{3.13}$$

or

$$\frac{dT}{dx} = \begin{bmatrix} -\frac{1}{l} & \frac{1}{l} \end{bmatrix} \begin{Bmatrix} T_i \\ T_j \end{Bmatrix} \tag{3.14}$$

where l is the length of an element equal to $(x_j - x_i)$.

Thus, we observe that the temperature gradient is constant within an element as the temperature variation is linear. We can rewrite Equation 3.14 as

$$g = [\mathbf{B}]\{\mathbf{T}\} \tag{3.15}$$

where g is the gradient of the field variable T

[**B**] is the derivative matrix, or strain matrix in structural mechanics, which relates the gradient of the field variable to the nodal values and $\{\mathbf{T}\}$ is the temperature vector.

The shape function matrix [**N**] and the derivative matrix [**B**] are the two important matrices that are used in the determination of the element properties as we shall see later in this chapter.

Example 3.2.1 *Calculate the temperature of an 8-cm long bar at a distance of 5 cm from one end where the temperature is 120°C with the other end at a temperature of 200°C. Assume the temperature variation between the two end points as being linear.*

From Equation 3.8, the temperature distribution over an element can be written as

$$T = N_i T_i + N_j T_j \tag{3.16}$$

where, at $x = 5$ *cm*

$$N_i = \frac{x_j - x}{x_j - x_i} = \frac{3}{8}$$

$$N_j = \frac{x - x_i}{x_j - x_i} = \frac{5}{8} \tag{3.17}$$

Substituting into Equation 3.16, we get $T = 170°C$. *Note that* $N_i + N_j = 1$.

3.2.2   One-dimensional quadratic element

We can see from Figure 3.3(d) that a better approximation for the temperature profile could be achieved if we use parabolic arcs over each element rather than linear segments. The function $T(x)$ would therefore be quadratic in x within each element and is of the form

$$T(x) = \alpha_1 + \alpha_2 x + \alpha_3 x^2 \tag{3.18}$$

We now have three parameters to determine and hence we need the temperature at one more point in addition to two end points of an element. We choose the mid-point in addition to the end values to get the following equations for the temperature at these three locations,

$$T_i = \alpha_1$$

$$T_j = \alpha_1 + \alpha_2 \frac{l}{2} + \alpha_3 \left(\frac{l}{2}\right)^2$$

$$T_k = \alpha_1 + \alpha_2 l + \alpha_3 l^2 \tag{3.19}$$

From the above three equations, we obtain the following values for the three constants α_1, α_2 and α_3.

$$\alpha_1 = T_i$$

$$\alpha_2 = \frac{1}{l}(-3T_i + 4T_j - T_k)$$

$$\alpha_3 = \frac{2}{l^2}(T_i - 2T_j + T_k) \tag{3.20}$$

Substituting the values of α_1, α_2 and α_3, into Equation 3.18 and collating the coefficients of T_i, T_j and T_k, we get

$$T = T_i\left[1 - \frac{3x}{l} + \frac{2x^2}{l^2}\right] + T_j\left[4\frac{x}{l} - 4\frac{x^2}{l^2}\right] + T_k\left[2\frac{x^2}{l^2} - \frac{x}{l}\right] \tag{3.21}$$

or

$$T = N_i T_i + N_j T_j + N_k T_k \qquad (3.22)$$

Hence the shape functions for a one-dimensional quadratic element are obtained from Equation 3.21 as follows:

$$N_i = \left[1 - \frac{3x}{l} + \frac{2x^2}{l^2} \right]$$

$$N_j = \left[4\frac{x}{l} - 4\frac{x^2}{l^2} \right]$$

$$N_k = \left[2\frac{x^2}{l^2} - \frac{x}{l} \right] \qquad (3.23)$$

The variation of temperature and shape functions of a typical quadratic element is shown in Figure 3.5. The first derivative of temperature can now be written as

$$\frac{dT}{dx} = \frac{dN_i}{dx} T_i + \frac{dN_j}{dx} T_j + \frac{dN_k}{dx} T_k \qquad (3.24)$$

or

$$\frac{dT}{dx} = \left[\frac{4x}{l^2} - \frac{3}{l} \right] T_i + \left[\frac{4}{l} - \frac{8x}{l^2} \right] T_j + \left[\frac{4x}{l^2} - \frac{1}{l} \right] T_k \qquad (3.25)$$

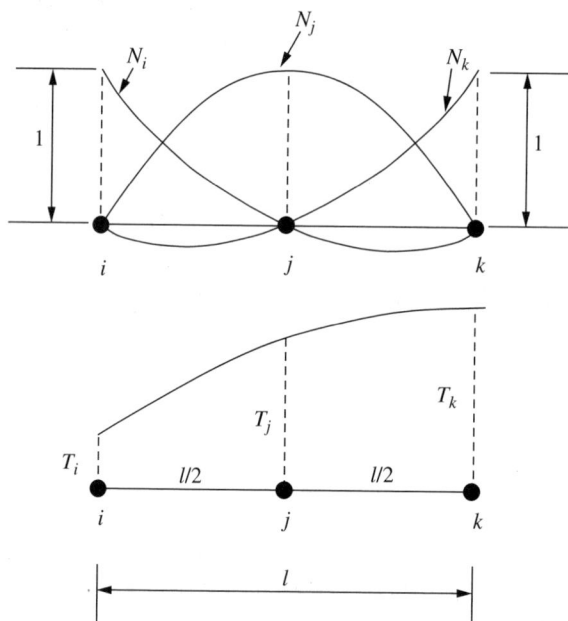

Figure 3.5 Variation of shape functions and their derivatives over a one-dimensional quadratic element

In matrix form,

$$g = [\mathbf{B}]\{\mathbf{T}\} \tag{3.26}$$

The [**B**] matrix is given as

$$[\mathbf{B}] = \left[\left(\frac{4x}{l^2} - \frac{3}{l} \right) \ \left(\frac{4}{l} - \frac{8x}{l^2} \right) \ \left(\frac{4x}{l^2} - \frac{1}{l} \right) \right] \tag{3.27}$$

Equation 3.23 shows that $N_i = 1$ at i and 0 at j and k, $N_j = 1$ at j and 0 at i and k and $N_k = 1$ at k and 0 at i and j.

It can be verified easily that within an element the summation over the shape functions is equal to unity, that is,

$$\sum_{i=1}^{3} N_i = 1 \tag{3.28}$$

For example at the point $x = l/4$, the shape function values are

$$N_i = 1 - \frac{3}{4} + \frac{2}{16} = \frac{6}{16}$$

$$N_j = 1 - \frac{4}{16} = \frac{12}{16}$$

$$N_k = \frac{2}{16} - \frac{1}{4} = -\frac{2}{16} \tag{3.29}$$

and it can be easily seen that the sum of the above three shape functions is equal to 1.

It can also be observed that even though the derivatives of the quadratic element are functions of the independent variable x, they will not be continuous at the inter-element nodes. The type of interpolation used here is known as Lagrangian (as they can be generated by Lagrangian interpolation formulae) and it only guarantees the continuity of the function across the inter-element boundaries. These types of elements are known as C^0 *elements*, in which the superscript indicates that only derivatives of zero order are continuous, that is, only the function is continuous. The elements that also assure the continuity of derivatives across inter-element boundaries, in addition to the continuity of functions, are known as C^1 *elements* and such functions are known as *Hermite polynomials*.

The C^0 shape functions can be determined in a general way by using Lagrangian polynomial formulae. The one-dimensional $(n - 1)$ th order Lagrange interpolation polynomial is the ratio of two products. For an element with n nodes, $(n - 1)$ order polynomial, the interpolation function is

$$N_k^e(x) = \Pi_{i=1}^{n} \frac{x - x_i}{x_k - x_i} \tag{3.30}$$

Note that in the above equation $k \neq i$. For a one-dimensional linear element, the shape functions can be written using Equation 3.30, as $(n = 2)$

$$N_1 = \frac{x - x_2}{x_1 - x_2} \quad \text{and} \quad N_2 = \frac{x - x_1}{x_2 - x_1} \tag{3.31}$$

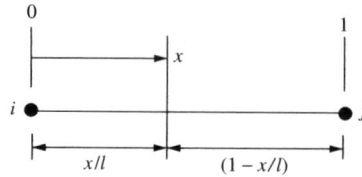

Figure 3.6   A one-dimensional linear element represented by local coordinates

Note that N_1 and N_2 are the shape functions corresponding to the two nodes of a one-dimensional linear element (N_i and N_j).

If we use local coordinates, as shown in Figure 3.6, with $x_1 = 0$ and $x_2 = 1$, then the shape functions (Equation 3.31) become

$$N_i = \left(1 - \frac{x}{l}\right) = L_i \quad \text{and} \quad N_j = \left(\frac{x}{l}\right) = L_j \tag{3.32}$$

where L_i and L_j are the shape functions defined by the local coordinate system. For a one-dimensional quadratic element, the shape functions using Lagrangian multipliers are given as follows:

$$N_1 = \frac{x - x_2}{x_1 - x_2} \frac{x - x_3}{x_1 - x_3}$$

$$N_2 = \frac{x - x_1}{x_2 - x_1} \frac{x - x_3}{x_2 - x_3}$$

$$N_3 = \frac{x - x_1}{x_3 - x_1} \frac{x - x_2}{x_3 - x_2} \tag{3.33}$$

If we substitute $x_1 = 0$, $x_2 = l/2$ and $x_3 = l$, in the above equation, we can immediately verify that the resulting equations are identical to the one derived from Equation 3.23.

Similarly, cubic elements, or any other one-dimensional higher-order element shape functions, can easily be derived using the Lagrangian interpolation formula.

For the case of quadratic and cubic elements, a better approximation of curved shapes is possible as we have more than two points placed along the boundaries of an element.

3.2.3   Two-dimensional linear triangular elements

When one-dimensional approximations are insufficient, multi-dimensional solution procedures need to be employed. In this section, we introduce for the first time a two-dimensional element. The simplest geometric shape that can be employed to approximate irregular surfaces is the triangle and it is one of the popular elements currently used in finite element calculations. This is partly due to the advances made on unstructured and adaptive mesh generation techniques in recent times (Thompson *et al.* 1999).

The two-dimensional linear triangular element, also known as a *simplex element*, is represented by

$$T(x, y) = \alpha_1 + \alpha_2 x + \alpha_3 y \tag{3.34}$$

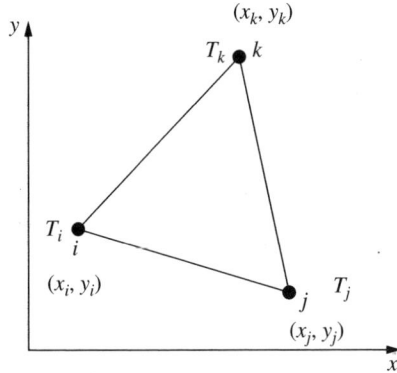

Figure 3.7   A linear triangular element

where the polynomial is linear in x and y and contains three coefficients. Since a linear triangle has three nodes (Figure 3.7), the values of α_1, α_2 and α_3 are determined from

$$T_i = \alpha_1 + \alpha_2 x_i + \alpha_3 y_i$$
$$T_j = \alpha_1 + \alpha_2 x_j + \alpha_3 y_j$$
$$T_k = \alpha_1 + \alpha_2 x_k + \alpha_3 y_k \tag{3.35}$$

which results in the following:

$$\alpha_1 = \frac{1}{2A} \left[(x_j y_k - x_k y_j) T_i + (x_k y_i - x_i y_k) T_j + (x_i y_j - x_j y_i) T_k \right]$$

$$\alpha_2 = \frac{1}{2A} \left[(y_j - y_k) T_i + (y_k - y_i) T_j + (y_i - y_j) T_k \right]$$

$$\alpha_3 = \frac{1}{2A} \left[(x_k - x_j) T_i + (x_i - x_k) T_j + (x_j - x_i) T_k \right] \tag{3.36}$$

where 'A' is the area of the triangle given by

$$2A = \det \begin{bmatrix} 1 & x_i & y_i \\ 1 & x_j & y_j \\ 1 & x_k & y_k \end{bmatrix} = (x_i y_j - x_j y_i) + (x_k y_i - x_i y_k) + (x_j y_k - x_k y_j) \tag{3.37}$$

Substituting the values of α_1, α_2 and α_3 into Equation 3.35 and collating the coefficients of T_i, T_j and T_k, we get

$$T = N_i T_i + N_j T_j + N_k T_k = \begin{bmatrix} N_i & N_j & N_k \end{bmatrix} \begin{Bmatrix} T_i \\ T_j \\ T_k \end{Bmatrix} \tag{3.38}$$

where,

$$N_i = \frac{1}{2A}(a_i + b_i x + c_i y)$$

$$N_j = \frac{1}{2A}(a_j + b_j x + c_j y)$$

$$N_k = \frac{1}{2A}(a_k + b_k x + c_k y) \tag{3.39}$$

and

$$a_i = x_j y_k - x_k y_j; \quad b_i = y_j - y_k; \quad c_i = x_k - x_j$$

$$a_j = x_k y_i - x_i y_k; \quad b_j = y_k - y_i; \quad c_j = x_i - x_k$$

$$a_k = x_i y_j - x_j y_i; \quad b_k = y_i - y_j; \quad c_k = x_j - x_i \tag{3.40}$$

If we evaluate N_i at node i, where the coordinates are (x_i, y_i), then we obtain

$$(N_i)_i = \frac{1}{2A}\left[(x_j y_k - x_k y_j) + (y_j - y_k)x_i + (x_k - x_j)y_i\right] = \frac{2A}{2A} = 1 \tag{3.41}$$

Similarly, it can readily be verified that $(N_j)_i = (N_k)_i = 0$.

Thus, we see that the shape functions have a value of unity at the designated vertex and zero at all other vertices. It is possible to show that

$$N_i + N_j + N_k = 1 \tag{3.42}$$

everywhere in the element, including the boundaries.

The gradients of the temperature T are given by

$$\frac{\partial T}{\partial x} = \frac{\partial N_i}{\partial x}T_i + \frac{\partial N_j}{\partial x}T_j + \frac{\partial N_k}{\partial x}T_k = \frac{b_i}{2A}T_i + \frac{b_j}{2A}T_j + \frac{b_k}{2A}T_k$$

$$\frac{\partial T}{\partial y} = \frac{\partial N_i}{\partial y}T_i + \frac{\partial N_j}{\partial y}T_j + \frac{\partial N_k}{\partial y}T_k = \frac{c_i}{2A}T_i + \frac{c_j}{2A}T_j + \frac{c_k}{2A}T_k \tag{3.43}$$

or

$$\{\mathbf{g}\} = \begin{Bmatrix} \dfrac{\partial T}{\partial x} \\[2mm] \dfrac{\partial T}{\partial y} \end{Bmatrix} = \frac{1}{2A}\begin{bmatrix} b_i & b_j & b_k \\ c_i & c_j & c_k \end{bmatrix}\begin{Bmatrix} T_i \\ T_j \\ T_k \end{Bmatrix} = [\mathbf{B}]\{\mathbf{T}\} \tag{3.44}$$

It should be noted that both $\partial T/\partial x$ and $\partial T/\partial y$ are constants within an element as b_i, b_j, b_k and c_i, c_j, c_k are constants for a given triangle. Hence, the heat fluxes q_x and q_y are also constants within a linear triangular element. Since the temperature varies linearly within an element, it is possible to draw the isotherms within a linear triangle and this is illustrated in the following example.

Example 3.2.2 *As an illustration of the method of calculation, let us calculate the temperature, T and heat fluxes q_x and q_y within an element for the data given in Table 3.2*

Calculate the temperature T, and the heat flux components q_x and q_y at (2.0, 1.0) if the thermal conductivity of the material is 2 W/cm K. Draw the isothermal line for $60°C$ in the triangle.

Table 3.2   Data for Example 3.2.2

Node	x (cm)	y (cm)	$T°C$
i	0.0	0.0	50.0
j	4.0	0.0	70.0
k	0.0	2.5	100.0

The temperature at any location within the triangle is given by Equation 3.38

The shape functions are calculated using Equation 3.39 with the x and y coordinates as given in Table 3.2. The result is

$$N_i = \frac{1}{10}$$

$$N_j = \frac{5}{10}$$

$$N_k = \frac{4}{10} \tag{3.45}$$

The substitution of the nodal temperatures and the above shape function values into Equation 3.38 results in the temperature of the point (2.0, 1.0) being

$$T = N_i T_i + N_j T_j + N_k T_k = \frac{1}{10}(50) + \frac{5}{10}(70) + \frac{4}{10}(100) = 80°C \tag{3.46}$$

The components of heat flux in the x and y directions are calculated as

$$\left\{ \begin{matrix} q_x \\ q_y \end{matrix} \right\} = -\frac{k}{2A} \begin{bmatrix} b_i & b_j & b_k \\ c_i & c_j & c_k \end{bmatrix} \left\{ \begin{matrix} T_i \\ T_j \\ T_k \end{matrix} \right\} = -\frac{2}{10} \begin{bmatrix} 50 \\ 200 \end{bmatrix} \tag{3.47}$$

The position of the 60°C isotherm may be obtained from Figure 3.8. From the given temperature values, it is clear that one 60°C point lies on the side ij (point P) and another lies on the side ik (point Q). It should be noted that the temperature varies linearly along these sides, that is, temperature is directly proportional to distance.

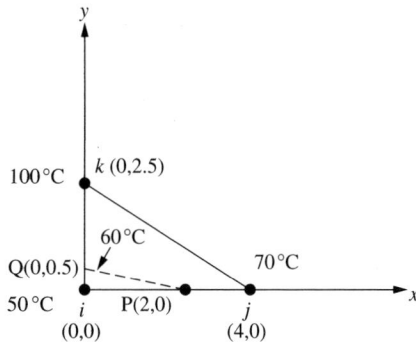

Figure 3.8   Isotherm within a linear triangular element

In order to determine the location of P on ij, we have the following linear relation between the distances and temperature values, namely,

$$\frac{60.0 - 50.0}{70.0 - 50.0} = \frac{\sqrt{(x_P - x_i)^2 + (y_P - y_i)^2}}{\sqrt{(x_j - x_i)^2 + (y_j - y_i)^2}} \tag{3.48}$$

From the data given, it is clear that the y coordinate on the ij side are equal to zero and thus the above equation is simplified to

$$\frac{10.0}{20.0} = \frac{(x_P - x_i)}{(x_j - x_i)} \tag{3.49}$$

which results in $x_P = 2.0$ cm. The location of Q along ik can be determined in a similar fashion as

$$\frac{60.0 - 50.0}{100.0 - 50.0} = \frac{y_Q - y_i}{y_k - y_i} \tag{3.50}$$

which gives $y_Q = 0.5$ cm. The x coordinate of this point is zero.

The line joining P and Q will be the $60°C$ isothermal (Figure 3.8). It should be noted that the same principle can be used for arbitrary triangles.

3.2.4 Area coordinates

An area, or natural, coordinate system will now be introduced for triangular elements in order to simplify the solution process. Let us consider a point P within a triangle at any location as shown in Figure 3.9. The local coordinates L_i, L_j and L_k of this point can be established by calculating appropriate non-dimensional distances or areas. For example, L_i is defined as the ratio of the perpendicular distance from point P to the side 'jk' (OP) to the perpendicular distance of point 'i' from the side 'jk' (QR). Thus,

$$L_i = \frac{OP}{QR} \tag{3.51}$$

Similarly, L_j and L_k are also defined. The value of L_i is also equal to the ratio of the area A_i (opposite to node 'i') to the total area of the triangle, that is,

$$L_i = \frac{A_i}{A} = \frac{0.5(OP)(jk)}{0.5(QR)(jk)} = \frac{OP}{QR} \tag{3.52}$$

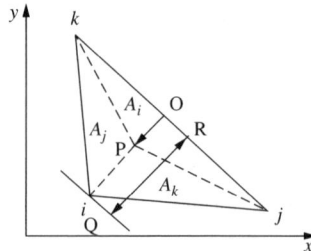

Figure 3.9   Area coordinates of a triangular element

Thus, the local coordinate L_i varies from 0 on the side jk to 1 at the node i. From Figure 3.9 it is obvious that

$$A_i + A_j + A_k = A \tag{3.53}$$

or

$$\frac{A_i}{A} + \frac{A_j}{A} + \frac{A_k}{A} = 1 \tag{3.54}$$

therefore

$$L_i + L_j + L_k = 1 \tag{3.55}$$

The relationship between the (x, y) coordinates and the natural, or area, coordinates are given by

$$x = L_i x_i + L_j x_j + L_k x_k \tag{3.56}$$

and

$$y = L_i y_i + L_j y_j + L_k y_k \tag{3.57}$$

From Equations 3.55, 3.56 and 3.57, the following relations for the local coordinates can be derived:

$$L_i = \frac{1}{2A}(a_i + b_i x + c_i y)$$

$$L_j = \frac{1}{2A}(a_j + b_j x + c_j y)$$

$$L_k = \frac{1}{2A}(a_k + b_k x + c_k y) \tag{3.58}$$

where the constants a, b and c are defined in Equation 3.40. Comparing with Equation 3.39, it is clear that

$$L_i = N_i$$

$$L_j = N_j$$

$$L_k = N_k \tag{3.59}$$

Thus, the local or area coordinates in a triangle are the same as the shape functions for a linear triangular element. In general, the local coordinates and shape functions are the same for linear elements irrespective of whether they are of one, two or three dimensions.

For a two-dimensional linear triangular element, with local coordinates L_i, L_j and L_k, we have a simple formula for integration over the triangle, that is,

$$\int_A L_i^a L_j^b L_k^c dA = \int_A N_i^a N_j^b N_k^c dA = \frac{a!b!c!}{(a+b+c+2)!} 2A \tag{3.60}$$

where 'A' is the area of a triangle. Note that L_i, L_j and L_k happen to be the shape functions for a linear triangular element. Example 3.2.2 can also be solved using the local coordinates via Equations 3.53 and 3.56, that is, on substituting the x and y coordinates of the three points (Table 3.2) of the triangle into Equation 3.56, we obtain

$$L_j = \frac{x}{4} \tag{3.61}$$

and

$$L_k = \frac{y}{2.5} \qquad (3.62)$$

From Equation 3.55, we get

$$L_i = 1 - \frac{x}{4} - \frac{y}{2.5} \qquad (3.63)$$

At $(x, y) = (2, 1)$, we have

$$L_i = 0.1 = N_i$$
$$L_j = 0.5 = N_j$$
$$L_k = 0.4 = N_k \qquad (3.64)$$

Note that these local coordinates are exactly the same as the shape function values calculated in Example 3.2.2

3.2.5 Quadratic triangular elements

We can write a quadratic approximation over a triangular element as

$$T = \alpha_1 + \alpha_2 x + \alpha_3 y + \alpha_4 x^2 + \alpha_5 y^2 + \alpha_6 xy \qquad (3.65)$$

Since there are six arbitrary constants, the quadratic triangle will have six nodes (Figure 3.10). The six constants $\alpha_1, \alpha_2, \ldots, \alpha_6$ can be evaluated by substitution of the nodal coordinates and the corresponding nodal temperatures $T_1, T_2, \ldots, T_6$. For example, we can write the following relationship for the first node:

$$T_1 = \alpha_1 + \alpha_2 x_1 + \alpha_3 y_1 + \alpha_4 x_1^2 + \alpha_5 y_1^2 + \alpha_6 x_1 y_1 \qquad (3.66)$$

Once $\alpha_1, \alpha_2, \ldots, \alpha_6$ are determined, then the substitution of these parameters into Equation 3.65 and collating the coefficients of $T_1, T_2, \ldots, T_6$, give relations for the shape functions. The process is both tedious and unnecessary. A much superior and more general

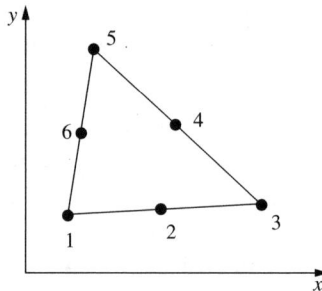

Figure 3.10   A quadratic triangular element

method of establishing the shape functions exists, which is based on local coordinates. The rationale behind this is given by Silvester (Silvester 1969) and can also be used to find the shape functions for a cubic triangular element.

Silvester introduced a triple-index numbering scheme $\alpha\beta\gamma$, which satisfies the following expression,

$$\alpha + \beta + \gamma = n \tag{3.67}$$

where n is the order of the interpolation polynomial used. We can write $N_{\alpha\beta\gamma}$ to denote the interpolation function for a node as a function of the area coordinates L_i, L_j and L_k, namely,

$$N_{\alpha\beta\gamma}(L_i, L_j, L_k) = N_\alpha(L_i)N_\beta(L_j)N_\gamma(L_k) \tag{3.68}$$

where

$$N_\alpha(L_i) = \Pi_{i=1}^\alpha \left[\frac{nL_i - i + 1}{i}\right] \quad \text{if} \quad \alpha \geq 1 \tag{3.69}$$

$$N_\alpha(L_i) = 1 \quad \text{if} \quad \alpha = 0 \tag{3.70}$$

Similarly, we can write relations for N_β and N_γ in terms of L_j and L_k respectively.

For a quadratic triangular element, as shown in Figure 3.11, the shape functions are designated as

Corner nodes: $N_1 = N_{200}$; $N_3 = N_{020}$; $N_5 = N_{002}$
Mid-side nodes: $N_2 = N_{110}$; $N_4 = N_{011}$; $N_6 = N_{101}$

Let us calculate typical terms, for example, N_{200} and N_{110}.

$$N_{200} = N_2(L_i)N_0(L_j)N_0(L_k) \tag{3.71}$$

In the above equation, $\alpha = 2, \beta = 0$ and $\gamma = 0$ and therefore, from equation 3.69 we have

$$N_\alpha = N_2(L_i) = \Pi_{i=1}^2 \left[\frac{nL_i - i + 1}{i}\right] = \left[\frac{2L_i - 1 + 1}{1}\right]\left[\frac{2L_i - 2 + 1}{2}\right] = L_i(2L_i - 1) \tag{3.72}$$

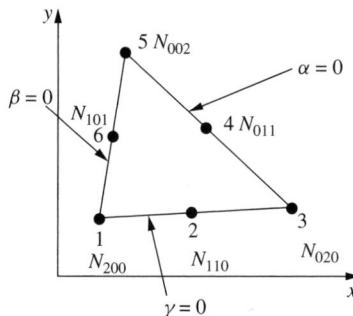

Figure 3.11   Shape function designations of a quadratic triangular element

and similarly
$$N_\beta = N_0(L_j) = 1 \quad \text{and} \quad N_\gamma = N_0(L_j) = 1 \tag{3.73}$$

Hence,
$$N_{200} = N_2(L_i)N_0(L_j)N_0(L_k) = L_i(2L_i - 1) = N_1 \tag{3.74}$$

is the shape function for node 1. Similarly,
$$N_3 = N_{020} = L_j(2L_j - 1) \quad \text{and}$$
$$N_5 = N_{002} = L_k(2L_k - 1) \tag{3.75}$$

For a middle node, with shape function N_{110}, we have
$$N_{110} = N_1(L_i)N_1(L_j)N_0(L_k)$$
$$= \left[\Pi_{i=1}^1 \left(\frac{2L_i - i + 1}{i}\right)\right]\left[\Pi_{i=1}^1 \left(\frac{2L_j - i + 1}{i}\right)\right]$$
$$= \left(\frac{2L_i - 1 + 1}{1}\right)\left(\frac{2L_j - 1 + 1}{1}\right) \tag{3.76}$$

Thus,
$$N_2 = N_{110} = 4L_iL_j \tag{3.77}$$

Similarly,
$$N_4 = N_{011} = 4L_jL_k$$
$$N_6 = N_{101} = 4L_kL_i \tag{3.78}$$

We can summarize the nodal shape functions for a quadratic triangle as follows:
For corner nodes,
$$N_m = L_n(2L_n - 1) \quad \text{with} \quad m = 1, 3, 5 \quad \text{and} \quad n = i, j, k \tag{3.79}$$

and for nodes at centres,
$$N_2 = 4L_iL_j$$
$$N_4 = 4L_jL_k$$
$$N_6 = 4L_kL_i \tag{3.80}$$

In a similar way, we can show that the interpolation functions for a 10-node cubic triangle are (see Figure 3.12) as follows:
For corner nodes,
$$N_m = \frac{1}{2}L_n(3L_n - 1)(3L_n - 2) \quad \text{with} \quad m = 1, 4, 7 \quad \text{and} \quad n = i, j, k \tag{3.81}$$

Side ij
$$N_2 = \frac{9}{2}L_iL_j(3L_i - 1)$$
$$N_3 = \frac{9}{2}L_iL_j(3L_j - 1) \tag{3.82}$$

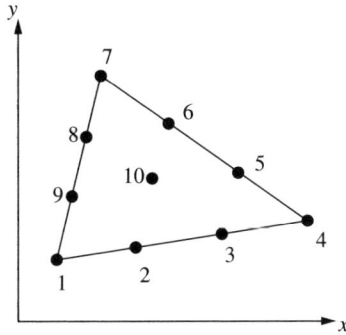

Figure 3.12   Ten-node cubic triangular element

Side jk

$$N_5 = \frac{9}{2} L_j L_k (3L_j - 1)$$

$$N_6 = \frac{9}{2} L_j L_k (3L_k - 1) \tag{3.83}$$

Side ki

$$N_8 = \frac{9}{2} L_k L_i (3L_k - 1)$$

$$N_9 = \frac{9}{2} L_k L_i (3L_i - 1) \tag{3.84}$$

and for the node at the centre of the triangle

$$N_{10} = 27 L_i L_j L_k \tag{3.85}$$

It is possible to derive shape functions for even higher-order elements using the same procedure.

3.2.6   Two-dimensional quadrilateral elements

The quadrilateral element has four nodes located at the vertices as shown in Figure 3.13. Eight and nine node quadrilaterals are also used in practice. The quadrilateral mesh resembles a finite difference mesh. However, for the case of a finite difference mesh, the mesh must be orthogonal, that is, all lines intersect at right angles to one another, whereas in the finite element mesh, each element can be unique in shape and each side may have a different slope. In its simplest form, the quadrilateral element becomes a *rectangular element* (Figure 3.14) with the boundaries of the element parallel to a coordinate system.

The temperature within a quadrilateral is represented by

$$T = \alpha_1 + \alpha_2 x + \alpha_3 y + \alpha_4 xy \tag{3.86}$$

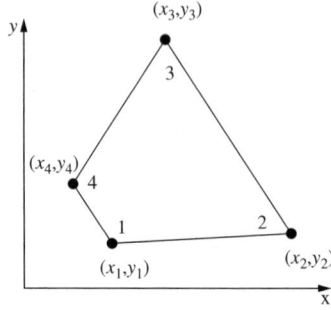

Figure 3.13   A typical quadrilateral element

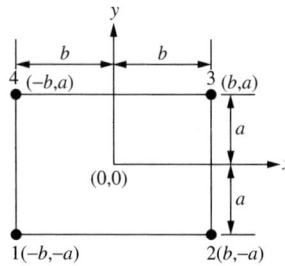

Figure 3.14   A simple rectangular element

and thus the temperature gradients may be written as

$$\frac{\partial T}{\partial x} = \alpha_2 + \alpha_4 y$$

$$\frac{\partial T}{\partial y} = \alpha_3 + \alpha_4 x \qquad (3.87)$$

Therefore, the gradient varies within the element in a linear way. On substituting the values of T_1, T_2, T_3 and T_4 into Equation 3.86 for the nodes $(x_1, y_1) \ldots (x_4, y_4)$ and solving, we obtain the values of α_1, α_2, α_3 and α_4. Substituting these relationships into Equation 3.86 and collating the coefficients of $T_1, T_2, \ldots, T_4$, we get

$$T = N_1 T_1 + N_2 T_2 + N_3 T_3 + N_4 T_4 \qquad (3.88)$$

where for a rectangular element (Figure 3.14),

$$N_1 = \frac{1}{4ab}(b - x)(a - y)$$

$$N_2 = \frac{1}{4ab}(b + x)(a - y)$$

$$N_3 = \frac{1}{4ab}(b + x)(a + y)$$

$$N_4 = \frac{1}{4ab}(b - x)(a + y) \qquad (3.89)$$

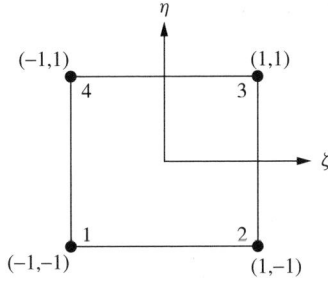

Figure 3.15   Non-dimensional coordinates of a rectangular element

We can express these shape functions in terms of length ratios x/b and y/a as

$$N_1 = \frac{1}{4ab}(b-x)(a-y) = \frac{1}{4}\left(1 - \frac{x}{b}\right)\left(1 - \frac{y}{a}\right) = \frac{1}{4}(1-\zeta)(1-\eta) \tag{3.90}$$

where

$$-1 \leq \zeta \leq 1 \quad \text{and} \quad -1 \leq \eta \leq 1 \tag{3.91}$$

are the non-dimensional coordinates of an element (Figure 3.15). The shape functions can also be obtained using Lagrange interpolation functions (Equation 3.30) as

$$N_1 = \frac{(x-b)(y-a)}{(-b-b)(-a-a)} = \frac{1}{4ab}(b-x)(a-y) = \frac{1}{4}(1-\zeta)(1-\eta)$$

$$N_2 = \frac{(x-(-b))(y-a)}{(b-(-b))(-a-a)} = \frac{1}{4ab}(b+x)(a-y) = \frac{1}{4}(1+\zeta)(1-\eta)$$

$$N_3 = \frac{(x-(-b))(y-(-a))}{(b-(-b))(-a-a)} = \frac{1}{4ab}(b+x)(a+y) = \frac{1}{4}(1+\zeta)(1+\eta)$$

$$N_4 = \frac{(x-b)(y-(-a))}{(-b-b)(a-(-a))} = \frac{1}{4ab}(b-x)(a+y) = \frac{1}{4}(1-\zeta)(1+\eta) \tag{3.92}$$

In general, the shape functions can be written as

$$N_i = (1 + \zeta\zeta_i)(1 + \eta\eta_i) \tag{3.93}$$

where (ζ_i, η_i) are the coordinates of the node 'i'.

Since the shape functions are linear in the x and y directions, they are referred to as a *bilinear* configuration. The derivatives can be expressed as follows:

$$\frac{\partial T}{\partial x} = \frac{\partial N_1}{\partial x}T_1 + \frac{\partial N_2}{\partial x}T_2 + \frac{\partial N_3}{\partial x}T_3 + \frac{\partial T_4}{\partial x}T_4$$

$$= \frac{1}{4ab}\left[-(a-y)T_1 + (a-y)T_2 + (a+y)T_3 - (a+y)T_4\right] \tag{3.94}$$

Similarly,

$$\frac{\partial T}{\partial y} = \frac{1}{4ab}\left[-(b-x)T_1 - (b+x)T_2 + (b+x)T_3 + (b-x)T_4\right] \tag{3.95}$$

The gradient matrix can be written as

$$\{\mathbf{g}\} = \begin{Bmatrix} \dfrac{\partial T}{\partial x} \\[2mm] \dfrac{\partial T}{\partial y} \end{Bmatrix} = \frac{1}{4ab} \begin{bmatrix} -(a-y) & (a-y) & (a+y) & -(a+y) \\ -(b-x) & -(b+x) & (b+x) & (b-x) \end{bmatrix} \begin{Bmatrix} T_1 \\ T_2 \\ T_3 \\ T_4 \end{Bmatrix}$$

$$= [\mathbf{B}]\{\mathbf{T}\} \tag{3.96}$$

The [**B**] matrix is written as

$$[\mathbf{B}] = \frac{1}{4} \begin{bmatrix} -(1-\eta) & (1-\eta) & (1+\eta) & -(1+\eta) \\ -(1-\zeta) & -(1+\zeta) & (1+\zeta) & (1-\zeta) \end{bmatrix} \tag{3.97}$$

Example 3.2.3 *Determine the temperature and the heat fluxes at a location (2, 1) in a square plate (Figure 3.16) with the data shown in Table 3.3. Draw the isothermal for 125°C.*

Note that the origin is at node 1. In order to use the shape functions already derived, we can determine the coordinates of the nodes with the origin at the centre of the square plate. Note that $2a = 2b = 5.0$

The temperature at any point within the element can be expressed as

$$T = N_1 T_1 + N_2 T_2 + N_3 T_3 + N_4 T_4 \tag{3.98}$$

The location of the point (2, 1), using the local coordinates and new origin at the centre, is $(-0.5, -1.5)$. The local co-ordinates of the four corner points are listed in Table 3.4.

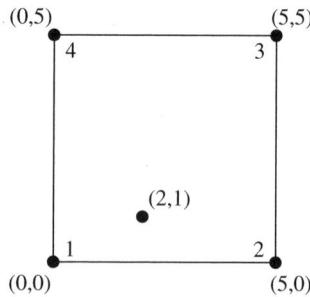

Figure 3.16   Square plate

Table 3.3   Data for Example 3.2.3

Node no.	x (cm)	y (cm)	Temperature (°C)
1	0.0	0.0	100.0
2	5.0	0.0	150.0
3	5.0	5.0	200.0
4	0.0	5.0	50.0

Table 3.4 Local coordinates for Example 3.2.3

Node	ζ	η
1	−2.5	−2.5
2	2.5	−2.5
3	2.5	2.5
4	−2.5	2.5

The shape functions at this point are calculated by substituting the new coordinates of point (2, 1), that is,

$$N_1 = \frac{1}{4ab}(b - x)(a - y) = \frac{12}{25}$$

$$N_2 = \frac{1}{4ab}(b + x)(a - y) = \frac{8}{25}$$

$$N_3 = \frac{1}{4ab}(b - x)(a + y) = \frac{2}{25}$$

$$N_4 = \frac{1}{4ab}(b - x)(a + y) = \frac{3}{25} \tag{3.99}$$

Note that $N_1 + N_2 + N_3 + N_4 = 1$.

Therefore, the temperature at the point $(-0.5, -1.5)$ is

$$T_{(-0.5,-1.5)} = \frac{12}{25}(100) + \frac{8}{25}(150) + \frac{2}{25}(200) + \frac{3}{25}(50) = 118°C \tag{3.100}$$

The heat fluxes can be calculated from Equation 3.96 as follows:

$$\begin{Bmatrix} q_x \\ q_y \end{Bmatrix} = - \begin{Bmatrix} k_x \dfrac{\partial T}{\partial x} \\ k_y \dfrac{\partial T}{\partial y} \end{Bmatrix}$$

$$= -\frac{2}{25} \begin{bmatrix} -4.0 & 4.0 & 1.0 & -1.0 \\ -3.0 & -2.0 & 2.0 & 3.0 \end{bmatrix} \begin{Bmatrix} 100.0 \\ 150.0 \\ 200.0 \\ 50.0 \end{Bmatrix}$$

$$= \begin{Bmatrix} 28.0 \\ 4.0 \end{Bmatrix} W/cm^2 \tag{3.101}$$

The isotherm of $125°C$ will not normally be a straight line owing to the bilinear nature of the elements. Thus, we need more than two points to represent an isotherm. It is certain that one point on side 1-2 and one on 3-4 will contain a point with a temperature of $125°C$. We know the y coordinates of both the sides 1-2 and 3-4. Thus, the x coordinate of the point on side 1-2 which has a temperature of $125°C$ is calculated by substituting $y = 0.0$ into the *temperature distribution of Equation 3.98, that is,*

$$125.0 = \frac{1}{25}[(2.5 - x)(2.5 - 0.0)100.0 + (2.5 + x)(2.5 - 0.0)150$$

$$+(2.5 + x)(2.5 + 0.0)200.0 + (2.5 - x)(2.5 + 0.0)50.0] \qquad (3.102)$$

which gives x = 2.5 and similarly, if we substitute a value of y = 5.0 for the side 3-4 the result is x = 2.5. These coordinates can be written in a local form as (0.0, −2.5) and (0.0, 2.5). From the two points found, it is clear that the 125°C isotherm crosses all horizontal lines between the bottom and top sides. Therefore, to determine another point, we can assume a 'y' value of 2.5 (0.0, in local form) and on substituting into Equation 3.98 results in an x coordinate of 2.5 (0.0, in local form). Connecting all three points will generate the 125°C isotherm.

3.2.7 Isoparametric elements

Many practical problems have curved boundaries, and it is often necessary to use a large number of straight-sided elements along the curved boundaries in order to achieve a reasonable geometric representation. The number of elements needed can be reduced considerably if curved elements are used with a consequential reduction in the total number of variables in the system. In the case of three-dimensional problems, the total number of variables is inherently large and a reduction in the total number of variables is very important, especially when there is a limitation on the computer memory/cost involved. While there are many methods of creating curved elements, the method most extensively used in practice involves isoparametric mapping from regular elements (Figure 3.17). Since the shape functions of the regular parent element are known in terms of a local coordinate system, those of the generated curvilinear element can also be determined. The mapping is simple and straightforward.

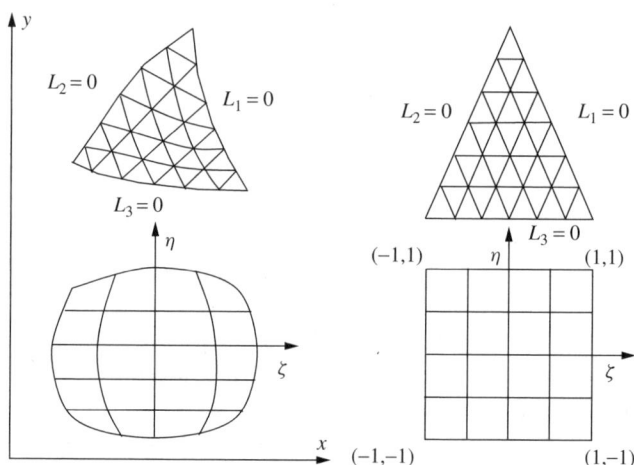

Figure 3.17   Isoparametric mapping of triangles and quadrilaterals

There are two sets of relations that must be defined when using the finite element method. One set determines the shape of the element and the other set defines the order of the interpolation function for the field variable. It is not necessary to use the same shape functions for the coordinate transformation and the interpolation equation. Thus, two different sets of global nodes can exist. Both sets of global nodes are identical in the case of isoparametric elements.

The natural coordinate system for the one-dimensional element is the length ratio defined such that $-1 \leq \zeta \leq 1$, where ζ is the natural coordinate. The origin of the coordinate is at the mid-point of the line segment. For a one-dimensional linear element (substituting $x = \zeta$, $x_1 = -1$ and $x_2 = 1$ into Equation 3.31), we obtain

$$N_i = \frac{\zeta - 1}{-1 - 1} = \frac{1}{2}(1 - \zeta)$$

$$N_j = \frac{\zeta - (-1)}{1 - (-1)} = \frac{1}{2}(1 + \zeta) \tag{3.103}$$

where i and j are the two nodes of a one-dimensional element. For a one-dimensional quadratic element, we have (Equation 3.33)

$$N_i = \frac{(\zeta - 0)(\zeta - 1)}{(-1 - 0)(-1 - 1)} = -\frac{\zeta}{2}(1 - \zeta)$$

$$N_j = \frac{(\zeta - (-1))(\zeta - 1)}{(0 - (-1))(0 - 1)} = (1 - \zeta^2)$$

$$N_k = \frac{(\zeta - (-1))\ (\zeta - 0)}{(1 - (-1))\ (1 - 0)} = \frac{\zeta}{2}(1 + \zeta) \tag{3.104}$$

where i, j and k represent the three nodes of the quadratic element. In order to calculate the stiffness matrix, we need the derivative of the shape functions with respect to the global coordinate, that is, with regard to x in this case. Therefore, a coordinate transformation of the type shown in Figure 3.17 should be determined. In either case, the functions $g(\zeta)$ and $g(x)$ are assumed to be one-to-one mappings.

The coordinate transformation can be written using the same functions as given in Equation 3.104, but substituting the coordinate value for the nodal parameter. Thus, the coordinate transformation becomes

$$x = N_i x_i + N_j x_j + N_k x_k \tag{3.105}$$

where N_i, N_j and N_k are given by Equation 3.104. The ζ derivative is

$$\frac{\mathrm{d}N_i}{\mathrm{d}\zeta} = \frac{\mathrm{d}N_i}{\mathrm{d}x}\frac{\mathrm{d}x}{\mathrm{d}\zeta} = \frac{\mathrm{d}N_i}{\mathrm{d}x}J_i \tag{3.106}$$

which gives

$$\frac{\mathrm{d}N_i}{\mathrm{d}x} = J_i^{-1}\frac{\mathrm{d}N_i}{\mathrm{d}\zeta} \tag{3.107}$$

The quantity $(dx/d\zeta)$ is called the *Jacobian of the coordinate transformation* and is denoted by $[J]$. For a one-dimensional coordinate, transformation $[J]$ is calculated using

$$[J] = \frac{dx}{d\zeta} = \frac{dN_i}{d\zeta}x_i + \frac{dN_j}{d\zeta}x_j + \frac{dN_k}{d\zeta}x_k \tag{3.108}$$

Example 3.2.4 *Derive the shape function derivatives for a one-dimensional quadratic element that has nodal coordinates $x_i = 2$, $x_j = 4$ and $x_k = 6$.*
The Jacobian matrix is written as

$$[J] = \frac{dx}{d\zeta}$$

$$= \frac{dN_i}{d\zeta}x_i + \frac{dN_j}{d\zeta}x_j + \frac{dN_k}{d\zeta}x_k$$

$$= \left(-\frac{1}{2}+\zeta\right)2 + (-2\zeta)4 + \left(\frac{1}{2}+\zeta\right)6$$

$$= 2 + 8\zeta - 8\zeta = 2 \tag{3.109}$$

thus,

$$[J]^{-1} = \frac{1}{2} \tag{3.110}$$

The shape function derivatives are written as follows:

$$\left\{\begin{array}{c} \dfrac{dN_i}{dx} \\[2mm] \dfrac{dN_j}{dx} \\[2mm] \dfrac{dN_k}{dx} \end{array}\right\} = [J]^{-1} \left\{\begin{array}{c} \dfrac{dN_i}{d\zeta} \\[2mm] \dfrac{dN_j}{d\zeta} \\[2mm] \dfrac{dN_k}{d\zeta} \end{array}\right\} = \frac{1}{2}\left\{\begin{array}{c} -\dfrac{1}{2}+\zeta \\[2mm] -2\zeta \\[2mm] \dfrac{1}{2}+\zeta \end{array}\right\} = \left\{\begin{array}{c} \dfrac{-1}{4}+\dfrac{\zeta}{2} \\[2mm] -\zeta \\[2mm] \dfrac{1}{4}+\dfrac{\zeta}{2} \end{array}\right\} \tag{3.111}$$

For two-dimensional cases, we may express x and y as functions of ζ and η, that is,

$$x = x(\zeta, \eta) \quad \text{and} \quad y = y(\zeta, \eta) \tag{3.112}$$

Since we deal with Cartesian derivatives for the calculation of the stiffness matrix, we transform the derivatives of the shape functions using the chain rule as follows,

$$\frac{\partial N_i}{\partial \zeta}(x, y) = \frac{\partial N_i}{\partial x}\frac{\partial x}{\partial \zeta} + \frac{\partial N_i}{\partial y}\frac{\partial y}{\partial \zeta}$$

$$\frac{\partial N_i}{\partial \eta}(x, y) = \frac{\partial N_i}{\partial x}\frac{\partial x}{\partial \eta} + \frac{\partial N_i}{\partial y}\frac{\partial y}{\partial \eta} \tag{3.113}$$

which can be written as

$$\left\{\begin{array}{c} \dfrac{\partial N_i}{\partial \zeta} \\[2mm] \dfrac{\partial N_i}{\partial \eta} \end{array}\right\} = \left[\begin{array}{cc} \dfrac{\partial x}{\partial \zeta} & \dfrac{\partial y}{\partial \zeta} \\[2mm] \dfrac{\partial x}{\partial \eta} & \dfrac{\partial y}{\partial \eta} \end{array}\right] \left\{\begin{array}{c} \dfrac{\partial N_i}{\partial x} \\[2mm] \dfrac{\partial N_i}{\partial y} \end{array}\right\} = [\mathbf{J}]\left\{\begin{array}{c} \dfrac{\partial N_i}{\partial x} \\[2mm] \dfrac{\partial N_i}{\partial y} \end{array}\right\} \tag{3.114}$$

Therefore, we can write

$$
\left\{
\begin{array}{c}
\dfrac{\partial N_i}{\partial x} \\[2mm]
\dfrac{\partial N_i}{\partial y}
\end{array}
\right\}
= [\mathbf{J}]^{-1}
\left\{
\begin{array}{c}
\dfrac{\partial N_i}{\partial \zeta} \\[2mm]
\dfrac{\partial N_i}{\partial \eta}
\end{array}
\right\}
\tag{3.115}
$$

Note that the inverse of the Jacobian matrix $[J]^{-1}$ is calculated as

$$
[\mathbf{J}]^{-1} = \frac{1}{\det [\mathbf{J}]}
\begin{bmatrix}
\dfrac{\partial y}{\partial \eta} & -\dfrac{\partial y}{\partial \zeta} \\[3mm]
-\dfrac{\partial x}{\partial \eta} & \dfrac{\partial x}{\partial \zeta}
\end{bmatrix}
\tag{3.116}
$$

The derivatives have to be numerically evaluated at each integration point, as a closed-form solution does not exist

For an eight-node isoparametric element (Figure 3.18) the values of the temperature T at any point are given by

$$
T = \sum_{i=1}^{8} N_i T_i
\tag{3.117}
$$

The coordinate values of x and y at any point within an element are given by the following expressions.

$$
x(\zeta, \eta) = \sum_{i=1}^{8} N_i(\zeta, \eta) x_i
$$

$$
y(\zeta, \eta) = \sum_{i=1}^{8} N_i(\zeta, \eta) y_i
\tag{3.118}
$$

where (x_i, y_i) are the coordinates of the node 'i' and the quadratic shape functions are given by

$$
N_1 = -\frac{1}{4}(1 - \zeta)(1 - \eta)(1 + \zeta + \eta)
$$

$$
N_2 = \frac{1}{2}(1 - \zeta^2)(1 - \eta)
$$

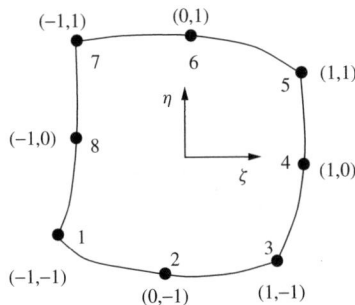

Figure 3.18   Eight-node isoparametric element

$$N_3 = \frac{1}{4}(1 + \zeta)(1 - \eta)(\zeta - \eta - 1)$$

$$N_4 = \frac{1}{2}(1 + \zeta)(1 - \eta^2)$$

$$N_5 = \frac{1}{4}(1 + \zeta)(1 + \eta)(\zeta + \eta - 1)$$

$$N_6 = \frac{1}{2}(1 - \zeta^2)(1 + \eta)$$

$$N_7 = \frac{1}{2}(1 - \zeta)(1 + \eta)(-\zeta + \eta - 1)$$

$$N_8 = \frac{1}{2}(1 - \zeta)(1 - \eta^2) \tag{3.119}$$

The ζ and η variables are curvilinear coordinates and as such their direction will vary with position. The nodes of the element are input in an anticlockwise sequence starting from any corner node. The directions of ζ and η are indicated on Figure 3.18, that is, positive ζ in the direction from nodes 1 to 3 and positive η in the direction from nodes 3 to 5.

Example 3.2.5 *Evaluate the partial derivatives of the shape functions at $\zeta = 1/2$, $\eta = 1/2$ of a quadrilateral element, assuming that the temperature is approximated by (a) bilinear and (b) quadratic interpolating polynomials.*

(a) Bilinear

The shape function derivatives in local coordinates are

$$\frac{\partial N_1}{\partial \zeta} = -\frac{1 - \eta}{4}; \quad \frac{\partial N_1}{\partial \eta} = -\frac{1 - \zeta}{4}$$

$$\frac{\partial N_2}{\partial \zeta} = \frac{1 - \eta}{4}; \quad \frac{\partial N_2}{\partial \eta} = -\frac{1 + \zeta}{4}$$

$$\frac{\partial N_3}{\partial \zeta} = \frac{1 + \eta}{4}; \quad \frac{\partial N_3}{\partial \eta} = \frac{1 + \zeta}{4}$$

$$\frac{\partial N_4}{\partial \zeta} = -\frac{1 + \eta}{4}; \quad \frac{\partial N_4}{\partial \eta} = \frac{1 - \zeta}{4} \tag{3.120}$$

The Jacobian matrix and its inverse are calculated from Equations 3.114 and 3.116, that is,

$$[\mathbf{J}] = \begin{bmatrix} \sum\limits_{i=1}^{4} \dfrac{\partial N_i}{\partial \zeta} x_i & \sum\limits_{i=1}^{4} \dfrac{\partial N_i}{\partial \zeta} y_i \\ \sum\limits_{i=1}^{4} \dfrac{\partial N_i}{\partial \eta} x_i & \sum\limits_{i=1}^{4} \dfrac{\partial N_i}{\partial \eta} y_i \end{bmatrix} = \frac{1}{8} \begin{bmatrix} 25 & 4 \\ 5 & 14 \end{bmatrix} \tag{3.121}$$

The determinant of the Jacobian matrix is

$$\det [\mathbf{J}] = \frac{(25)(14)}{(8)(8)} - \frac{(5)(4)}{(8)(8)} = \frac{330}{64} \tag{3.122}$$

Employing Equation 3.116

$$[\mathbf{J}]^{-1} = \frac{8}{330}\begin{bmatrix} 14 & -4 \\ -5 & 25 \end{bmatrix} \tag{3.123}$$

Substituting $\zeta = 1/2$ and $\eta = 1/2$ into Equation 3.120

$$\frac{\partial N_1}{\partial \zeta} = -\frac{1}{8} \quad \text{and} \quad \frac{\partial N_1}{\partial \eta} = -\frac{1}{8} \tag{3.124}$$

Substituting into Equation 3.115

$$\left\{ \begin{array}{c} \dfrac{\partial N_1}{\partial x} \\[2ex] \dfrac{\partial N_1}{\partial y} \end{array} \right\} = \frac{1}{330}\left\{ \begin{array}{c} -10 \\ -20 \end{array} \right\} \tag{3.125}$$

In a similar fashion, all other nodal derivatives can be calculated.

(b) *Quadratic variation*

The shape function at node 1 is

$$N_1 = -\frac{1}{4}(1 - \zeta)(1 - \eta)(\zeta + \eta + 1) \tag{3.126}$$

The derivatives with respect to the transformed coordinates are

$$\frac{\partial N_1}{\partial \zeta} = \frac{1}{16} \quad \text{and} \quad \frac{\partial N_1}{\partial \eta} = \frac{3}{16} \tag{3.127}$$

The derivatives with respect to the global coordinates are

$$\left\{ \begin{array}{c} \dfrac{\partial N_1}{\partial x} \\[2ex] \dfrac{\partial N_1}{\partial y} \end{array} \right\} = \frac{1}{660}\left\{ \begin{array}{c} 30 \\ 60 \end{array} \right\} \tag{3.128}$$

Other derivatives can be established in a similar manner.

It is a simple matter to transform the area coordinate system for triangular elements $(L_i, i = 1, 2, 3)$ to the $\zeta - \eta$ coordinates.

The shape functions for the three-node linear triangle can be expressed in the ζ and η coordinate system as shown in Figure 3.19, that is,

$$N_1 = L_1 = 1 - \zeta - \eta$$
$$N_2 = L_2 = \zeta; 0 \le \zeta \le 1$$
$$N_3 = L_3 = \eta; 0 \le \eta \le 1 \tag{3.129}$$

For a quadratic triangle with six nodes, the shape functions at the corner codes are

$$N_1 = L_1(2L_1 - 1) = [2(1 - \zeta - \eta) - 1](1 - \zeta - \eta)$$
$$N_3 = L_2(2L_2 - 1) = \zeta(2\zeta - 1)$$
$$N_5 = L_3(2L_3 - 1) = \eta(2\eta - 1) \tag{3.130}$$

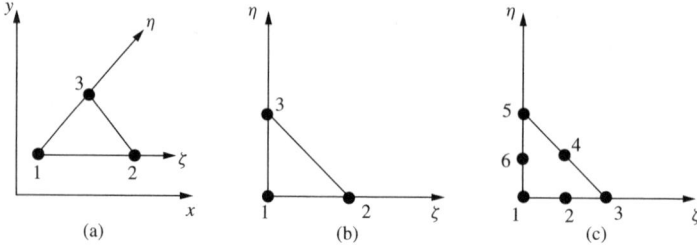

Figure 3.19   Isoparametric transformation of a single triangular element. (a) Global, (b) local - linear and (c) local - quadratic

For the mid-side nodes,

$$N_2 = 4L_1L_2 = 4\zeta(1 - \zeta - \eta)$$

$$N_4 = 4L_2L_3 = 4\zeta\eta$$

$$N_6 = 4L_3L_1 = 4\eta(1 - \zeta - \eta) \tag{3.131}$$

Consider the linear triangular element shown in Figure 3.19(a).

$$x(L_1, L_2) = N_1(L_1, L_2)x_1 + N_2(L_1, L_2)x_2 + N_3(L_1, L_2)x_3$$

$$y(L_1, L_2) = N_1(L_1, L_2)y_1 + N_2(L_1, L_2)y_2 + N_3(L_1, L_2)y_3 \tag{3.132}$$

Where x_1, x_2, x_3, y_1, y_2 and y_3 are the global coordinates of the three-node triangular element, which are used for representing the geometry. Replacing the shape functions by the area coordinate gives

$$x(L_1, L_2) = x_1L_1 + x_2L_2 + x_3(1 - L_1 - L_2)$$

$$y(L_1, L_2) = y_1L_1 + y_2L_2 + y_3(1 - L_1 - L_2) \tag{3.133}$$

The components of the Jacobian matrix are

$$[\mathbf{J}] = \begin{bmatrix} \dfrac{\partial x}{\partial L_1} & \dfrac{\partial y}{\partial L_1} \\ \dfrac{\partial x}{\partial L_2} & \dfrac{\partial y}{\partial L_2} \end{bmatrix} = \begin{bmatrix} (x_1 - x_3) & (y_1 - y_3) \\ (x_2 - x_3) & (y_2 - y_3) \end{bmatrix} \tag{3.134}$$

The determinant of the Jacobian matrix is

$$\det [\mathbf{J}] = (x_1 - x_3)(y_2 - y_3) - (x_2 - x_3)(y_1 - y_3) = 2A \tag{3.135}$$

where A is the area of the element. The inverse of the Jacobian matrix is

$$[\mathbf{J}]^{-1} = \frac{1}{\det J} \begin{bmatrix} (y_2 - y_3) & -(y_1 - y_3) \\ -(x_2 - x_3) & (x_1 - x_3) \end{bmatrix} = \frac{1}{2A} \begin{bmatrix} (y_2 - y_3) & -(y_1 - y_3) \\ -(x_2 - x_3) & (x_1 - x_3) \end{bmatrix} \tag{3.136}$$

Finally, the derivatives in global coordinates are written as

$$\left\{ \begin{array}{c} \dfrac{\partial N_1}{\partial x} \\ \dfrac{\partial N_1}{\partial y} \end{array} \right\} = [\mathbf{J}]^{-1} \left\{ \begin{array}{c} \dfrac{\partial N_1}{\partial L_1} \\ \dfrac{\partial N_1}{\partial L_2} \end{array} \right\} \tag{3.137}$$

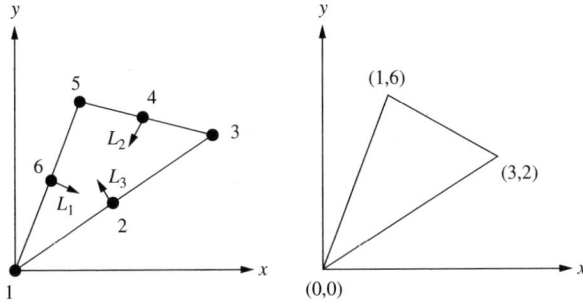

Figure 3.20   Triangular elements

Example 3.2.6 *Calculate $\partial N_4/\partial x$ and $\partial N_4/\partial y$ at a point (1, 4) for the quadratic triangular element shown in Figure 3.20 (left) when the geometry is represented by a three-node triangle (right).*

The coordinates are expressed as

$$x = x_1 L_1 + x_2 L_2 + x_3 L_3$$
$$y = y_1 L_1 + y_2 L_2 + y_3 L_3 \tag{3.138}$$

After substituting the coordinates of the three points, we have

$$x = 3L_2 + L_3$$
$$y = 2L_2 + 6L_3 \tag{3.139}$$

The determinant of the Jacobian matrix is (Equation 3.135)

$$\det [\mathbf{J}] = (-1)(-4) - (2)(-6) = 16 \tag{3.140}$$

The inverse of the Jacobian is therefore (Equation 3.136)

$$[\mathbf{J}]^{-1} = \frac{1}{16} \begin{bmatrix} -4 & 6 \\ -2 & -1 \end{bmatrix} \tag{3.141}$$

The shape function N_4 is given by $4L_2 L_3 = 4L_2(1 - L_1 - L_2)$

$$\begin{Bmatrix} \dfrac{\partial N_4}{\partial x} \\ \dfrac{\partial N_4}{\partial y} \end{Bmatrix} = [\mathbf{J}]^{-1} \begin{Bmatrix} \dfrac{\partial N_4}{\partial L_1} \\ \dfrac{\partial N_4}{\partial L_2} \end{Bmatrix} = \begin{Bmatrix} L_2 + 1.5L_3 \\ 0.5L_2 - 0.25L_3 \end{Bmatrix} \tag{3.142}$$

To determine the local coordinates corresponding to $(x, y) = (1, 4)$, we have the following three equations (Equation 3.139):

$$3L_2 + L_3 = 1$$
$$2L_2 + 6L_3 = 4$$
$$L_1 + L_2 + L_3 = 1 \tag{3.143}$$

which gives

$$L_1 = \frac{1}{4}$$

$$L_2 = \frac{1}{8}$$

$$L_3 = \frac{5}{8} \tag{3.144}$$

Substituting into Equation 3.142 gives

$$\left\{ \begin{array}{c} \dfrac{\partial N_4}{\partial x} \\[2mm] \dfrac{\partial N_4}{\partial y} \end{array} \right\} = \left\{ \begin{array}{c} \dfrac{8.5}{8} \\[2mm] \dfrac{-1.5}{16} \end{array} \right\} \tag{3.145}$$

Similarly, other derivatives can also be calculated.

3.2.8   Three-dimensional elements

The amount of data required to establish the computational domain and boundary conditions become significantly greater in three dimensions than for two-dimensional problems. It is therefore obvious that the amount of computational work/cost increases by a considerable extent. Therefore, appropriate three-dimensional elements need to be used. The tetrahedron and brick-shaped hexahedron elements are developed (Figure 3.21) in this section, which are extensions of the linear triangle and quadrilateral elements in two dimensions.

The linear temperature representation for a tetrahedron element (three-dimensional linear element) is given by

$$T = \alpha_1 + \alpha_2 x + \alpha_3 y + \alpha_4 z \tag{3.146}$$

As discussed previously for 2D elements, the constants of Equation 3.146 can be determined and may be written in the following form:

$$T = N_1 T_1 + N_2 T_2 + N_3 T_3 + N_4 T_4 \tag{3.147}$$

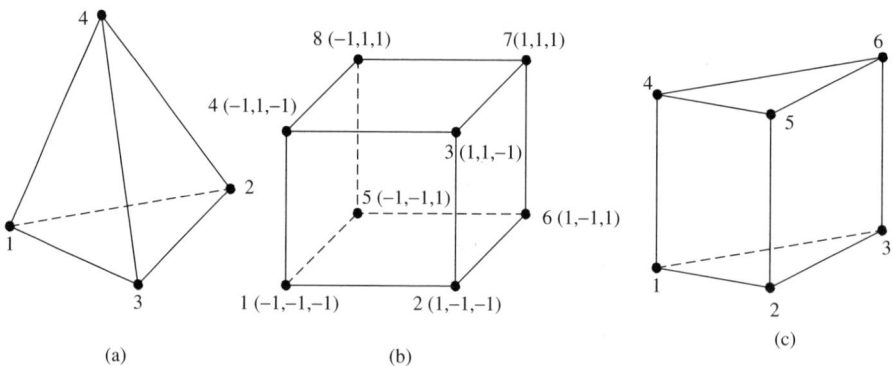

Figure 3.21   Three-dimensional elements, (a) tetrahedron, (b) hexahedron and (c) prism

where

$$N_i = \frac{1}{6V}(a_i + b_i x + c_i y + d_i z) \quad \text{with} \quad i = 1, 2, 3, 4 \tag{3.148}$$

The volume of the tetrahedron is expressed as

$$6V = \det \begin{bmatrix} 1 & x_1 & y_1 & z_1 \\ 1 & x_2 & y_2 & z_2 \\ 1 & x_3 & y_3 & z_3 \\ 1 & x_4 & y_4 & z_4 \end{bmatrix} \tag{3.149}$$

Also note that

$$\frac{\partial N_1}{\partial x} = \frac{b_1}{6V}$$

$$\frac{\partial N_1}{\partial y} = \frac{c_1}{6V}$$

$$\frac{\partial N_1}{\partial z} = \frac{d_1}{6V} \tag{3.150}$$

Therefore, the gradient matrix of the shape functions can be written as

$$[\mathbf{B}] = \frac{1}{6V} \begin{bmatrix} b_1 & b_2 & b_3 & b_4 \\ c_1 & c_2 & c_3 & c_4 \\ d_1 & d_2 & d_3 & d_4 \end{bmatrix} \tag{3.151}$$

where

$$b_1 = -\det \begin{bmatrix} 1 & y_2 & z_2 \\ 1 & y_3 & z_3 \\ 1 & y_4 & z_4 \end{bmatrix} \tag{3.152}$$

$$c_1 = -\det \begin{bmatrix} x_2 & 1 & z_2 \\ x_3 & 1 & z_3 \\ x_4 & 1 & z_4 \end{bmatrix} \tag{3.153}$$

$$d_1 = -\det \begin{bmatrix} x_2 & y_2 & 1 \\ x_3 & y_3 & 1 \\ x_4 & y_4 & 1 \end{bmatrix} \tag{3.154}$$

Similarly, the other terms in Equation 3.151 can also be determined. We therefore summarize all the terms as follows:

b-terms

$$b_1 = (y_2 - y_4)(z_3 - z_4) - (y_3 - y_4)(z_2 - z_4)$$

$$b_2 = (y_3 - y_4)(z_1 - z_4) - (y_1 - y_4)(z_3 - z_4)$$

$$b_3 = (y_1 - y_4)(z_2 - z_4) - (y_2 - y_4)(z_1 - z_4)$$

$$b_4 = b_1 + b_2 + b_3 \tag{3.155}$$

c-terms

$$c_1 = (x_3 - x_4)(z_2 - z_4) - (x_2 - x_4)(z_3 - z_4)$$

$$c_2 = (x_1 - x_4)(z_3 - z_4) - (x_3 - x_4)(z_1 - z_4)$$

$$c_3 = (x_2 - x_4)(z_1 - z_4) - (x_1 - x_4)(z_2 - z_4)$$

$$c_4 = -(c_1 + c_2 + c_3) \tag{3.156}$$

d-terms

$$d_1 = (x_2 - x_4)(y_3 - y_4) - (x_3 - x_4)(y_3 - y_4)$$

$$d_2 = (x_3 - x_4)(y_1 - y_4) - (x_1 - x_4)(y_3 - y_4)$$

$$d_3 = (x_1 - x_4)(y_2 - y_4) - (x_2 - x_4)(y_1 - y_4)$$

$$d_4 = -(d_1 + d_2 + d_3) \tag{3.157}$$

A volume coordinate system for the tetrahedron can be established in a similar manner as were the area coordinates for a triangle. In the tetrahedron, four distance ratios are used, each normal to sides L_1, L_2, L_3 and L_4.

Note that $L_1 + L_2 + L_3 + L_4 = 1$.

The linear shape functions are related to the volume coordinate as follows:

$$N_1 = L_1; \quad N_2 = L_2; \quad N_3 = L_3 \quad \text{and} \quad N_4 = L_4 \tag{3.158}$$

The volume integrals can easily be evaluated from the relationship,

$$\int_V L_1^a L_2^b L_3^c L_4^d dV = \frac{a!b!c!d!}{(a+b+c+d+3)!} 6V \tag{3.159}$$

For a quadratic tetrahedron,

$$T = \alpha_1 + \alpha_2 x + \alpha_3 y + \alpha_4 z + \alpha_5 x^2 + \alpha_6 y^2 + \alpha_7 z^2 + \alpha_8 xy + \alpha_9 yz + \alpha_{10} zx \tag{3.160}$$

Therefore, ten nodes will exist in a quadratic tetrahedron as shown in Figure 3.22. The element may also have curved surfaces on the boundaries. As before, the temperature distribution can be rewritten in terms of the shape functions as

$$T = N_1 T_1 + N_2 T_2 + N_3 T_3 + N_4 T_4 + N_5 T_5$$

$$+ N_6 T_6 + N_7 T_7 + N_8 T_8 + N_9 T_9 + N_{10} T_{10} \tag{3.161}$$

The shape functions can be expressed in terms of local coordinates as

$$N_1 = L_1(2L_1 - 1)$$

$$N_2 = L_2(2L_2 - 1)$$

$$N_3 = L_3(2L_3 - 1)$$

$$N_4 = L_4(2L_4 - 1)$$

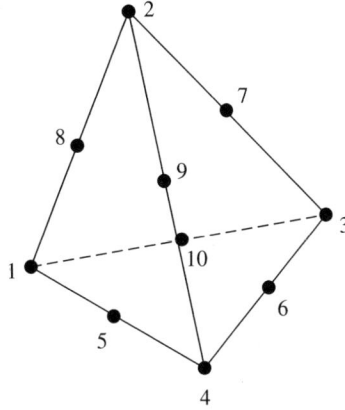

Figure 3.22   Quadratic tetrahedral element

$$N_5 = 4L_4L_1$$

$$N_6 = 4L_3L_4$$

$$N_7 = 4L_3L_2$$

$$N_8 = 4L_1L_2$$

$$N_9 = 4L_2L_4$$

$$N_{10} = 4L_1L_3 \tag{3.162}$$

The brick, or hexahedron element shown in Figure 3.21(b), is a simple element, which is easy to visualize when the domain is discretized. The bilinear interpolation function is

$$T = \alpha_1 + \alpha_2 x + \alpha_3 y + \alpha_4 z + \alpha_5 xy + \alpha_6 yz + \alpha_7 zx + \alpha_8 xyz \tag{3.163}$$

which can be written as

$$T = \sum_{i=1}^{8} N_i T_i \tag{3.164}$$

where

$$N_i = \frac{1}{8}(1 + \zeta \zeta_i)(1 + \eta \eta_i)(1 + \rho \rho_i) \tag{3.165}$$

where ζ_i, η_i and ρ_i are the local coordinates.

For a quadratic 20-node hexahedron, which can represent arbitrary solids with curved surfaces as shown in Figure 3.23, the shape functions can be written as follows.

Corner nodes

$$N_i = \frac{1}{8}(1 + \zeta \zeta_i)(1 + \eta \eta_i)(1 + \rho \rho_i)(\zeta \zeta_i + \eta \eta_i + \rho \rho_i - 1) \quad \text{with} \quad i = 1, 2, \ldots, 8.$$

$$\tag{3.166}$$

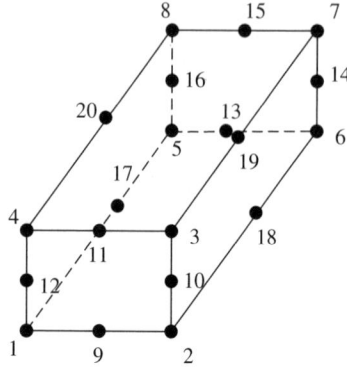

Figure 3.23   20-node hexahedral element

Mid-side nodes

$$N_i = \frac{1}{4}(1 - \zeta^2)(1 + \eta\eta_i)(1 + \rho\rho_i) \quad \text{with} \quad i = 9, 13, 15, 11$$

$$N_i = \frac{1}{4}(1 - \eta^2)(1 + \zeta\zeta_i)(1 + \rho\rho_i) \quad \text{with} \quad i = 10, 14, 16, 12$$

$$N_i = \frac{1}{4}(1 - \rho^2)(1 + \zeta\zeta_i)(1 + \eta\eta_i) \quad \text{with} \quad i = 18, 19, 20, 17 \qquad (3.167)$$

The shape functions for a linear pentahedran element (which is used in cylindrical geometries) can be generated from the product of triangular and one-dimensional interpolation functions (Refer to Figure 3.21(c)).

$$N_1 = \frac{1}{2}L_1(1 - w)$$

$$N_2 = \frac{1}{2}L_2(1 - w)$$

$$N_3 = \frac{1}{2}L_3(1 - w)$$

$$N_4 = \frac{1}{2}L_1(1 + w)$$

$$N_5 = \frac{1}{2}L_2(1 + w)$$

$$N_6 = \frac{1}{2}L_3(1 + w) \qquad (3.168)$$

where $w = -1$ at the bottom surface and 1 at the top surface. In conclusion, isoparametric elements are very useful as they can be used for modelling irregular solids and the element can be mapped onto a unit cube.

3.3   Formulation (Element Characteristics)

After briefly describing the various elements used in the context of finite element analysis, we shall now focus our attention on determining the element characteristics, that is, the relation between the nodal unknowns and the corresponding loads or forces in the form of the following matrix equation, namely,

$$[K]\{T\} = \{f\} \tag{3.169}$$

where $[K]$ is the thermal stiffness matrix, $\{T\}$ is the vector of unknown temperatures and $\{f\}$ is the thermal load, or forcing vector.

Several methods are available for the determination of the approximate solution to a given problem. We shall consider three methods in the first instance.

1. Ritz method (Heat balance integral)

2. Rayleigh Ritz method (Variational)

3. Weighted residual methods.

In order to illustrate the above methods, we shall consider a one-dimensional fin problem as shown in Figure 3.24.

Heat balance on the differential volume of length dx as shown in Figure 3.24 gives

$$-kA\frac{dT}{dx}\Big|_x = hP\,dx(T - T_a) - kA\frac{dT}{dx}\Big|_{x+dx}$$

$$= hP\,dx(T - T_a) - kA\frac{dT}{dx}\Big|_x - kA\frac{d^2T}{dx^2}dx \tag{3.170}$$

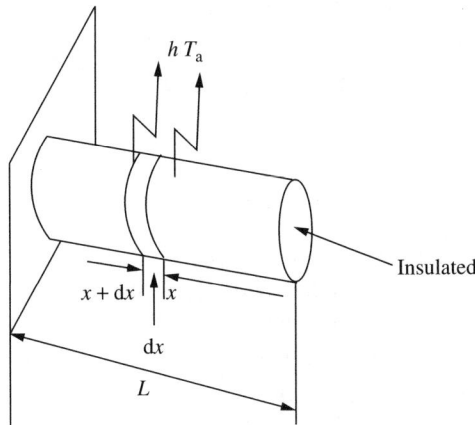

Figure 3.24   A fin problem

where k is the thermal conductivity, A is the cross-sectional area, h is the heat transfer coefficient, P is the perimeter and the suffix a represents atmospheric condition.

Simplifying, the governing differential equation becomes

$$kA\frac{d^2T}{dx^2} - hP(T - T_a) = 0 \tag{3.171}$$

with the following boundary conditions:

At $x = 0$, $dT/dx = 0$ (tip) and at $x = L$, $T = T_b$ (base)

Let $(T - T_a) = \theta$, $\zeta = x/L$, $hP/kA = m^2$ and $m^2L^2 = \mu^2$, then the governing equation reduces to

$$\frac{d^2\theta}{d\zeta^2} - \mu^2\theta = 0 \tag{3.172}$$

with the following new boundary conditions:

$$\text{At} \quad \zeta = 0, d\theta/d\zeta = 0 \quad \text{and at} \quad \zeta = 1, \theta = \theta_b \tag{3.173}$$

3.3.1 Ritz method (Heat balance integral method - Goodman's method)

An approximate solution of Equation 3.172 along with the appropriate boundary conditions may be found using the following function:

$$T \approx \overline{T} = \overline{T}(x, a_1, a_2, \ldots, a_n) = \sum_{i=1}^{n} a_i N_i(x) \tag{3.174}$$

which has one or more unknown parameters $a_1, a_2, \ldots, a_n$ and functions $N_i(x)$ that exactly satisfy the boundary conditions given by Equation 3.173. The functions $N_i(x)$ are referred to as trial functions, which must be continuous and differentiable up to the highest order present in the integral form of the governing equation.

The approximations may be carried out using one, two or n terms as follows:

$$\overline{T} = a_1 N_1(x)$$

$$\overline{T} = a_1 N_1(x) + a_2 N_2(x) \tag{3.175}$$

or

$$\overline{T} = \sum_{i=1}^{n} a_i N_i(x) \tag{3.176}$$

When $\overline{T}$ is substituted into the governing differential equation, it is not satisfied exactly, leaving a residual 'R'. The exact solution results when the residual 'R' is zero for all points in the domain. In approximate solution methods, the residual is not in general zero everywhere in the domain even though it may be zero at some preferred points.

Let us select a profile that satisfies the boundary conditions (Equation 3.173) in the global sense. By inspection, we find that

$$\frac{\theta(\zeta)}{\theta_b} = 1 - (1 - \zeta^2)B \tag{3.177}$$

satisfies the boundary conditions, where 'B' is an unknown parameter to be determined.

In the Ritz method, we insert the approximate profile into the governing differential equation, Equation 3.172, and then the integral of the residual 'R' over the domain is equated to zero to determine the constant B, that is,

$$\int_0^1 \left(\frac{d^2\theta(\zeta)}{d\zeta^2} - \mu^2\theta \right) d\zeta = 0 \tag{3.178}$$

Differentiating Equation 3.177 gives

$$\frac{d^2\theta(\zeta)}{d\zeta^2} = 2B\theta_b \tag{3.179}$$

Substituting Equation 3.179 into Equation 3.178, we have

$$\int_0^1 [2B - \mu^2(1 - \{1 - \zeta^2\}B)]\theta_b d\zeta = \left[2\theta_b B\zeta - \mu^2\theta_b \left(\zeta - B\zeta + \frac{B\zeta^3}{3} \right) \right]_0^1$$

$$= 2B\theta_b - \left(1 - B + \frac{B}{3} \right)\mu^2\theta_b$$

$$= 0 \tag{3.180}$$

which gives

$$B = \frac{\frac{\mu^2}{2}}{1 + \frac{\mu^2}{3}} \tag{3.181}$$

Substituting Equation 3.181 into 3.177 gives the following solution:

$$\frac{\theta(\zeta)}{\theta_b} = 1 - (1 - \zeta^2)\frac{\frac{\mu^2}{2}}{1 + \frac{\mu^2}{3}} \tag{3.182}$$

For the case of a stainless steel fin ($k = 16.66$ W/m°C) of circular cross section with a diameter of 2 cm and length of 10 cm exposed to a convection environment with $h = 25$ W/m²°C and $\mu^2 = 3.0$ and $m^2 = 300$, the approximate solution is

$$\frac{\overline{\theta}(\zeta)}{\theta_b} = 1 - \frac{3}{4}(1 - \zeta^2) \tag{3.183}$$

where the exact solution is

$$\frac{\theta(\zeta)}{\theta_b} = \frac{\cosh m(L - x)}{\cosh mL} \tag{3.184}$$

Note that the distance x is taken from the tip of the fin as shown in Figure 3.24. The comparison between the exact and approximate solutions is given in Figure 3.25. As seen, the temperatures agree excellently at the base at $x = 1$ but differ close to the insulated end at $x = 0$.

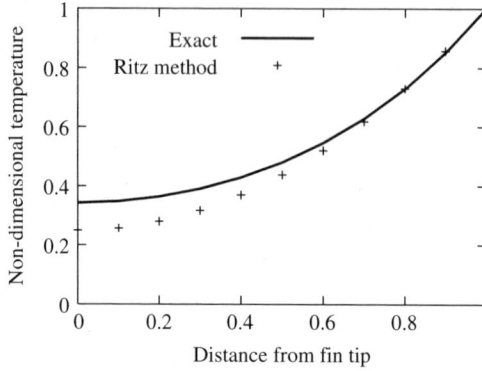

Figure 3.25   Comparison between the Ritz method and the exact solution

3.3.2   Rayleigh–Ritz method (Variational method)

In the case of the variational method, we make use of an important theorem from the theory of the calculus of variations, which states, 'The function $T(x)$ that extremises the variational integral corresponding to the governing differential equation (called Euler or Euler–Lagrange equation) is the solution of the original governing differential equation and boundary conditions'. This implies that the solution obtained is unique, which is the case for well-posed problems. Thus, the first step is to determine the variational integral 'I', which corresponds to the governing differential equation and its boundary conditions. The differential equation is, Equation 3.172,

$$\frac{d^2\theta}{d\zeta^2} - \mu^2\theta = 0 \tag{3.185}$$

with the following boundary conditions:

$$\frac{d\theta(0)}{d\zeta} = 0 \quad \text{and} \quad \theta(1) = \theta_b \tag{3.186}$$

Using the differential equation as the Euler–Lagrange equation, we can write

$$\delta I = \int_0^1 \left(\frac{d^2\theta}{d\zeta^2} - \mu^2\theta\right)\delta\theta\,d\zeta = 0 \tag{3.187}$$

Integrating by parts gives

$$\left[\frac{d\theta}{d\zeta}\delta\theta\right]_0^1 - \int_0^1 \left(\frac{d\theta}{d\zeta}\right)\frac{d}{d\zeta}(\delta\theta)\,d\zeta - \mu^2\int_0^1 \theta\delta\theta\,d\zeta = 0 \tag{3.188}$$

Using the relations

$$\frac{d}{d\zeta}(\delta\theta) = \delta\left(\frac{d\theta}{d\zeta}\right)$$

$$\frac{d\theta}{d\zeta}\delta\left(\frac{d\theta}{d\zeta}\right) = \frac{1}{2}\delta\left(\frac{d\theta}{d\zeta}\right)^2$$

and

$$\theta\delta\theta = \frac{1}{2}\delta\theta^2 \tag{3.189}$$

Then, Equation 3.188 is simplified to the following:

$$\left[\frac{d\theta}{d\zeta}\delta\theta\right]_0^1 - \frac{1}{2}\delta\int_0^1\left[\left(\frac{d\theta}{d\zeta}\right)^2 + \mu^2\theta^2\right]d\zeta = 0 \tag{3.190}$$

When we apply the boundary conditions (Equation 3.186), the first term of the above equation becomes zero. Thus, the variational formulation for the given problem is

$$\delta\int_0^1\frac{1}{2}\left[\left(\frac{d\theta}{d\zeta}\right)^2 + \mu^2\theta^2\right]d\zeta = 0 \tag{3.191}$$

and the corresponding variational integral is given by

$$I = \int_0^1\frac{1}{2}\left[\left(\frac{d\theta}{d\zeta}\right)^2 + \mu^2\theta^2\right]d\zeta \tag{3.192}$$

Now, the profile that minimizes the integral Equation 3.192 is the solution to the differential Equation 3.185 with its boundary conditions given by Equation 3.186.

Let us assume the same profile as before (Equation 3.177) and substitute into Equation 3.192, that is,

$$I = \int_0^1\frac{1}{2}\theta_b^2\{(2B\zeta)^2 + \mu^2[1 - (1 - \zeta^2)B]^2\}d\zeta \tag{3.193}$$

After integration and substitution of limits, we have

$$I = \frac{1}{2}\theta_b\left\{B^2\left(\frac{4}{3} + \mu^2 - \frac{2}{3}\mu^2 + \frac{1}{5}\mu^2\right) + \mu^2 + B\left(-2\mu^2 + \frac{2}{3}\mu^2\right)\right\} \tag{3.194}$$

For I to be minimum, $\frac{\partial I}{\partial B} = 0$, that is,

$$\frac{\partial I}{\partial B} = \frac{1}{2}\theta_b\left\{2B\left(\frac{4}{3} + \mu^2 - \frac{2}{3}\mu^2 + \frac{1}{5}\mu^2\right) + \mu^2 + \left(-2\mu^2 + \frac{2}{3}\mu^2\right)\right\} = 0 \tag{3.195}$$

which gives

$$2B\left(\frac{4}{3} + \frac{8}{15}\mu^2\right) = \frac{4}{3}\mu^2 \tag{3.196}$$

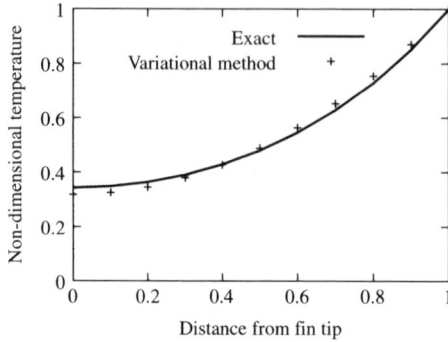

Figure 3.26   Comparison between variational method and exact solution

or

$$B = \frac{\dfrac{\mu^2}{2}}{1 + \dfrac{2}{5}\mu^2} \tag{3.197}$$

Substituting into Equation 3.177 gives the solution as

$$\frac{\theta(\zeta)}{\theta} = 1 - (1 - \zeta^2)\frac{\dfrac{\mu^2}{2}}{1 + \dfrac{2}{5}\mu^2} \tag{3.198}$$

For the fin problem of the previous subsection with $\mu^2 = 3$ and $m^2 = 300$, the comparison between the variational method and the exact solution is shown in Figure 3.26. As seen, the agreement between the solutions is better than the agreement between the exact and Ritz solutions.

It can be observed from the variational Integral Equation 3.192 that it contains only a first-order derivative even though the original differential Equation 3.185 contains a second-order derivative.

If a body has two materials, the second derivative of the temperature, required by the original differential equation at the point where the two materials meet, may not exist. In this case, the variational formulation of the problem would readily yield an accurate solution, since the second derivative in this example is not needed in the formulation. For this reason, the variational formulation of a physical problem is often referred to as the *weak formulation*.

3.3.3   The method of weighted residuals

For those differential equations for which we cannot write a variational formulation, there is a need to find an alternative method of formulation. The method of weighted residuals provides a very powerful approximate solution procedure that is applicable to a wide variety of problems and thus makes it unnecessary to search for variational formulations in order to apply the finite element method for these problems.

Let the governing equations be represented by

$$L(T) = 0 \quad \text{in} \quad \Omega \tag{3.199}$$

Let

$$T \approx \overline{T} = \sum_{i=1}^{n} a_i N_i(x) \tag{3.200}$$

Substitution of the above equation into Equation 3.199 results in

$$L(\overline{T}) \neq 0$$

$$= R \text{ (residual)} \tag{3.201}$$

The method of weighted residual requires that the parameters $a_1, a_2, \ldots, a_n$ be determined by satisfying

$$\int_{\Omega} w_i(x) R \, dx = 0 \quad \text{with} \quad i = 1, 2, \ldots, n \tag{3.202}$$

where the functions $w_i(x)$ are the n arbitrary weighting functions. There are an infinite number of choices for $w_i(x)$ but four particular functions are most often used. Depending on the choice of the weighting functions, different names are given

Collocation: $w_i = \delta(x - x_i)$

$$\int_{\Omega} R\delta(x - x_i) dx = R_{x=x_i} = 0 \tag{3.203}$$

Sub-domain: $w_i = 1$ (Note the sub-domain Ω_i in the integration)

$$\int_{\Omega_i} R \, dx = 0 \quad \text{with} \quad i = 1, 2, \ldots, n \tag{3.204}$$

Galerkin: $w_i(x) = N_i(x)$, that is, the same trial functions as used in $T(x)$

$$\int_{\Omega} N_i(x) R \, dx = 0 \quad \text{with} \quad i = 1, 2, \ldots, n \tag{3.205}$$

Least Squares: $w_i = \partial R / \partial a_i$

$$\int_{\Omega} \frac{\partial R}{\partial a_i} dx = 0 \quad \text{with} \quad i = 1, 2, \ldots, n \tag{3.206}$$

For illustration purposes the fin problem is re-solved with each of the above methods.

Collocation method

The weight is $w_i = \delta(x - x_i)$

Let $\zeta_i = 1/2$ as there is only one unknown in the fin problem. Rewriting the equation in collocation form in the non-dimensional coordinates gives the following:

$$\int_0^1 \left[\frac{d^2\overline{\theta}}{d\zeta^2} - \mu^2\overline{\theta} \right] \delta(\zeta - \zeta_i) d\zeta = 0 \tag{3.207}$$

From the above equation, we can write

$$\left[\frac{d^2\overline{\theta}}{d\zeta^2} - \mu^2\overline{\theta}\right]_{\zeta_i=\frac{1}{2}} = 0 \tag{3.208}$$

Substituting Equation 3.207 into 3.208, with $\zeta = 1/2$, we have

$$2B - \mu^2\left[1 - \left(1 - \frac{1}{2}\right)^2\right]B = 0 \tag{3.209}$$

which gives

$$B = \frac{\left(\dfrac{\mu^2}{2}\right)}{1 + \dfrac{3}{8}\mu^2} \tag{3.210}$$

Substituting into Equation 3.177, the solution is obtained as

$$\frac{\overline{\theta}(\zeta)}{\theta_b} = 1 - (1 - \zeta^2)\frac{\left(\dfrac{\mu^2}{2}\right)}{1 + \dfrac{3}{8}\mu^2} \tag{3.211}$$

For a problem with $\mu^2 = 3$, then

$$\frac{\overline{\theta}(\zeta)}{\theta_b} = 1 - \frac{12}{17}(1 - \zeta^2) \tag{3.212}$$

Sub-domain method

The weighting function $w_i = 1$ that results in the sub-domain formulation being

$$\int_0^1 (1)\left[\frac{d^2\overline{\theta}}{d\zeta^2} - \mu^2\overline{\theta}\right]d\zeta = 0 \tag{3.213}$$

Substituting Equation 3.177 and integrating, we get

$$B = \frac{\dfrac{\mu^2}{2}}{1 + \dfrac{\mu^2}{3}} \tag{3.214}$$

The solution becomes

$$\frac{\overline{\theta}(\zeta)}{\theta_b} = 1 - (1 - \zeta^2)\frac{\left(\dfrac{\mu^2}{2}\right)}{1 + \dfrac{\mu^2}{3}} \tag{3.215}$$

For the particular case of $\mu^2 = 3$

$$\frac{\overline{\theta}(\zeta)}{\theta_b} = 1 - \frac{3}{4}(1 - \zeta^2) \tag{3.216}$$

The result from the sub-domain method coincides with the heat balance integral solution as in the present case integration is carried out over the entire domain in view of only one constant being involved.

Galerkin method

This is one of the most important methods used in finite element analysis. The weight function is $N_i(x) = (1 - \zeta^2)$. The Galerkin formulation of the fin equation is

$$\int_0^1 N_i(x) \left[\frac{d^2\overline{\theta}}{d\zeta^2} - \mu^2\overline{\theta} \right] d\zeta = 0 \tag{3.217}$$

Substituting Equation 3.177 and integrating, we obtain

$$2B - \frac{2B}{3} + \mu^2 \left(\frac{8}{15}B \right) - \frac{2\mu^2}{3} = 0 \tag{3.218}$$

and

$$B = \frac{\mu^2}{1 + \frac{2}{5}\mu^2} \tag{3.219}$$

Thus, the solution is

$$\frac{\overline{\theta}(\zeta)}{\theta_b} = 1 - (1 - \zeta^2)\frac{\left(\dfrac{\mu^2}{2}\right)}{1 + \dfrac{2}{5}\mu^2} \tag{3.220}$$

It can be observed that the solution using Galerkin's method is exactly the same as that obtained by the variational method. It can also be shown that the variational and Galerkin methods give the same results, provided the problem has a classical variational statement. In fact, later we will see that when the finite element formulation is carried out on a quasi-harmonic equation, using both the variational and Galerkin methods, the same results are obtained since a classical variational principle does exist for a quasi-harmonic equation.

Least-squares method

In this case, the minimization of the error is carried out in a least squares sense, that is,

$$\frac{\partial}{\partial a_i} \int_\Omega R^2 dx = 0 \tag{3.221}$$

which can also be written as

$$\int_\Omega \frac{\partial R}{\partial a_i} dx = 0 \tag{3.222}$$

where the weighting function is

$$w_i(x) = \frac{\partial R}{\partial a_i} \tag{3.223}$$

and the error E is given by

$$E = \int_0^1 R^2 d\zeta$$

$$= \int_0^1 \left[\frac{d^2\overline{\theta}}{d\zeta^2} - \mu^2\overline{\theta} \right]^2 d\zeta \tag{3.224}$$

Substituting Equation 3.177 into Equation 3.224 and integrating, we have

$$E = 4B^2 - 4B\mu\left(1 - \frac{2}{3}B\right) + \mu^4 - 2B\mu^4\left(\frac{2}{3}\right) + B^2\left(\frac{8}{15}\right)\mu^4 \tag{3.225}$$

The error is minimized by satisfying $\partial E / \partial B = 0$, that is,

$$\frac{\partial E}{\partial B} = 8B - \frac{4\mu^4}{3} + \frac{16B\mu^4}{15} - 4\mu^2 + \frac{16B\mu^2}{3} = 0 \tag{3.226}$$

which gives

$$B = \frac{\dfrac{\mu^2}{2}\left(1 + \dfrac{\mu^2}{3}\right)}{1 + 2\mu^2\left(\dfrac{1}{3} + \dfrac{\mu^2}{15}\right)} \tag{3.227}$$

Therefore, the solution is given by

$$\frac{\bar{\theta}(\zeta)}{\theta_b} = 1 - (1 - \zeta^2)\frac{\dfrac{\mu^2}{2}\left(1 + \dfrac{\mu^2}{3}\right)}{1 + 2\mu^2\left(\dfrac{1}{3} + \dfrac{\mu^2}{15}\right)} \tag{3.228}$$

For the particular problem where $\mu^2 = 3$, then

$$\frac{\bar{\theta}(\zeta)}{\theta_b} = 1 - \frac{15}{24}(1 - \zeta^2) \tag{3.229}$$

Figure 3.27 shows the comparison between all the different weighted residual methods. As seen, the Galerkin method is the most accurate method.

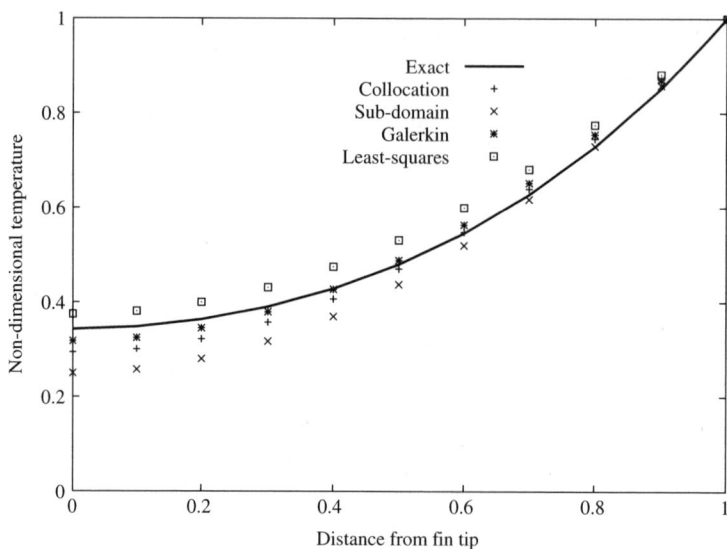

Figure 3.27   Comparison between various weighted residual methods and exact solution

3.3.4 Galerkin finite element method

We shall work out the fin problem by using the Galerkin finite element method and discretizing the domain into five linear elements with a total of six nodal points as shown in Figure 3.28. Unlike the weighted residual methods discussed in the previous section, we need no *a priori* assumption of the temperature profile in this case.

For a linear element,

$$\bar{\theta} = N_i \theta_i + N_j \theta_j \tag{3.230}$$

and

$$\frac{d\theta}{d\zeta} = \frac{dN_i}{d\zeta}\theta_i + \frac{dN_j}{d\zeta}\theta_j = -\frac{1}{\zeta_e}\theta_i + \frac{1}{\zeta_e}\theta_j \tag{3.231}$$

The Galerkin method requires that

$$\int_\zeta N_k \left(\frac{d^2\bar{\theta}}{d\zeta^2} - \mu^2\bar{\theta}\right) d\zeta = 0 \tag{3.232}$$

where the subscript k represents the nodes in the domain. Integration by parts of the above equation for one element, with the weight being the shape function at the first node of the element, results in the following:

$$\tilde{n}\left[N_i \frac{d\theta}{d\zeta}\right]_0^{\zeta_e} - \int_0^{\zeta_e} \frac{dN_i}{d\zeta}\frac{dN_j}{d\zeta}d\zeta\{\theta\} - \int_0^{\zeta_e} N_i \mu^2(N_i\theta_i + N_j\theta_j)d\zeta \tag{3.233}$$

where $\tilde{n}$ is the outward normal to the boundary. In one dimension, the magnitude of $\tilde{n}$ is unity but the sign changes appropriately. Note the following:

$$\int_0^{\zeta_e} N_i^2 d\zeta = \frac{2!0!\zeta_e}{(2+0+1)!} = \frac{\zeta_e}{3}$$

$$\int_0^{\zeta_e} N_i N_j d\zeta = \frac{1!1!\zeta_e}{(1+1+1)!} = \frac{\zeta_e}{6} \tag{3.234}$$

For the first element, with N_i being the weight, Equation 3.233 simplifies to

$$\frac{1}{\zeta_e}[1 \quad -1]\begin{Bmatrix}\theta_i \\ \theta_j\end{Bmatrix} + \frac{\mu^2\zeta_e}{6}[2 \quad 1]\begin{Bmatrix}\theta_i \\ \theta_j\end{Bmatrix} + \begin{Bmatrix}\dfrac{d\theta}{d\zeta} \\ 0\end{Bmatrix} \tag{3.235}$$

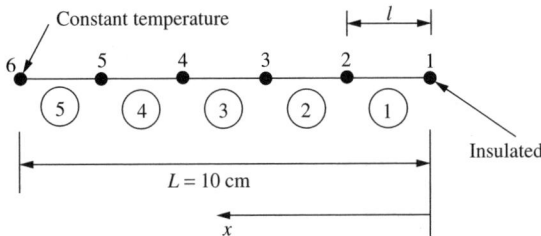

Figure 3.28 Heat dissipation from a fin (Figure 3.24). Spatial discretization. Nodes: 6. Elements: 5

Note that the outward normal at node 1 is 1. Also, note that the gradient terms of Equation 3.233 become zero at node j as $N_i = 0$ at j. Now weighting the equation using N_j, we have

$$\frac{1}{\zeta_e}[-1 \ 1]\begin{Bmatrix}\theta_i \\ \theta_j\end{Bmatrix} + \frac{\mu^2\zeta_e}{6}[2 \ 1]\begin{Bmatrix}\theta_i \\ \theta_j\end{Bmatrix} + \begin{Bmatrix}0 \\ -d\theta \\ \dfrac{}{d\zeta}\end{Bmatrix} \tag{3.236}$$

In this case, the gradient term disappears for node i as N_j is zero at node i. The outward normal value of point j is -1 (see Figure 3.28). The element characteristics are given by

$$\left\{\frac{1}{\zeta_e}\begin{bmatrix}1 & -1 \\ -1 & 1\end{bmatrix} + \frac{\mu^2\zeta_e}{6}\begin{bmatrix}2 & 1 \\ 1 & 2\end{bmatrix}\right\}\begin{Bmatrix}\theta_i \\ \theta_j\end{Bmatrix} + \begin{Bmatrix}\dfrac{d\theta}{d\zeta} \\ +\dfrac{d\theta}{d\zeta}\end{Bmatrix} \tag{3.237}$$

For the given problem with $\zeta_e = 0.2$, which is a non-dimensional element length, l/L (Figure 3.28), and $\mu^2 = 3$, the element characteristics for the first element are derived as follows:

$$\begin{bmatrix}5.2 & -4.9 \\ -4.9 & 5.2\end{bmatrix}\begin{Bmatrix}\theta_i \\ \theta_j\end{Bmatrix} + \begin{Bmatrix}\dfrac{d\theta}{d\zeta} \\ +\dfrac{d\theta}{d\zeta}\end{Bmatrix} \tag{3.238}$$

In a similar fashion, we can write the element characteristics equation for all the other four elements. On assembling over all the five elements, we obtain

$$\begin{bmatrix}5.2 & -4.9 & 0.0 & 0.0 & 0.0 & 0.0 \\ -4.9 & 10.4 & -4.9 & 0.0 & 0.0 & 0.0 \\ 0.0 & -4.9 & 10.4 & -4.9 & 0.0 & 0.0 \\ 0.0 & 0.0 & -4.9 & 10.4 & -4.9 & 0.0 \\ 0.0 & 0.0 & 0.0 & -4.9 & 10.4 & -4.9 \\ 0.0 & 0.0 & 0.0 & 0.0 & -4.9 & 5.2\end{bmatrix}\begin{Bmatrix}\theta_1 \\ \theta_2 \\ \theta_3 \\ \theta_4 \\ \theta_5 \\ \theta_6\end{Bmatrix} = \begin{Bmatrix}0.0 \\ 0.0 \\ 0.0 \\ 0.0 \\ 0.0 \\ \dfrac{d\theta}{d\zeta}\end{Bmatrix} \tag{3.239}$$

where $\theta_1, \theta_2, \ldots, \theta_6$ are the temperature values at all the six nodes. The assembly procedure has already been discussed in the previous chapter. Further details on the assembly procedure are given in Appendix C. Note that $d\theta/d\zeta$ at node 1 is zero because of the zero flux boundary condition but we also have the boundary condition at $\zeta = 1$, as $\theta = 1$. The resulting nodal simultaneous equations can be written as

$$5.2\theta_1 - 4.9\theta_2 = 0.0$$

$$-4.9\theta_1 + 10.4\theta_2 - 4.9\theta_3 = 0.0$$

$$-4.9\theta_2 + 10.4\theta_3 - 4.9\theta_4 = 0.0$$

$$-4.9\theta_3 + 10.4\theta_4 - 4.9\theta_5 = 0.0$$

$$-4.9\theta_4 + 10.4\theta_5 - 4.9\theta_6 = 0.0$$

$$\theta_6 = 1.0 \tag{3.240}$$

Table 3.5 Comparison of solutions obtained from different methods

Location (ζ)	Exact	FEM 5 linear elements	Collocation	Sub-domain	Variational or Galerkin	Least squares
0.0	0.343	0.340	0.294	0.250	0.318	0.375
0.1	0.348	–	0.301	0.258	0.325	0.381
0.2	0.364	0.361	0.322	0.280	0.345	0.400
0.3	0.390	–	0.358	0.316	0.380	0.431
0.4	0.429	0.426	0.407	0.370	0.427	0.475
0.5	0.480	–	0.471	0.438	0.490	0.531
0.6	0.546	0.543	0.548	0.520	0.563	0.600
0.7	0.628	–	0.640	0.618	0.652	0.681
0.8	0.729	0.727	0.746	0.730	0.755	0.755
0.9	0.851	–	0.866	0.858	0.870	0.881
1.00	1.00	1.00	1.00	1.00	1.00	1.00

Note that the last equation arises because of the constant temperature boundary condition at node 6. On solving the system of equations using Gaussian elimination, we finally obtain all the θ values. Table 3.5 shows the comparison between the exact result and all the other computations from each of the different methods.

It can be observed from Table 3.5 that the methods used in conjunction with the assumed profile satisfying the boundary conditions for the entire domain are less accurate compared to the finite element method solution even with only five linear elements. It can also be observed that the nodal values in the finite element method solution are very close to those of the exact solution.

3.4 Formulation for the Heat Conduction Equation

In many practical situations, finding the temperature in a solid body is of vital importance in terms of the maximum allowable temperature, for example, as in semiconductor devices, maximum allowable displacement, for example, as in steam and gas turbines, maximum allowable thermal stress and the maximum number of repeated thermal cycles in fatigue-dominated problems. In this section, we shall give the derivation of the finite element equations, both by the variational method as well as the Galerkin method, for the three-dimensional heat conduction equation of stationary systems under steady state conditions.

The governing differential equation, as given in Chapter 2, is

$$\frac{\partial}{\partial x}\left(k_x \frac{\partial T}{\partial x}\right) + \frac{\partial}{\partial y}\left(k_y \frac{\partial T}{\partial y}\right) + \frac{\partial}{\partial z}\left(k_z \frac{\partial T}{\partial z}\right) + G = 0 \tag{3.241}$$

with the following boundary conditions

$$T = T_{\mathrm{b}} \quad \text{on surface } S_1$$

$$k_x \frac{\partial T}{\partial x}\tilde{l} + k_y \frac{\partial T}{\partial y}\tilde{m} + k_z \frac{\partial T}{\partial z}\tilde{n} + q = 0 \quad \text{on surface } S_2$$

$$k_x \frac{\partial T}{\partial x}\tilde{l} + k_y \frac{\partial T}{\partial y}\tilde{m} + k_z \frac{\partial T}{\partial z}\tilde{n} + h(T - T_a) = 0 \quad \text{on surface } S_3 \qquad (3.242)$$

where $\tilde{l}, \tilde{m}$ and $\tilde{n}$ are surface normals, h is the heat transfer coefficient, k is the thermal conductivity and q is the heat flux.

3.4.1 Variational approach

The variational integral, I, corresponding to the above differential equation with its boundary conditions is given by

$$I(T) = \frac{1}{2}\int_{\Omega}\left[k_x\left(\frac{\partial T}{\partial x}\right)^2 + k_y\left(\frac{\partial T}{\partial y}\right)^2 + k_z\left(\frac{\partial T}{\partial z}\right)^2 - 2GT\right]d\Omega$$

$$+ \int_{S_2} qT\,ds + \int_{S_3}\frac{1}{2}h(T - T_a)^2 ds \qquad (3.243)$$

The given domain Ω is divided into 'n' number of finite elements with each element having 'r' nodes. The temperature is expressed in each element by

$$T^e = \sum_{i=1}^{r} N_i T_i = [\mathbf{N}]\{\mathbf{T}\} \qquad (3.244)$$

where $[\mathbf{N}] = [N_i, N_j, \ldots, N_r]$ = shape function matrix and

$$\{\mathbf{T}\} = \begin{Bmatrix} T_i \\ T_j \\ \ldots \\ T_r \end{Bmatrix} \qquad (3.245)$$

is the vector of nodal temperatures.

The finite element solution to the problem involves selecting the nodal values of T so as to make the function $I(T)$ stationery. In order to make $I(T)$ stationery, with respect to the nodal values of T, we require that

$$\delta I(T) = \sum_{i=1}^{n}\frac{\partial I}{\partial T_i} = 0 \qquad (3.246)$$

where n is the total number of discrete values of T assigned to the solution domain. Since T_i are arbitrary, Equation 3.246 holds good only if

$$\frac{\partial I}{\partial T_i} = 0 \quad \text{for} \quad i = 1, 2, \ldots, n \qquad (3.247)$$

The functional $I(T)$ can be written as a sum of individual functions, defined for the assembly of elements, only if the shape functions giving piece-wise representation of T

obey certain continuity and compatibility conditions. These conditions will be discussed later in the text.

$$I(T) = \sum_{e=1}^{n} I^e(T^e) \tag{3.248}$$

Thus, instead of working with a functional defined over the whole solution region, our attention is now focused on a functional defined for the individual elements. Hence,

$$\delta I = \sum_{e=1}^{n} \delta I^e = 0 \tag{3.249}$$

where the variation in I^e is taken only with respect to the r nodal values associated with the element e, that is,

$$\left\{ \frac{\partial I^e}{\partial T} \right\} = \frac{\partial I^e}{\partial T_j} = 0 \quad \text{with} \quad j = 1, 2, \ldots, r \tag{3.250}$$

Equation 3.250 comprises a set of r equations that characterize the behavior of the element e. The fact that we can represent the functional for the assembly of elements as a sum of the functional for all individual elements provides the key to formulating individual element equations from a variational principle. The complete set of assembled finite element equations for the problem is obtained by adding all the derivatives of I, as given by Equation 3.250, for all the elements. We can write the complete set of equations as

$$\frac{\partial I}{\partial T_i} = \sum_{e=1}^{n} \frac{\partial I^e}{\partial T_i} = 0 \quad \text{with} \quad i = 1, 2, \ldots, M \tag{3.251}$$

The problem is complete when the M set of equations are solved simultaneously for the M nodal values of T. We now give the details for formulating the individual finite element equations from a variational principle.

$$I^e = \frac{1}{2} \int_{\Omega} \left[k_x \left(\frac{\partial T^e}{\partial x} \right)^2 + k_y \left(\frac{\partial T^e}{\partial y} \right)^2 + k_z \left(\frac{\partial T^e}{\partial z} \right)^2 - 2G T^e \right] d\Omega$$
$$+ \int_{S_{2e}} q T^e ds + \int_{S_{3e}} \frac{1}{2} h (T^e - T_a)^2 ds \tag{3.252}$$

with

$$T^e = [\mathbf{N}]\{\mathbf{T}\} = [N_1, N_2, \ldots, N_r] \begin{Bmatrix} T_1 \\ T_2 \\ \ldots \\ T_r \end{Bmatrix} = N_1 T_1 + N_2 T_2 + \cdots N_r T_r \tag{3.253}$$

and

$$\frac{\partial T^e}{\partial T_1} = N_1$$

$$\frac{\partial T^e}{\partial T_2} = N_2$$

$$\frac{\partial T^e}{\partial T_r} = N_r \tag{3.254}$$

or

$$\frac{\partial T^e}{\partial \{T\}} = \begin{Bmatrix} N_1 \\ N_2 \\ \cdots \\ N_r \end{Bmatrix} = \{N\} = [N]^T \tag{3.255}$$

The gradient matrix is written as

$$\{g\} = \begin{Bmatrix} \dfrac{\partial T^e}{\partial x} \\ \dfrac{\partial T^e}{\partial y} \\ \dfrac{\partial T^e}{\partial z} \end{Bmatrix} = \begin{bmatrix} \dfrac{\partial N_1}{\partial x} & \dfrac{\partial N_2}{\partial x} & \cdots & \dfrac{\partial N_r}{\partial x} \\ \dfrac{\partial N_1}{\partial y} & \dfrac{\partial N_2}{\partial y} & \cdots & \dfrac{\partial N_r}{\partial y} \\ \dfrac{\partial N_1}{\partial z} & \dfrac{\partial N_2}{\partial z} & \cdots & \dfrac{\partial N_r}{\partial z} \end{bmatrix} \begin{Bmatrix} T_1 \\ T_2 \\ \cdots \\ T_r \end{Bmatrix} = [B]\{T\} \tag{3.256}$$

Consider

$$\{g\}^T [D]\{g\} = \begin{Bmatrix} \dfrac{\partial T^e}{\partial x} & \dfrac{\partial T^e}{\partial y} & \dfrac{\partial T^e}{\partial z} \end{Bmatrix} \begin{bmatrix} k_x & 0 & 0 \\ 0 & k_y & 0 \\ 0 & 0 & k_z \end{bmatrix} \begin{Bmatrix} \dfrac{\partial T^e}{\partial x} \\ \dfrac{\partial T^e}{\partial y} \\ \dfrac{\partial T^e}{\partial z} \end{Bmatrix}$$

$$= k_x \left(\frac{\partial T^e}{\partial x} \right)^2 + k_y \left(\frac{\partial T^e}{\partial y} \right)^2 + k_z \left(\frac{\partial T^e}{\partial z} \right)^2 \tag{3.257}$$

substituting into Equation 3.252, we have

$$I^e = \frac{1}{2} \int_\Omega \left[\{g\}^T [D]\{g\} - 2GT^e \right] d\Omega + \int_{S_{2e}} qT^e ds + \int_{S_{3e}} \frac{1}{2} h(T^e - T_a)^2 ds \tag{3.258}$$

From Equation 3.256 we can substitute $\{g\}^T [D]\{g\} = \{T\}^T [B]^T [D][B]\{T\}$ and minimizing the integral, we have (employing Equation 3.255)

$$\frac{\partial I^e}{\partial \{T\}} = \int_\Omega \frac{1}{2} 2[B]^T [D][B]\{T\} d\Omega - \int_\Omega \frac{1}{2} 2G[N]^T \{T\} d\Omega$$

$$+ \int_{S_{2e}} q[N]^T \{T\} ds + \int_{S_{3e}} h[N]^T \{T\} ds$$

$$- \int_{S_{3e}} h[N]^T T_a ds = 0 \tag{3.259}$$

The above equation can be written in a compact form as

$$[\mathbf{K}]\{\mathbf{T}\} = \{\mathbf{f}\} \tag{3.260}$$

where

$$[\mathbf{K}] = \int_{\Omega} [\mathbf{B}]^T [\mathbf{D}][\mathbf{B}] d\Omega + \int_{S_3} h[\mathbf{N}]^T [\mathbf{N}] ds$$

$$\{\mathbf{f}\} = \int_{\Omega} G[\mathbf{N}]^T d\Omega - \int_{S_2} q[\mathbf{N}]^T ds + \int_{S_3} hT_a[\mathbf{N}]^T ds \tag{3.261}$$

Equations 3.260 form the backbone of the calculation method for a finite element analysis of heat conduction problems. It can be easily noted that when there is no heat generation within an element ($G = 0$), the corresponding term disappears. Similarly, for an insulated boundary (i.e., $q = 0$ or $h = 0$) the corresponding term again disappears. Thus, for an insulated boundary, we do not have to specify any contribution, but leave it unattended. In this respect, this is a great deal more convenient as compared to the finite difference method, where nodal equations have to be written for insulated boundaries.

3.4.2 The Galerkin method

The method requires that the following expression be satisfied:

$$\int_{\Omega} w_k \mathbf{L}(\overline{T}) d\Omega = 0 \tag{3.262}$$

where the weight w_k is replaced by the shape functions at nodes, $N_k(x)$, that is,

$$\int_{\Omega} N_k \left\{ \frac{\partial}{\partial x} \left(k_x \frac{\partial \overline{T}}{\partial x} \right) + \frac{\partial}{\partial y} \left(k_y \frac{\partial \overline{T}}{\partial y} \right) + \frac{\partial}{\partial z} \left(k_z \frac{\partial \overline{T}}{\partial z} \right) + G \right\} d\Omega = 0 \tag{3.263}$$

Integration by parts is often essential when dealing with second-order derivatives. Using Green's lemma (see Appendix A), we can rewrite the second derivatives in two parts as

$$\int_{\Omega} N_k \frac{\partial}{\partial x} \left(k_x \frac{\partial \overline{T}}{\partial x} \right) d\Omega = \int_{S} N_k \left(k_x \frac{\partial \overline{T}}{\partial x} \right) ds - \int_{\Omega} \frac{\partial N_k}{\partial x} k_x \frac{\partial N_m}{\partial x} \{\overline{T}_m\} d\Omega \tag{3.264}$$

where m represents nodes. With the boundary conditions (3.242), we can rewrite Equation 3.263 as

$$-\int_{\Omega} \left(k_x \frac{\partial N_k}{\partial x} \frac{\partial N_m}{\partial x} + k_y \frac{\partial N_k}{\partial y} \frac{\partial N_m}{\partial y} + k_z \frac{\partial N_k}{\partial z} \frac{\partial N_m}{\partial z} \right) \{\overline{T}_m\} d\Omega$$

$$+ \int_{\Omega} G N_k d\Omega - \int_{S} N_k q ds + \int_{S} h N_k N_m \{\overline{T}_m\} ds + \int_{S} h T_a N_k ds = 0 \tag{3.265}$$

Now collecting the coefficients of the nodal variables $\{\overline{T}_m\}$, we get

$$[\mathbf{K}]\{\overline{T}\} = \{\mathbf{f}\} \tag{3.266}$$

or

$$[K_{km}]\{\overline{T}_m\} = \{f_k\} \tag{3.267}$$

where

$$K_{km} = -\int_\Omega \left(k_x \frac{\partial N_k}{\partial x} \frac{\partial N_m}{\partial x} + k_y \frac{\partial N_k}{\partial y} \frac{\partial N_m}{\partial y} + k_z \frac{\partial N_k}{\partial z} \frac{\partial N_m}{\partial z} \right) d\Omega$$

$$+ \int_S h N_k N_m \, dS$$

$$f_k = \int_\Omega G N_k \, d\Omega - \int_S q N_k \, dS + \int_S h T_a N_k \, dS \tag{3.268}$$

It may be observed that Equations 3.260 and 3.266 are identical, which substantiates the fact that both the variational and Galerkin methods give the same result because there exists a classical variational integral for the heat conduction equation.

3.5 Requirements for Interpolation Functions

The procedure for formulating the individual element equations from a variational principle and the assemblage of these equations relies on the assumption that the interpolation functions satisfy the following requirements. This arises from the need to ensure that Equation 3.248 holds and that our approximate solution converges to the correct solution when we use an increasing number of elements, that is, when we refine the mesh.

a. Compatibility: At element interfaces, the field variable T and any of its partial derivatives up to one order less than the highest-order derivative appearing in $I(T)$ must be continuous.

b. Completeness: All uniform states of T and its partial derivatives up to the highest order appearing in $I(T)$ should have representation in T, when in the limit the element size decreases to zero.

If the field variables are continuous at the element interfaces, then we have C^0 continuity. If, in addition, the first derivatives are continuous, we have C^1 continuity, and if the second derivatives are continuous, then we have C^2 continuity, and so on. If the functions appearing in the integrals of the element equations contain derivatives up to the $(r + 1)$th order, then to have a rigorous assurance of convergence as the element size decreases, we must satisfy the following requirements.

For compatibility: At the element interfaces, we must have C^r continuity.

For completeness: Within an element, we must have C^{r+1} continuity.

These requirements will hold regardless of whether the element equations (integral expressions) were derived using the variation method, the Galerkin method, the energy balance methods or any other method yet to be devised. These requirements govern the selection of proper interpolation functions depending on the order of the differential equation. Thus, for a conduction heat transfer problem, the highest derivative in I is of the first order. Thus, the shape function selected should provide for the continuity of temperature at the interface between two elements and also ensure the continuity of temperature and heat flux within each element.

In addition to the requirements of continuity of the field variable and convergence to the correct solution as the element size reduces, we require that the field variable representation (polynomials used) within an element remain unchanged under a linear transformation from one Cartesian coordinate system to another. Polynomials that exhibit this invariance property are said to possess 'Geometric Isotropy'. Clearly, we cannot expect a realistic approximation if our field variable representation changes with respect to a movement in origin, or in the orientation of the coordinate system. Hence, the need to ensure geometric isotropy in our polynomial interpolation functions is apparent. Fortunately, we have two simple guidelines that allow us to construct polynomial series with geometric isotropy. These are as follows:

(i) Polynomials of order 'n' that are complete, that is, those that contain all terms have geometric isotropy. The triangle family satisfies this condition whether it be a linear, quadratic or cubic form.

(ii) Polynomials of order 'n' that are incomplete yet contain the appropriate terms to preserve 'symmetry' have geometric isotropy. We neglect only these terms that occur in symmetric pairs that is, (x^3, y^3), $(x^2 y, xy^2)$, and so on.

Example: For an eight-node element, the following polynomial, P, satisfies geometric isotropy, that is,

$$P(x, y) = \alpha_1 + \alpha_2 x + \alpha_3 y + \alpha_4 x^2 + \alpha_5 xy + \alpha_6 y^2 \tag{3.269}$$

with either

$$\alpha_7 x^3 + \alpha_8 y^3 \tag{3.270}$$

or

$$\alpha_7 x^2 y + \alpha_8 y^2 x \tag{3.271}$$

added to it.

Example 3.5.1 *Before concluding this chapter, it is important to consider a numerical problem for illustrating the theory presented. For this purpose, we consider again a fin problem as shown in Figure 3.29. The linear variation for the temperature within each finite element is assumed. We shall derive the element equations from the most general formulation given*

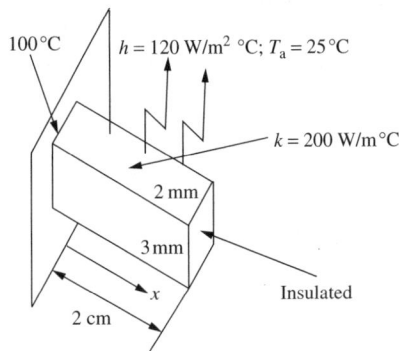

100 °C

$h = 120$ W/m^2 °C; $T_a = 25$ °C

$k = 200$ W/m °C

2 mm

3 mm

x

Insulated

2 cm

Figure 3.29   Heat transfer from a rectangular fin

Table 3.6   Element and node numbers
of linear one-dimensional elements

Element No.	Node i	Node j
1	1	2
2	2	3
e	i	j
n	n	$n + 1$

in Section 3.4 and determine the temperature distribution, heat dissipation capacity and the efficiency of the fin, assuming that the tip is insulated.

Since we are using linear elements, the element will only have two nodes. First, we divide the given length of the fin into number of divisions—say 'n' elements. Therefore, we will have $(n + 1)$ nodes to represent the fin (see Table 3.6).

The variation of temperature in the elements is linear. Hence,

$$T = N_i T_i + N_j T_j \tag{3.272}$$

and the first derivative is given by

$$\frac{dT}{dx} = \frac{dN_i}{dx} T_i + \frac{dN_j}{dx} T_j$$

$$= -\frac{1}{l} T_i + \frac{1}{l} T_j \tag{3.273}$$

that is, the gradient matrix is

$$g = \frac{dT}{dx} = \left[-\frac{1}{l} \ \ \frac{1}{l} \right] \begin{Bmatrix} T_i \\ T_j \end{Bmatrix} = [\mathbf{B}]\{\mathbf{T}\} \tag{3.274}$$

where

$$[\mathbf{B}] = \frac{1}{l} \begin{bmatrix} -1 & 1 \end{bmatrix} \tag{3.275}$$

With the above relationships, we can write the relevant element matrices as follows:

$$[\mathbf{K}]_e = \int_l \frac{1}{l} \begin{bmatrix} -1 \\ 1 \end{bmatrix} [k_x] \frac{1}{l} \begin{bmatrix} -1 & 1 \end{bmatrix} A \, dx + \int_S h \begin{bmatrix} N_i \\ N_j \end{bmatrix} \begin{bmatrix} N_i & N_j \end{bmatrix} P \, dx \tag{3.276}$$

Where A is the cross-sectional area of the fin and P is the perimeter of the fin from which convection takes place. Note that $[D] = k_x$ for one-dimensional problems.

Rearranging Equation 3.276, we have

$$[\mathbf{K}]_e = \int_l \frac{A k_x}{l^2} \begin{bmatrix} 1 & -1 \\ -1 & 1 \end{bmatrix} dx + \int_l h P \begin{bmatrix} N_i^2 & N_i N_j \\ N_i N_j & N_j^2 \end{bmatrix} dx \tag{3.277}$$

Here $N_i = L_i$ and $N_j = L_j$, which is generally true for all linear elements. Hence, we can make use of the formula

$$\int_l L_i^a L_j^b dl = \frac{a!b!l}{(a+b+1)!} \tag{3.278}$$

For example,

$$\int_l N_i^2 dl = \int_l L_i^2 dl = \frac{2!0!l}{(2+0+1)!} = \frac{l}{3} \tag{3.279}$$

and other terms can be similarly integrated.

If A, k_x, P and h are all assumed to be constant throughout the element (see Figure 3.29), we obtain the following [K] matrix:

$$[K]_e = \frac{Ak_x}{l} \begin{bmatrix} 1 & -1 \\ -1 & 1 \end{bmatrix} + \frac{hPl}{6} \begin{bmatrix} 2 & 1 \\ 1 & 2 \end{bmatrix} \tag{3.280}$$

Let us next consider the thermal loading. From Equation 3.261, we can write

$$\{f\}_e = \frac{GAl}{2} \begin{Bmatrix} 1 \\ 1 \end{Bmatrix} - \frac{qPl}{2} \begin{Bmatrix} 1 \\ 1 \end{Bmatrix} + \frac{hT_a Pl}{2} \begin{Bmatrix} 1 \\ 1 \end{Bmatrix} \tag{3.281}$$

In this case, the loads are distributed equally between the two nodes, which is a general characteristic of linear elements.

The solution of the given problem may be found by substitution of the numerical values.

(a) First let us consider a one-element solution for the case where $l = 2$ cm, as shown in Figure 3.30. The element stiffness matrix is

$$
\begin{aligned}
[K]_e &= \frac{Ak_x}{l} \begin{bmatrix} 1 & -1 \\ -1 & 1 \end{bmatrix} + \frac{hPl}{6} \begin{bmatrix} 2 & 1 \\ 1 & 2 \end{bmatrix} \\
&= \begin{bmatrix} 0.06 & -0.06 \\ -0.06 & 0.06 \end{bmatrix} + \begin{bmatrix} 0.008 & 0.004 \\ 0.004 & 0.008 \end{bmatrix} \\
&= \begin{bmatrix} 0.068 & -0.056 \\ -0.056 & 0.068 \end{bmatrix}
\end{aligned} \tag{3.282}
$$

and the loading term is given by

$$
\begin{aligned}
\{f\} &= \frac{hPlT_a}{2} \begin{Bmatrix} 1 \\ 1 \end{Bmatrix} \\
&= \begin{Bmatrix} 0.30 \\ 0.30 \end{Bmatrix}
\end{aligned} \tag{3.283}
$$

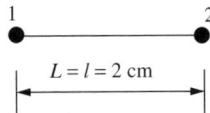

Figure 3.30 Heat transfer from a rectangular fin. One linear element

Note that T_a is in $°C$ as h is expressed in $W/m^2°C$.

Since only one element is employed, no assemblage of element contribution is necessary. Thus, the simultaneous equation system may be written as

$$\begin{bmatrix} 0.068 & -0.056 \\ -0.056 & 0.068 \end{bmatrix} \begin{Bmatrix} T_1 \\ T_2 \end{Bmatrix} = \begin{Bmatrix} 0.30 \\ 0.30 \end{Bmatrix} \tag{3.284}$$

We now incorporate the known base temperature of $100°C$ at node 1. It is done in such a way that the symmetry of the $[\mathbf{K}]$ matrix is retained. This is essential if a symmetric matrix solution procedure is employed in the solution of the simultaneous equations. The following steps give a typical implementation procedure for the temperature boundary condition:

(i) *The diagonal element of the first row is assigned a value of 1 and the remaining elements on that row are zero.*

(ii) *Replace the first row value of the loading vector $\mathbf{f}$ by the known value of T_1, that is, 100.*

(iii) *In order to retain the symmetry, the first term of the second row in the $[\mathbf{K}]$ matrix is transferred to the right-hand side and replaced with a zero value as given below:*

$$\begin{bmatrix} 1.0 & 0.0 \\ 0.0 & 0.068 \end{bmatrix} \begin{Bmatrix} T_1 \\ T_2 \end{Bmatrix} = \begin{Bmatrix} 100.0 \\ 0.30 + 0.056(100.0) \end{Bmatrix} \tag{3.285}$$

The equation to be solved is

$$0.068T_2 = 0.3 + 0.056(100) \tag{3.286}$$

Therefore, the solution is $T_1 = 100°C$ and $T_2 = 86.765°C$.
Heat dissipated is

$$Q = \frac{kA}{l}(T_1 - T_2) = 0.7941 \text{ W} \tag{3.287}$$

The above answer is very approximate. However, a more accurate value can be determined by using the following convection condition, that is,

$$Q = \sum_{e=1}^{M} hPl \left(\frac{T_1 + T_2}{2} - T_a \right) = 1.64 \text{ W} \tag{3.288}$$

where M is the total number of elements. The maximum theoretically possible heat transfer is

$$Q_{max} = \sum_{e=1}^{M} hPl\,(T_1 - T_a) = 1.8 \text{ W} \tag{3.289}$$

The efficiency is defined as

$$\eta_f = \frac{Q}{Q_{max}} = \frac{1.64}{1.80} = 91.11\% \tag{3.290}$$

The exact solution for this problem is

$$Q_{\text{exact}} = kAm(T_b - T_a) \tanh (kml) = 1.593 \text{ W} \qquad (3.291)$$

where $m = \sqrt{hP/kA} = 31.62$. *Therefore, the exact fin efficiency is*

$$(\eta_f)_{\text{exact}} = \frac{Q}{Q_{\text{exact}}} = 88.48\%. \qquad (3.292)$$

(b) Let us consider a two-element solution of the same problem (3 nodes)
The length of the fin is divided equally into two elements, that is, l = 1.0 cm.
The stiffness matrix calculation is similar to the one for the single-element case, that is,

$$[\mathbf{K_1}] = [\mathbf{K_2}] = \begin{bmatrix} 0.124 & -0.118 \\ -0.118 & 0.124 \end{bmatrix} \qquad (3.293)$$

and the loading vectors are

$$\{\mathbf{f_1}\} = \{\mathbf{f_2}\} = \begin{Bmatrix} 0.15 \\ 0.15 \end{Bmatrix} \qquad (3.294)$$

On assembly we obtain

$$\begin{bmatrix} 0.124 & -0.118 & 0.0 \\ -0.118 & 0.124 + 0.124 & -0.118 \\ 0.0 & -0.118 & 0.124 \end{bmatrix} \begin{Bmatrix} T_1 \\ T_2 \\ T_3 \end{Bmatrix} = \begin{Bmatrix} 0.15 \\ 0.15 + 0.15 \\ 0.15 \end{Bmatrix} \qquad (3.295)$$

Now we have to incorporate the known value of base temperature, that is, $T_1 = 100°C$.

$$\begin{bmatrix} 1.0 & 0.0 & 0.0 \\ 0.0 & 0.248 & -0.118 \\ 0.0 & -0.118 & 0.124 \end{bmatrix} \begin{Bmatrix} T_1 \\ T_2 \\ T_3 \end{Bmatrix} = \begin{Bmatrix} 100.0 \\ 0.30 + 0.118(100) \\ 0.15 \end{Bmatrix} \qquad (3.296)$$

Therefore, the two equations to be solved are

$$0.248T_2 - 0.118T_3 = 12.1$$

and

$$-0.118T_2 + 0.124T_3 = 0.15$$

Solving these equations, we get $T_2 = 90.209°C$, $T_3 = 87.057°C$.
Results, which have been generated using different number of elements are tabulated in Tables 3.7 and 3.8.
As can be seen, the two-element solution is very good and is further improved with the use of four elements. As a first idealization, even the one element solution is reasonably good considering the small effort involved.

Table 3.7   Summary of results—temperatures

x mm	Exact	1 element	2 elements	4 elements
0.0	100.00	100.00	100.00	100.00
5.0	94.28	–	–	94.26
10.0	90.28	–	90.209	90.25
15.0	87.93	–	–	87.908
20.0	87.15	86.77	87.07	87.128

Table 3.8   Summary of results—
heat dissipated and efficiency

case	$Q(W)$	η_f
1 element	1.640	91.11
2 elements	1.604	89.11
4 elements	1.596	88.65
Exact	1.590	88.48

3.6   Summary

In this chapter, we have discussed the basic principles of the finite element method as applied to heat transfer problems. Different types of elements have been discussed and various examples have been presented. In the authors' opinion, this is the most important chapter for beginners. Readers already familiar with the topic of finite elements may find it trivial to follow but it would be beneficial for the novice to work out the exercises provided in the following section.

3.7   Exercise

Exercise 3.7.1 *A one-dimensional linear element is used to approximate the temperature variation in a fin. The solution gives the temperature at two nodes i and j of an element as 100 and 80°C respectively. The distance from the origin to node i is 6 cm and to node j is 10 cm. Determine the temperature at a point 9 cm from the origin. Also, calculate the temperature gradient in the element. Show that the sum of the shape functions at the location 9 cm from the origin is unity.*

Exercise 3.7.2 *A one-dimensional quadratic element is used to approximate the temperature distribution in a long fin. The solution gives the temperature at three nodes as 100, 90, and 80°C at distances of 10, 15 and 20 cm respectively from the origin. Calculate the temperature and temperature gradient at a location of 12 cm from the origin.*

Exercise 3.7.3 *During the implementation of the finite element method, the evaluation of the integrals that contain shape functions and their derivatives are required. Evaluate the* *following integrals for a linear one-dimensional element:*

$$\int_l N_i dl; \quad \int_l N_i^2 dl; \quad \int_l \frac{dN_i}{dx}\frac{dN_j}{dx} dl; \quad \int_l N_i^3 dl; \quad \int_l N_i N_j dl \qquad (3.297)$$

Exercise 3.7.4 *Derive the shape functions for a one-dimensional linear element in which both the temperature and the heat fluxes should continuously be varying in the element. (Note that degrees of freedom for a one-dimensional linear element are T_i, q_i, T_j, q_j.)*

Exercise 3.7.5 *The solution for temperature distribution in a linear triangle gives the nodal temperature as $T_i = 200°C$, $T_j = 180°C$ and $T_k = 160°C$. The coordinates of i, j and k are $(x_i = 2$ cm, $y_i = 2$ cm), $(x_j = 6$ cm, $y_j = 4$ cm) and $(x_k = 4$ cm, $y_k = 6$ cm). Calculate the temperature at a location given by $x = 3$ cm and $y = 4$ cm. Calculate the coordinates of the isotherm corresponding to $170°C$. Calculate the heat flux in the x and y directions if the thermal conductivity is 0.5 W/m°C. Also, show that the sum of the shape functions at $(x = 3$ cm, $y = 4$ cm) is unity.*

Exercise 3.7.6 *For a one-dimensional quadratic element evaluate the integrals (Note : convert N_i, N_j and N_k to local coordinates and then integrate.)*

$$\int_l N_i dl; \quad \int_l N_j dl; \quad \int_l N_k dl; \quad \int_l N_i N_j dl \qquad (3.298)$$

Exercise 3.7.7 *The nodal values for a rectangular element are given as follows, $x_i = 0.25$ cm, $y_i = 0.20$ cm, $x_j = 0.30$ cm, $y_m = 0.25$ cm, $T_i = 150°C$, $T_j = 120°C$, $T_k = 100°C$, $T_m = 110°C$ Calculate (a) The temperature at the point $C(x = 0.27$ cm, $y = 0.22$ cm). (b) x, y coordinates of the isotherm $130°C$ (c) Evaluate $\partial T/\partial x$ and $\partial T/\partial y$ at the point C.*

Exercise 3.7.8 *Calculate the shape functions for the six-node rectangle shown in Figure 3.31.*

Exercise 3.7.9 *Evaluate the partial derivatives of the shape functions at $\psi = 1/4$ and $\eta = 1/2$ of a quadrilateral element shown in Figure 3.32 assuming that the temperature is approximated by (a) Bilinear (b) Quadratic interpolating polynomials.*

Exercise 3.7.10 *Calculate the derivatives $\partial N_6/\partial x$ and $\partial N_6/\partial y$ at the point $(2, 5)$ for a quadratic triangle element, when the geometry is represented by a three-node triangle as shown in Figure 3.33.*

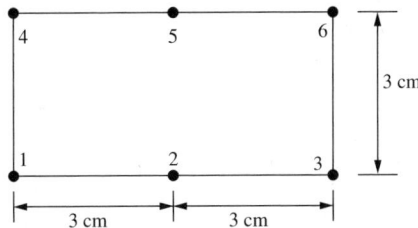

Figure 3.31   Rectangular element

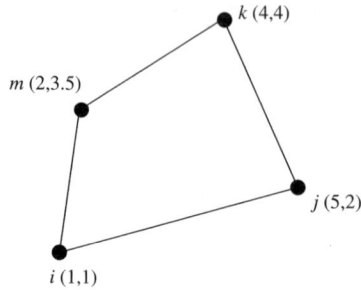

Figure 3.32   Quadrilateral element

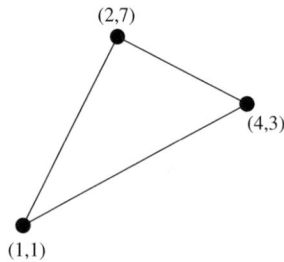

Figure 3.33   Triangular element

Exercise 3.7.11 *In a double pipe heat exchanger, hot fluid flows inside a pipe and cold fluid flows outside in the annular space. The heat exchange between the two fluids is given by the differential equations, (refer to Exercise 2.5.12)*

$$C_1 \frac{dT_h}{dA} = -U(T_h - T_c)$$

$$C_2 \frac{dT_c}{dA} = U(T_h - T_c) \tag{3.299}$$

Develop the stiffness matrix and forcing vector using (a) Sub-domain method (b) Galerkin method.

Exercise 3.7.12 *Calculate (using one, two and four elements) the temperature distribution and the heat dissipation capacity of a fin of length 4 cm and cross-sectional dimensions of 6 mm × 4 mm with a heat transfer coefficient of 0.1 $W/m^2°C$ and a thermal conductivity of the material of the fin as 0.5 $W/m°C$. Base temperature is 90°C.*

Bibliography

Baker, AJ 1995 *Finite Element Computational Fluid Mechanics*, Student Edition, McGraw-Hill Book Company, New York.

Bathe KJ 1982 *Finite Element Procedures in Engineering Analysis*, Prentice Hall, Englewood Cliffs, NJ.

Chandrupatla TR and Belegundu AD 1991 *Introduction to Finite Elements in Engineering*, Prentice Hall of India Pvt Ltd.

Clough RW 1960 The finite element analysis in plane stress analysis, *Proc. 2nf ASCE Conf. on Electronic Computation*, Pittsburgh, PA, September.

Gupta KK and Meek JL 1996 A brief history of the beginning of the finite element method, *International Journal for Numerical Methods in Engineering*, **39**, 3761–3774.

Huebner K and Thornton EA 1982 *The Finite Element Method for Engineers*, Second Edition, John Wiley & Sons.

Hughes TJR 2000 *The Finite Element Method: Linear Static and Dynamic Finite Element Analysis*, Dover Publications, New York.

Lewis RW, Morgan K, Thomas HR and Seetharamu KN 1996 *Finite Element Methods in Heat Transfer Analysis*, John Wiley & Sons.

Malan AG, Lewis, RW and Nithiarasu P 2002 An improved unsteady, unstructured, artificial compressibility, finite volume scheme for viscous incompressible flows, Part I - Theory and implementation, *International Journal for Numerical Methods in Engineering*, **54**, 695–714.

Oden JT 1996 Finite elements: an introduction, *Handbook of Numerical Analysis*, P.G. Ciarlet and J.L. Lions (eds), 2, 3–16, Elsevier, Amsterdam.

Ozisik MN and Czisik MN 1994 *Finite Difference Methods in Heat Transfer*, CRC Press.

Patankar SV 1980 *Numerical Heat Transfer and Fluid Flow*, Hemisphere Publishers.

Rao SS 1989 *The Finite Element Methods in Engineering*, Second Edition, Pergamon Press, New York.

Reddy JN 1993 *An Introduction to Finite Element Method*, Second Edition, McGraw-Hill Book Company.

Segerlind LJ 1984 *Applied Finite Element Analysis*, Second Edition, John Wiley & Sons.

Silvester P 1969 Higher-order polynomial triangular finite elements for potential problems, *International Journal of Engineering Science*, **7**, 849–861.

Thompson JF, Soni BK and Weatherill NP 1999 *Handbook of grid Generation*, CRC press.

Zienkiewicz, OC 1996 Origins, milestones and directions of the finite element method—a personal view, *Handbook of Numerical Analysis*, P.G. Ciarlet and J.L. Lions (eds), 4, 7–67, Elsevier, Amsterdam.

Zienkiewicz OC and Cheung K 1965 Finite elements in the solution of field problems, *Engineer*, **200**, 507–510.

Zienkiewicz OC and Morgan K 1983 *Finite Elements and Approximation*, Wiley-Inter Science, New York.

Zienkiewicz OC and Taylor RL 2000 *The Finite Element Method, Vol. 1, The Basis*, Butterworth and Heinemann, London.

4

Steady State Heat Conduction in One Dimension

4.1 Introduction

A one-dimensional approximation of the heat conduction equation is feasible for many physical problems, for example, plane walls, fins, and so on (Bejan 1993; Holman 1989; Incropera and Dewitt 1990; Ozisik 1968). In these problems, any major temperature variation is in one direction only and the variation in all other directions can be ignored. Other examples of one-dimensional heat transfer occur in cylindrical and spherical solids in which the temperature variation occurs only in the radial direction. In this chapter, such one-dimensional problems are considered for steady state conditions, in which the temperature does not depend on time. Time-dependent and multi-dimensional problems will be discussed in later chapters.

4.2 Plane Walls

4.2.1 Homogeneous wall

The differential equations that govern the heat conduction through plane walls have already been discussed in Chapter 1. The steady state heat conduction equation for a plane wall, shown in Figure 4.1, is

$$kA\frac{\mathrm{d}^2 T}{\mathrm{d}x^2} = 0 \qquad (4.1)$$

where k is the thermal conductivity and A is the cross-sectional area perpendicular to the direction of heat flow. The problem is complete with the following description of the

Fundamentals of the Finite Element Method for Heat and Fluid Flow   R. W. Lewis, P. Nithiarasu and K. N. Seetharamu
© 2004 John Wiley & Sons, Ltd   ISBNs: 0-470-84788-3 (HB); 0-470-84789-1 (PB)

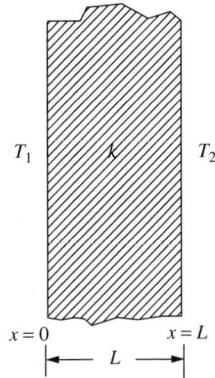

Figure 4.1   Heat conduction through a homogeneous wall

boundary conditions:

$$\text{At} \quad x = 0, T = T_1; \quad \text{and at} \quad x = L, T = T_2$$

The exact solution to Equation 4.1 is

$$kAT = C_1 x + C_2 \tag{4.2}$$

On applying the appropriate boundary conditions to Equation 4.3, we obtain

$$C_2 = kAT_1 \tag{4.3}$$

and

$$C_1 = -\frac{kA(T_1 - T_2)}{L} \tag{4.4}$$

Therefore, substituting constants C_1 and C_2 into Equation 4.3 results in

$$T = -\frac{(T_1 - T_2)}{L} x + T_1 \tag{4.5}$$

The above equation indicates that the temperature distribution within the wall is linear. The heat flow, Q, can be written as

$$Q = -kA\frac{dT}{dx} = -\frac{kA}{L}(T_2 - T_1) \tag{4.6}$$

4.2.2   Composite wall

Even if more than one material is used to construct the plane wall, as shown in Figure 4.2, at steady state, the heat flow will be constant (conservation of energy), that is,

$$Q = -\frac{k_1 A}{x_1}(T_2 - T_1) = -\frac{k_2 A}{x_2}(T_3 - T_2) = -\frac{k_3 A}{x_3}(T_4 - T_3) \tag{4.7}$$

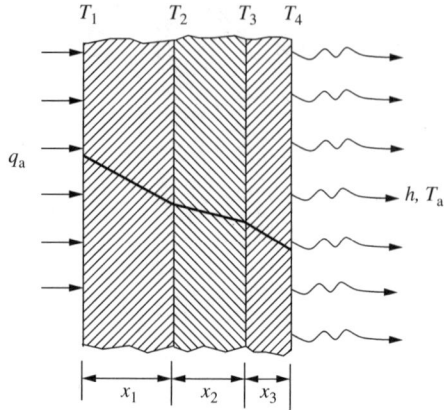

Figure 4.2   Heat conduction in a composite wall

Rearranging, we obtain

$$\frac{Q}{\dfrac{k_1 A}{x_1}} = -(T_2 - T_1)$$

$$\frac{Q}{\dfrac{k_2 A}{x_2}} = -(T_3 - T_2)$$

$$\frac{Q}{\dfrac{k_3 A}{x_3}} = -(T_4 - T_3) \tag{4.8}$$

Adding the above equations and rearranging,

$$Q = \frac{(T_1 - T_4)}{\left[\dfrac{x_1}{k_1 A} + \dfrac{x_2}{k_2 A} + \dfrac{x_3}{k_3 A}\right]} \tag{4.9}$$

The numerator in the above equation is often referred to as the *thermal potential differ-ence* and the denominator is known as the *thermal resistance*. In general, all x/kA terms are called *thermal resistances* (See Figure 4.2). If there is a convective resistance, say on the right face, then we have ($Q = hA(T_4 - T_a)$).

$$Q = \frac{(T_1 - T_a)}{\dfrac{x_1}{k_1 A} + \dfrac{x_2}{k_2 A} + \dfrac{x_3}{k_3 A} + \dfrac{1}{h A}} \tag{4.10}$$

where h is the heat transfer coefficient from the right wall surface to the atmosphere and T_a is the atmospheric temperature. Let us now consider a finite element solution for Equation 4.1. As shown in Equation 4.6, the temperature distribution is linear for a homogeneous material.

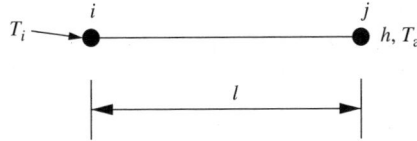

Figure 4.3 Heat conduction through a homogeneous wall subjected to heat convection on one side and constant temperature on the other. Approximation using a single linear element

4.2.3 Finite element discretization

If we consider a typical homogeneous slab as shown in Figure 4.1, with nodes 'i' and 'j' on either side (see Figure 4.3), we can write

$$T = N_i T_i + N_j T_j \tag{4.11}$$

where

$$N_i = \frac{x_j - x}{x_j - x_i} \text{ and } N_j = \frac{x - x_i}{x_j - x_i} \tag{4.12}$$

In local coordinates,

$$N_i = 1 - \frac{x}{l} \text{ and } N_j = \frac{x}{l} \tag{4.13}$$

and the temperature derivative is

$$\frac{dT}{dx} = -\frac{1}{l} T_i + \frac{1}{l} T_j$$

$$= \left[-\frac{1}{l} \quad \frac{1}{l} \right] \left\{ \begin{array}{c} T_i \\ T_j \end{array} \right\} = [\mathbf{B}]\{\mathbf{T}\} \tag{4.14}$$

where l is the length of the element.

The elemental stiffness matrix (Chapter 3) is given as

$$[\mathbf{K}]_e = \int_\Omega [\mathbf{B}]^T [\mathbf{D}][\mathbf{B}] \, d\Omega + \int_{A_s} h[\mathbf{N}]^T [\mathbf{N}] \, dA_s$$

$$= \int_l [\mathbf{B}]^T [\mathbf{D}][\mathbf{B}] A \, dx + \int_{A_s} h[\mathbf{N}]^T [\mathbf{N}] \, dA_s \tag{4.15}$$

where Ω is the volume integral, A_s indicates surface area and h is the convective heat transfer coefficient. After integration,

$$[\mathbf{K}]_e = \frac{A k_x}{l} \begin{bmatrix} 1 & -1 \\ -1 & 1 \end{bmatrix} + h A_s \begin{bmatrix} 0 & 0 \\ 0 & 1 \end{bmatrix} \tag{4.16}$$

In a one-dimensional problem, $[\mathbf{D}]$ has only one entry, which is equal to k_x.

Note that the convective heat transfer boundary condition is assumed to act on the right face where $N_i = 0$ and $N_j = 1$. This is the reason we have $h A_s$ added to the last nodal equation in Equation 4.16. In the plane wall problems considered here, the cross-sectional area A and convective surface area A_s are equal.

The forcing vector can be written as

$$\{f\}_e = \int_\Omega G[N]^T \, d\Omega - \int_{A_s} q[N]^T \, dA_s + \int_{A_s} hT_a[N]^T \, dA_s \tag{4.17}$$

where G is the internal heat generation per unit volume, q is the boundary surface heat flux and T_a is the atmospheric temperature. If $G = 0$, then there is no heat generation inside the slab. The no heat flux boundary condition is denoted by $q = 0$. If neither internal heat generation nor external heat flux boundary conditions occur, then the finite element equation for a homogeneous slab (Figure 4.3) with only two nodes becomes

$$\left\{ \frac{k_x A}{l} \begin{bmatrix} 1 & -1 \\ -1 & 1 \end{bmatrix} + hA \begin{bmatrix} 0 & 0 \\ 0 & 1 \end{bmatrix} \right\} \begin{Bmatrix} T_i \\ T_j \end{Bmatrix} = \begin{Bmatrix} 0 \\ hT_a A \end{Bmatrix} \tag{4.18}$$

The element equations can now be written for each slab of the composite wall shown in Figure 4.2 separately and may be assembled. If we assume a discretization as shown in Figure 4.4, we obtain the following element equations:

Element 1—(Slab 1)

$$[K]_1 = \begin{bmatrix} \dfrac{k_1 A}{x_1} & -\dfrac{k_1 A}{x_1} \\ -\dfrac{k_1 A}{x_1} & \dfrac{k_1 A}{x_1} \end{bmatrix} ; \quad \{f\}_1 = \begin{Bmatrix} qA \\ 0 \end{Bmatrix} \tag{4.19}$$

Element 2—(Slab 2)

$$[K]_2 = \begin{bmatrix} \dfrac{k_2 A}{x_2} & -\dfrac{k_2 A}{x_2} \\ -\dfrac{k_2 A}{x_2} & \dfrac{k_2 A}{x_2} \end{bmatrix} ; \quad \{f\}_2 = \begin{Bmatrix} 0 \\ 0 \end{Bmatrix} \tag{4.20}$$

Element 3—(Slab 3)

$$[K]_3 = \begin{bmatrix} \dfrac{k_3 A}{x_3} & -\dfrac{k_3 A}{x_3} \\ -\dfrac{k_3 A}{x_3} & \dfrac{k_3 A}{x_3} + hA \end{bmatrix} ; \quad \{f\}_3 = \begin{Bmatrix} 0 \\ hAT_a \end{Bmatrix} \tag{4.21}$$

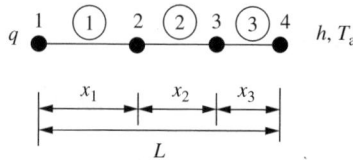

Figure 4.4   Heat conduction through a composite wall subjected to heat convection on one side and constant heat flux on the other side. Approximation using three linear elements

Assembly gives (see Appendix C)

$$
\begin{bmatrix}
\dfrac{k_1 A}{x_1} & -\dfrac{k_1 A}{x_1} & 0 & 0 \\[2ex]
-\dfrac{k_1 A}{x_1} & \left(\dfrac{k_1 A}{x_1} + \dfrac{k_2 A}{x_2}\right) & -\dfrac{k_1 A}{x_2} & 0 \\[2ex]
0 & -\dfrac{k_2 A}{x_2} & \left(\dfrac{k_2 A}{x_1} + \dfrac{k_3 A}{x_3}\right) & \dfrac{k_3 A}{x_3} \\[2ex]
0 & 0 & -\dfrac{k_3 A}{x_3} & \dfrac{k_3 A}{x_3} + hA
\end{bmatrix}
\begin{Bmatrix} T_1 \\ T_2 \\ T_3 \\ T_4 \end{Bmatrix}
=
\begin{Bmatrix} qA \\ 0 \\ 0 \\ hAT_a \end{Bmatrix}
\tag{4.22}
$$

A solution of the above system of simultaneous equations will result in the values of T_1, T_2, T_3 and T_4. In a similar way, we can extend this solution method to any number of materials that might constitute a composite wall. Note that the heat flux imposed on the left-hand face is q.

4.2.4 Wall with varying cross-sectional area

Let us now consider a case in which the cross-sectional area varies linearly from section 'i' to 'j' as shown in Figure 4.5.

Let A_i and A_j be the areas of cross section at distances x_i and x_j respectively. Therefore, the area A at an intermediate distance x is given by

$$
A = A_i - \frac{x}{l}(A_i - A_j)
\tag{4.23}
$$

Rearranging, we obtain

$$
A = A_i \left(1 - \frac{x}{l}\right) + \frac{x}{l} A_j
$$
$$
= A_i N_i + A_j N_j
\tag{4.24}
$$

Thus, the linear variation of area with distance can be represented in terms of the areas at the points 'i' and 'j', using the same shape functions. The stiffness matrix for the

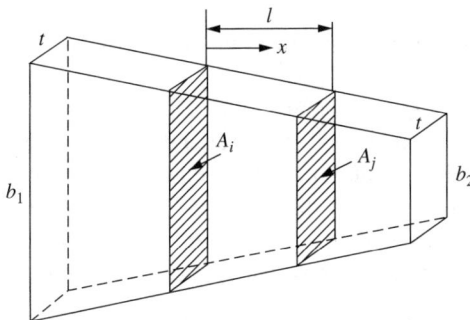

Figure 4.5   Heat conduction through a wall with linearly varying area of cross section

element connecting i and j can be written as

$$[\mathbf{K}] = \int_\Omega [\mathbf{B}]^T [\mathbf{D}][\mathbf{B}]\, d\Omega$$

$$= \int_l \frac{k}{l^2} \begin{bmatrix} 1 & -1 \\ -1 & 1 \end{bmatrix} (N_i A_i + N_j A_j)\, dx$$

$$= \frac{k}{l}\left(\frac{A_i + A_j}{2}\right)\begin{bmatrix} 1 & -1 \\ -1 & 1 \end{bmatrix} \qquad (4.25)$$

where l is the distance between i and j. In the above equation, it has been assumed that convection is ignored.

Thus, when the area varies linearly, we can substitute an average area value and use the constant area formulation if there is no heat dissipation from the perimeter. This assumption will not hold good if the body is circular in cross section, in which case the cross-sectional area varies quadratically with the axial distance. This case can be dealt with by the use of a quadratic variation within the element.

Example 4.2.1 *A composite wall, with three layers of different material as shown in Figure 4.2, has the following properties for the different layers:*

Layer-1: Gypsum, $k_3 = 0.05$ W/m $^\circ$C, $x_3 = 1$ cm and $q = 15$ W/m^2
Layer-2: Fibre-glass, $k_2 = 0.0332$ W/m $^\circ$C and $x_2 = 5$ cm
Layer-3: Concrete, $k_1 = 1.2$ W/m $^\circ$C, $x_1 = 15$ cm, $h = 15$ W/m^2 $^\circ$C and $T_a = 25\,^\circ C$
Calculate the temperatures T_1, T_2, T_3 and T_4 assuming unit area of heat flow.
On substituting the given parameter values into Equation 4.22, we obtain

$$\begin{bmatrix} 5.0 & -5.0 & 0.0 & 0.0 \\ -5.0 & 5.66 & -0.66 & 0.0 \\ 0.0 & -0.66 & 5.66 & 8.66 \\ -8.0 & 0.0 & -8.0 & 8.15 \end{bmatrix} \begin{Bmatrix} T_1 \\ T_2 \\ T_3 \\ T_4 \end{Bmatrix} = \begin{Bmatrix} 15 \\ 0.0 \\ 0.0 \\ 375 \end{Bmatrix} \qquad (4.26)$$

The solution of the above simultaneous equations results in $T_1 = 53.6\,^\circ C$, $T_2 = 50.60\,^\circ C$, $T_3 = 27.875\,^\circ C$ and $T_4 = 26\,^\circ C$

4.2.5 Plane wall with a heat source: solution by linear elements

Many examples of heat transfer problems involve internal heat generation, for example, in nuclear reactors, electrical conductors, chemical and biological reactors, and so on. In this section, the heat conduction through a wall is considered with internal heat generation as shown in Figure 4.6. Let us assume that the one-dimensional approximation is valid and that G W/m^3 represents the quantity of heat generated per unit volume inside the wall. Therefore, under steady state conditions, the applicable differential equation is

$$\frac{d^2 T}{dx^2} + \frac{G}{k} = 0 \qquad (4.27)$$

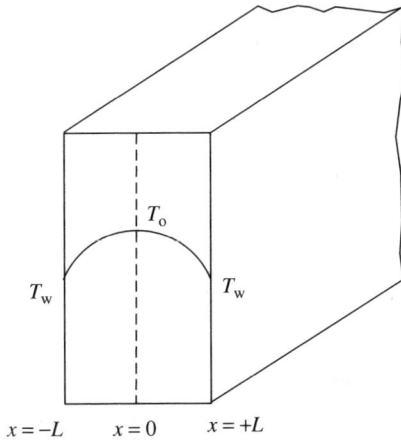

Figure 4.6 Plane wall with heat source

The boundary conditions are

$$\text{at} \quad x = \pm L, T = T_w \tag{4.28}$$

Integrating twice, we get

$$T = -\frac{G}{k}\frac{x^2}{2} + C_1 x + C_2 \tag{4.29}$$

From the symmetry of the problem, we find at $x = 0$, $dT/dx = 0$. Since T is a maximum at the centre, then $C_1 = 0$ and $C_2 = T_o$. Therefore, Equation 4.29 becomes

$$T = -\frac{G}{k}\frac{x^2}{2} + T_o \tag{4.30}$$

The temperature, T_w, at both ends can be obtained by substituting $x = \pm L$, which results in

$$T_w = -\frac{G}{k}\frac{L^2}{2} + T_o \tag{4.31}$$

Similarly, at the centre, that is, $x = 0$,

$$T_o = T_w + \frac{GL^2}{2k} \tag{4.32}$$

From Equations 4.30, 4.31 and 4.32, we can write

$$\frac{T - T_o}{T_w - T_o} = \left(\frac{x}{L}\right)^2 \tag{4.33}$$

which shows that the temperature distribution is parabolic.

In the case of a finite element formulation, we have to account for the heat generation in the forcing vector such that

$$\{\mathbf{f}\}_e = \int_\Omega G[\mathbf{N}]^T \, d\Omega = \int_l G \begin{Bmatrix} N_i \\ N_j \end{Bmatrix} A \, dx = \frac{GAL}{2} \begin{Bmatrix} 1 \\ 1 \end{Bmatrix} \tag{4.34}$$

The heat generated is distributed equally between the two nodes 'i' and 'j'. In all linear elements, we observe that the heat generated, or any other type of load, is equally distributed among the participating nodes.

Because of the symmetry of the problem, it is sufficient in this case if we take only one half of the domain.

Example 4.2.2 *Determine the temperature distribution in a plane wall of thickness 60 mm, which has an internal heat source of $0.3\,MW/m^3$ and the thermal conductivity of the material is $21\,W/m\,°C$. Assume that the surface temperature of the wall is $40\,°C$.*

Because of symmetry, we may consider only one half of the plane wall as shown in Figure 4.7. Let us consider four elements, each of length 7.5 mm. Let the cross-sectional area for heat flow, $A = 1\,m^2$.

The element stiffness matrix is

$$[\mathbf{K}]_e = \frac{kA}{L} \begin{bmatrix} 1 & -1 \\ -1 & 1 \end{bmatrix} = \begin{bmatrix} 2800 & -2800 \\ -2800 & 2800 \end{bmatrix} \tag{4.35}$$

which is identical for every element and

$$\{\mathbf{f}\}_e = \frac{GAL}{2} \begin{Bmatrix} 1 \\ 1 \end{Bmatrix} = \begin{Bmatrix} 1125 \\ 1125 \end{Bmatrix} \tag{4.36}$$

which also is identical for all elements. Assembly gives

$$\begin{bmatrix} 2800 & -2800 & 0.0 & 0.0 & 0.0 \\ -2800 & 5600 & 5600 & 0.0 & 0.0 \\ 0.0 & -2800 & 5600 & -2800 & 0.0 \\ 0.0 & 0.0 & -2800 & 5600 & -2800 \\ 0.0 & 0.0 & 0.0 & -2800 & 2800 \end{bmatrix} \begin{Bmatrix} T_1 \\ T_2 \\ T_3 \\ T_4 \\ T_5 \end{Bmatrix} = \begin{Bmatrix} 1125 \\ 2250 \\ 2250 \\ 2250 \\ 1125 \end{Bmatrix} \tag{4.37}$$

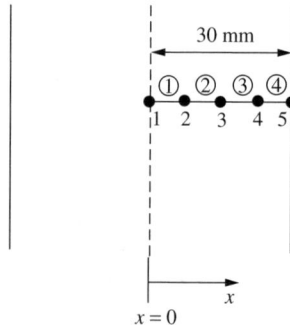

Figure 4.7   Finite element discretization

Table 4.1 Summary of results—temperatures

T	FEM (°C)	Exact (°C)
T_1	46.43	46.43
T_2	46.03	46.03
T_3	44.83	44.82
T_4	42.82	42.81
T_5	40.0	40.0

Applying the boundary condition, $T_5 = 40°$, the modifications are necessary to retain the symmetry of the stiffness matrix, as discussed in Chapter 3.

$$\begin{bmatrix} 2800 & -2800 & 0.0 & 0.0 & 0.0 \\ -2800 & 5600 & 5600 & 0.0 & 0.0 \\ 0.0 & -2800 & 5600 & -2800 & 0.0 \\ 0.0 & 0.0 & -2800 & 5600 & 0.0 \\ 0.0 & 0.0 & 0.0 & 0.0 & 1 \end{bmatrix} \begin{Bmatrix} T_1 \\ T_2 \\ T_3 \\ T_4 \\ T_5 \end{Bmatrix} = \begin{Bmatrix} 1125 \\ 2250 \\ 2250 \\ 2250 + 2800(40) \\ 40 \end{Bmatrix} \quad (4.38)$$

Solving the above system of equations, we obtain the temperature distribution as shown in Table 4.1.

We observe that the finite element method results are either very close or equal to the exact solution. The method can be extended for the case of either a known wall heat flux, or a convection boundary condition at the wall, as shown in Example 4.2.3.

Example 4.2.3 *In Example 4.2.2, the left-hand face is insulated and the right-hand face is subjected to a convection environment at $93°C$ with a surface heat transfer coefficient of $570 \, W/m^2 \, °C$. Determine the temperature distribution within the wall.*

Since there is no symmetry, we have to consider the entire domain. Let us subdivide the domain into eight elements (Figure 4.8), each of 7.5 mm width. Then,

$$[\mathbf{K}]_1 = [\mathbf{K}]_2 = \cdots [\mathbf{K}]_7 = \begin{bmatrix} 2800 & -2800 \\ -2800 & 2800 \end{bmatrix} \quad (4.39)$$

$$[\mathbf{K}]_8 = \begin{bmatrix} 2800 & -2800 \\ -2800 & 2800 \end{bmatrix} + 570 \begin{bmatrix} 0 & 0 \\ 0 & 1 \end{bmatrix} = \begin{bmatrix} 2800 & -2800 \\ -2800 & 3370 \end{bmatrix} \quad (4.40)$$

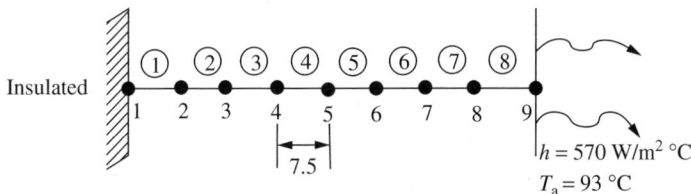

Figure 4.8   Finite element discretization for the example with convection

Table 4.2   Summary of results–
temperatures

T	FEM (°C)	Analytical (°C)
T_1	150.28	150.29
T_2	149.88	149.89
T_3	148.68	148.68
T_4	146.67	146.67
T_5	143.86	143.86
T_6	140.24	140.24
T_7	135.82	135.83
T_8	130.60	130.60
T_9	124.59	124.59

The elemental forcing vectors are the same as for Example 4.2.2, except for the last element, which is

$$\{f\}_8 = \begin{Bmatrix} 1125 \\ 1125 \end{Bmatrix} + hAT_a \begin{Bmatrix} 0 \\ 1 \end{Bmatrix} = \begin{Bmatrix} 1125 \\ 54135 \end{Bmatrix} \tag{4.41}$$

Assembly may be carried out as in Example 4.2.2. The solution of the assembled equation results in the temperature distribution within the wall. The FEM solution is compared with the analytical[1] results, as shown in Table 4.2, and compare very favourably.

4.2.6   Plane wall with a heat source: solution by quadratic elements

We have seen from the previous section that the analytical solution to the problem of a plane wall with a heat source gives a quadratic temperature distribution. Thus, it is appropriate to solve such a problem using quadratic elements. Let us consider the problem shown in Figure 4.6. We require three nodes for each element in order to represent a quadratic variation as discussed in Section 3.2.2, that is,

$$T = N_i T_i + N_j T_j + N_k T_k \tag{4.42}$$

with

$$N_i = \left[1 - \frac{3x}{l} + \frac{2x^2}{l^2} \right]$$

---

[1] Analytical solution is obtained by solving

$$\frac{d^2 T}{dx^2} + \frac{G}{k} = 0$$

subjected to boundary conditions. The final exact relation is

$$T = \frac{G}{2k}(L^2 - x^2) + \left(\frac{GL}{h} + T_a \right)$$

$$N_j = \frac{4x}{l} - \frac{4x^2}{l^2}$$

$$N_k = \frac{2x^2}{l^2} - \frac{x}{l} \tag{4.43}$$

From Chapter 3, the stiffness matrix is defined as

$$[\mathbf{K}] = \int_\Omega [\mathbf{B}]^T [\mathbf{D}][\mathbf{B}]\, d\Omega$$

$$= \frac{Ak}{6l} \begin{bmatrix} 14 & -16 & 2 \\ -16 & 32 & -16 \\ 2 & -16 & 14 \end{bmatrix} \tag{4.44}$$

where

$$[\mathbf{B}] = \left[\left(\frac{4x}{l^2} - \frac{3}{l} \right) \quad \left(\frac{4}{l} - \frac{8x}{l^2} \right) \quad \left(\frac{4x}{l^2} - \frac{1}{l} \right) \right] \tag{4.45}$$

The loading vector is

$$\{\mathbf{f}\} = \int_\Omega G[\mathbf{N}]^T\, d\Omega$$

$$= \int_l G \left\{ \begin{array}{c} L_i(2L_i - 1) \\ 4L_i L_j \\ L_j(2L_j - 1) \end{array} \right\} A\, dx$$

$$= \frac{GAl}{6} \left\{ \begin{array}{c} 1 \\ 4 \\ 1 \end{array} \right\} \tag{4.46}$$

In the above equation, the shape functions N_i, N_j and N_k are expressed in terms of the local coordinate system L_i and L_j, the use of which will facilitate the integration process by using

$$\int_l N_i^a N_j^b\, dl = \frac{a!b!}{(a+b+1)!} l \tag{4.47}$$

Example 4.2.4 *We shall now solve Example 4.2.2 using one quadratic element only as shown in Figure 4.9.*

As before, we consider only one half of the wall, where L is equal to 30 mm.

Substituting values into Equations 4.44 and 4.46, we obtain

$$[\mathbf{K}]_e = \begin{bmatrix} 1633.33 & -1866.66 & 233.33 \\ -1866.66 & 3733.33 & -1866.66 \\ 233.33 & -1866.66 & 1633.33 \end{bmatrix} \tag{4.48}$$

and

$$\{\mathbf{f}\}_e = \left\{ \begin{array}{c} 1500 \\ 6000 \\ 1500 \end{array} \right\} \tag{4.49}$$

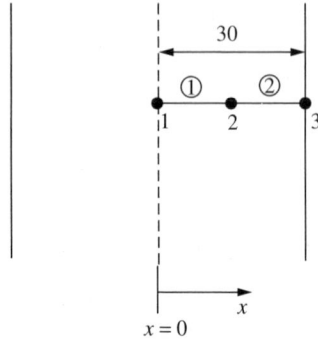

Figure 4.9   Quadratic finite element discretization

Incorporating the boundary condition, that is, $T_3 = 40\,^\circ C$, results in the following set of equations:

$$
\begin{bmatrix}
1633.33 & -1866.66 & 0.0 \\
-1866.66 & 3733.33 & 0.0 \\
0.0 & 0.0 & 1.0
\end{bmatrix}
\begin{Bmatrix} T_1 \\ T_2 \\ T_3 \end{Bmatrix}
=
\begin{Bmatrix}
1500 - 233.33(40) \\
6000 + 1866.66(40) \\
40.0
\end{Bmatrix}
\qquad (4.50)
$$

The solution to the above system gives $T_1 = 46.43\,^\circ C$ and $T_2 = 44.82\,^\circ C$, which are identical to the exact solution.

4.2.7   Plane wall with a heat source: solution by modified quadratic equations (static condensation)

In many transient and nonlinear problems, it will be necessary to obtain the temperature distribution several times. Hence, any possible reduction in the number of nodes, without sacrificing accuracy, is important. For one-dimensional quadratic elements, it is possible to transfer the central node contribution to the side nodes. Thus, there will be only two nodes but the influence of the quadratic variation is inherently present. This process is referred to as static condensation and the procedure will be demonstrated by considering a typical quadratic element equation, namely,

$$
\begin{bmatrix}
K_{11} & K_{12} & K_{13} \\
K_{21} & K_{22} & K_{23} \\
K_{31} & K_{32} & K_{33}
\end{bmatrix}
\begin{Bmatrix} T_1 \\ T_2 \\ T_3 \end{Bmatrix}
=
\begin{Bmatrix} f_1 \\ f_2 \\ f_3 \end{Bmatrix}
\qquad (4.51)
$$

In order to eliminate the middle node, that is, node 2, we transfer its contribution to nodes 1 and 3. This is accomplished by expressing the temperature at node 2 in terms of the temperatures at nodes 1 and 3, that is,

$$
T_2 = \frac{f_2}{K_{22}} - \left[\frac{K_{21} T_1}{K_{22}} + \frac{K_{23} T_3}{K_{22}} \right]
\qquad (4.52)
$$

Now, on substituting the above relation into the first and third nodal equations, we have

$$\left[K_{11} - \frac{K_{21}}{K_{22}}K_{12}\right]T_1 + \left[K_{13} - \frac{K_{23}}{K_{22}}K_{12}\right]T_3 = \left[f_1 - f_2\frac{K_{12}}{K_{22}}\right] \tag{4.53}$$

for the first node, and

$$\left[K_{31} - \frac{K_{21}}{K_{22}}K_{32}\right]T_1 + \left[K_{33} - \frac{K_{23}}{K_{22}}K_{32}\right]T_3 = \left[f_3 - f_2\frac{K_{32}}{K_{22}}\right] \tag{4.54}$$

for the second node. Now the matrix form of the equation can be rewritten as

$$\begin{bmatrix} \left(K_{11} - \frac{K_{21}}{K_{22}}K_{12}\right) & \left(K_{13} - \frac{K_{23}}{K_{22}}K_{12}\right) \\ \left(K_{31} - \frac{K_{21}}{K_{22}}K_{32}\right) & \left(K_{33} - \frac{K_{23}}{K_{22}}K_{32}\right) \end{bmatrix} \begin{Bmatrix} T_1 \\ T_3 \end{Bmatrix} = \begin{Bmatrix} f_1 - f_2\frac{K_{12}}{K_{22}} \\ f_3 - f_2\frac{K_{32}}{K_{22}} \end{Bmatrix} \tag{4.55}$$

Note that the number of equations have been reduced, which leads to a small decrease in computational cost. However, extending this procedure to multi-dimensional problems is difficult and therefore not widely used.

Example 4.2.5 *Repeat Example 4.2.4 using the static condensation procedure.*
Substituting all relevant values into Equation 4.55 and applying the boundary condition ($T_3 = 40\,^\circ C$) leads to the following:

$$\begin{bmatrix} 700.0 & 0.0 \\ 0.0 & 1 \end{bmatrix} \begin{Bmatrix} T_1 \\ T_3 \end{Bmatrix} = \begin{Bmatrix} 4499.89 + 700(40) \\ 40.0 \end{Bmatrix} \tag{4.56}$$

The solution to the above equation results in $T_1 = 46.43\,^\circ C$, which is identical to the exact solution.

4.3 Radial Heat Flow in a Cylinder

Many problems in industry, such as heat exchangers, crude oil transport, and so on, involve the flow of hot fluids in very long pipes that have uniform boundary conditions along the circumference, both inside and outside as shown in Figure 4.10. In such problems, the heat transfer mainly takes place along the radial direction apart from the end effects. The governing differential equation for heat flow in cylindrical geometries is

$$\frac{1}{r}\frac{d}{dr}\left(rk\frac{dT}{dr}\right) = 0 \tag{4.57}$$

The boundary conditions are as follows:

$$\text{At} \quad r = r_i, T = T_w$$

$$\text{and at} \quad r = r_o, -k\frac{dT}{dr} = h(T_o - T_a) \tag{4.58}$$

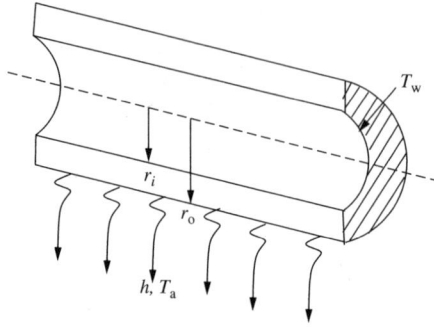

Figure 4.10   Radial heat conduction in an infinitely long cylinder

where T_w is the inside wall temperature, T_o is the outside wall temperature, k is the thermal conductivity, h is the heat transfer coefficient at the outside surface and T_a is the atmospheric temperature.

Integrating Equation 4.57, we obtain

$$kT = C_1 \ln r + C_2 \tag{4.59}$$

Subjecting the above equation to the boundary conditions of Equation 4.58 results in

$$C_1 = -hr_o(T_o - T_a) \quad \text{and} \quad C_2 = kT_w - C_1 \ln r_i \tag{4.60}$$

Substituting the constants and rearranging Equation 4.59, we obtain the exact solution as

$$\frac{(T - T_w)}{(T_o - T_a)} = \frac{hr_o}{k} \ln \frac{r_i}{r_o} \tag{4.61}$$

With the use of the finite element method and assuming a linear variation of temperature, the resulting stiffness matrix is given by

$$[\mathbf{K}] = \int_\Omega [\mathbf{B}]^T [\mathbf{D}][\mathbf{B}] \, d\Omega + \int_{A_s} h[\mathbf{N}]^T [\mathbf{N}] \, dA_s$$

$$= \int_{r_i}^{r_o} \begin{bmatrix} -\dfrac{1}{l} \\ \dfrac{1}{l} \end{bmatrix} k \begin{bmatrix} -\dfrac{1}{l} & \dfrac{1}{l} \end{bmatrix} 2\pi r \, dr + \int_{A_s} h \begin{bmatrix} N_i \\ N_j \end{bmatrix} \begin{bmatrix} N_i & N_j \end{bmatrix} \, dA_s$$

$$= \frac{2\pi k \, (r_i + r_j)}{l} \frac{}{2} \begin{bmatrix} 1 & -1 \\ -1 & 1 \end{bmatrix} + 2\pi r_o h \begin{bmatrix} 0 & 0 \\ 0 & 1 \end{bmatrix} \tag{4.62}$$

per unit length of a cylinder. In the above equation, the variation of r is expressed as $r = N_i r_i + N_j r_j$. The surface area per unit length is $A_s = 2\pi r_o$. The loading vector is

$$\{\mathbf{f}\} = \int_{A_s} hT_a[N]^T \, dA_s = hT_a 2\pi r_o \begin{Bmatrix} 0 \\ 1 \end{Bmatrix} \tag{4.63}$$

Example 4.3.1 *Calculate the outer wall surface temperature and the temperature distribution in a thick wall cylinder with the following data:*

$$r_i = 40\,\text{cm}, \ r_o = 60\,\text{cm}, \ k = 10\,\text{W/m}\,^\circ\text{C}, \ h_o = 10\,\text{W/m}^2\,\text{C}, \ T_a = 30\,^\circ\text{C}.$$

Consider a one-element solution with an element length of l = 60 − 40 = 20 cm. The element stiffness matrix and the loading vectors are given by

$$[\mathbf{K}]_e = \frac{2\pi k}{l} \frac{r_i + r_j}{2} \begin{bmatrix} 1 & -1 \\ -1 & 1 \end{bmatrix} + 2\pi r_o h \begin{bmatrix} 0 & 0 \\ 0 & 1 \end{bmatrix}$$

$$= \pi \begin{bmatrix} 50 & -50 \\ -50 & 62 \end{bmatrix} \tag{4.64}$$

and

$$\{\mathbf{f}\}_e = \pi \begin{Bmatrix} 0 \\ 360 \end{Bmatrix} \tag{4.65}$$

The complete system of equations can be written as

$$\pi \begin{bmatrix} 50 & -50 \\ -50 & 62 \end{bmatrix} \begin{Bmatrix} T_i \\ T_j \end{Bmatrix} = \pi \begin{Bmatrix} 0 \\ 360 \end{Bmatrix} \tag{4.66}$$

The solution to the above system, with $T_i = 100\,^\circ C$ results in $T_j = T_o = 86.45\,^\circ C$, which is greater than the analytical solution, that is, $86.30\,^\circ C$. A more accurate solution may be obtained if two elements, each 10 cm long, are employed. The assembled equation for the two-element system is

$$\begin{bmatrix} 90 & -90 & 0 \\ -90 & 200 & -110 \\ 0 & -110 & 122 \end{bmatrix} \begin{Bmatrix} T_1 \\ T_2 \\ T_3 \end{Bmatrix} = \begin{Bmatrix} 0 \\ 0 \\ 360 \end{Bmatrix} \tag{4.67}$$

The solution to the above equations with boundary condition $T_1 = 100\,^\circ C$, gives $T_2 = 92.48\,^\circ C$ and $T_3 = T_o = 86.34\,^\circ C$. The accuracy of the outer wall temperature has been greatly improved by using two elements.

4.3.1 Cylinder with heat source

Consider a homogeneous cylinder as shown in Figure 4.10 with uniformly distributed heat sources. If we assume a very long cylinder, the temperature in the cylinder will be a function of the radius only. Thus,

$$k \left(\frac{d^2 T}{dr^2} + \frac{1}{r} \frac{dT}{dr} \right) + G = 0 \tag{4.68}$$

The boundary conditions are

$$\text{at} \quad r = r_o, T = T_w \quad \text{and} \quad -k \frac{dT}{dr} = h(T_w - T_a) \tag{4.69}$$

and the heat generated will be equal to the heat lost at the surface, that is,

$$G\pi r_o^2 L = -k2\pi r_o L \left(\frac{dT}{dr}\right)_{r_o} \tag{4.70}$$

Equation 4.68 can be rewritten as

$$\frac{1}{r}k\frac{d}{dr}\left(r\frac{dT}{dr}\right) + G = 0 \tag{4.71}$$

The analytical solution for this problem is

$$\frac{T - T_w}{T_c - T_w} = 1 - \left(\frac{r}{r_o}\right)^2 \tag{4.72}$$

where T_c is the temperature at $r = 0$ and is given by

$$T_c = T_w + \frac{Gr_o^2}{4k} \tag{4.73}$$

Let us now consider a finite element solution employing linear elements. The stiffness matrix is (Equation 4.62 without convection)

$$[\mathbf{K}] = \frac{2\pi k}{l}\left(\frac{r_i + r_j}{2}\right)\begin{bmatrix} 1 & -1 \\ -1 & 1 \end{bmatrix} \tag{4.74}$$

and the forcing vector is

$$\{\mathbf{f}\} = \int_r G[\mathbf{N}]^T 2\pi r\, dr \tag{4.75}$$

per unit length.

In cylindrical coordinates, r may be expressed as

$$r = N_i r_i + N_j r_j \tag{4.76}$$

Substituting the above equation into Equation 4.75 and integrating between r_i and r_j, we obtain

$$\{\mathbf{f}\} = \frac{2\pi Gl}{6}\begin{Bmatrix} 2r_i + r_j \\ r_i + 2r_j \end{Bmatrix} \tag{4.77}$$

where l is the length of an element.

Example 4.3.2 *Calculate the surface temperature in a circular solid cylinder of radius 25 mm with a volumetric heat generation of 35.3 MW/m³. The external surface of the cylinder is exposed to a liquid at a temperature of 20°C with a surface heat transfer coefficient of 4000 W/m² °C. The thermal conductivity of the material is 21 W/m °C.*

Let us divide half of the region into four elements as shown in Figure 4.11, each of width 6.25 cm.

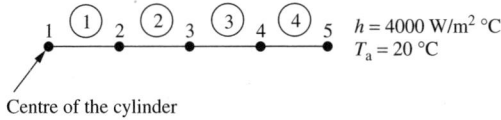

Figure 4.11 Radial heat conduction in an infinitely long cylinder. Finite element discretization

On substituting the given data into Equation 4.74, the stiffness matrix of the four elements may be calculated as follows:

$$[\mathbf{K}]_1 = 2\pi \begin{bmatrix} 10.5 & -10.5 \\ -10.5 & 10.5 \end{bmatrix} \tag{4.78}$$

$$[\mathbf{K}]_2 = 2\pi \begin{bmatrix} 31.5 & -31.5 \\ -31.5 & 31.5 \end{bmatrix} \tag{4.79}$$

$$[\mathbf{K}]_3 = 2\pi \begin{bmatrix} 52.5 & -52.5 \\ -52.5 & 52.5 \end{bmatrix} \tag{4.80}$$

and

$$[\mathbf{K}]_4 = 2\pi \begin{bmatrix} 73.5 & -73.5 \\ -73.5 & 73.5 \end{bmatrix} + 2\pi \begin{bmatrix} 0 & 0 \\ 0 & 100 \end{bmatrix} \tag{4.81}$$

Similarly, the forcing vectors for all four elements can be calculated as

$$\{\mathbf{f}\}_1 = 2\pi \begin{Bmatrix} 229.82 \\ 459.63 \end{Bmatrix} \tag{4.82}$$

$$\{\mathbf{f}\}_2 = 2\pi \begin{Bmatrix} 919.27 \\ 1149.09 \end{Bmatrix} \tag{4.83}$$

$$\{\mathbf{f}\}_3 = 2\pi \begin{Bmatrix} 1608.18 \\ 1838.54 \end{Bmatrix} \tag{4.84}$$

and

$$\{\mathbf{f}\}_4 = 2\pi \begin{Bmatrix} 2298.18 \\ 2528.00 \end{Bmatrix} + 2\pi \begin{Bmatrix} 0 \\ 2000.0 \end{Bmatrix} \tag{4.85}$$

Assembly gives

$$\begin{bmatrix} 10.5 & -10.5 & 0.0 & 0.0 & 0.0 \\ -10.5 & 42.0 & -31.5 & 0.0 & 0.0 \\ 0.0 & -31.5 & 84.0 & -52.5 & 0.0 \\ 0.0 & 0.0 & -52.5 & 126.0 & -73.5 \\ 0.0 & 0.0 & 0.0 & -73.5 & 173.5 \end{bmatrix} \begin{Bmatrix} T_1 \\ T_2 \\ T_3 \\ T_4 \\ T_5 \end{Bmatrix} = \begin{Bmatrix} 229.82 \\ 1378.9 \\ 2757.81 \\ 4136.72 \\ 4528.00 \end{Bmatrix} \tag{4.86}$$

The solution obtained by solving the above system of equations is tabulated in Table 4.3
We can see that the surface temperature, T_5, is predicted very well but the deviation from the exact solution increases as we proceed towards the centre. If two linear elements replace the one element near the centre, then the solution for the maximum temperature is improved to $398.43\,°C$. It is also possible to improve the accuracy of the temperature solution by using quadratic elements.

Table 4.3 Summary of results–temperatures

T	FEM ($^\circ$C)	Exact ($^\circ$C)
T_1	402.19	392.26
T_2	380.28	376.54
T_3	329.20	327.29
T_4	246.02	245.22
T_5	130.32	130.31

4.4 Conduction–Convection Systems

Many physical situations involve the transfer of heat in a material by conduction and its subsequent dissipation by exchange with a fluid or the environment by convection. The heat sinks used in the electronic industry to dissipate heat from electronic components to the ambient are an example of a conduction–convection system. Other examples include the dissipation of heat in electrical windings to the coolant, the heat exchange process in heat exchangers and the cooling of gas turbine blades in which the temperature of the hot gases is greater than the melting point of the blade material. In Section 3.6, we have already demonstrated the applications of the finite element method for extended surfaces with different cross sections. Also, the problems discussed in the previous section of this chapter include the influence of convective boundary conditions. However, all the problems studied previously in this chapter assumed that the domains were of infinite length.

Figure 4.12 shows various types of fins used in practice. Let us now consider the case of a tapered fin (extended surfaces) with plane surfaces on the top and bottom. The fin also loses heat to the ambient via the tip. The thickness of the fin varies linearly from t_2 at the base to t_1 at the tip as shown in Figure 4.13. The width, b, of the fin remains constant along the whole length.

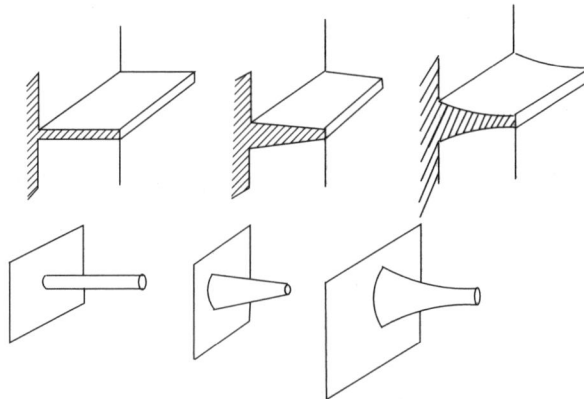

Figure 4.12   Different types of fins

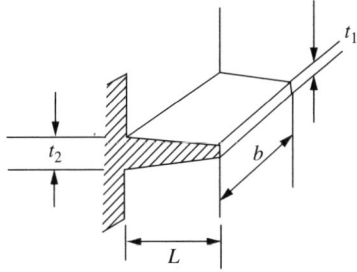

Figure 4.13   Tapered fin

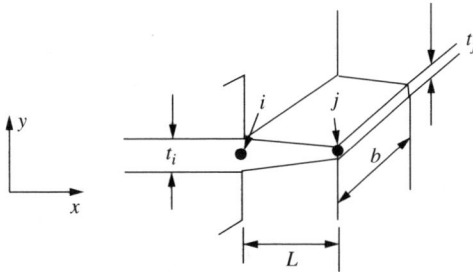

Figure 4.14   Tapered fin. Locations i and j

Let us consider a typical element e, with thicknesses t_i and t_j, areas A_i and A_j and perimeter P_i and P_j at locations 'i' and 'j' respectively as shown in Figure 4.14.

$$A_i = bt_i; \; A_j = bt_j; \; P_i = 2(b + t_i) \quad \text{and} \quad P_j = 2(b + t_j) \tag{4.87}$$

Since 'A' varies linearly with 'x', we can write

$$A = A_i - \frac{A_i - A_j}{L} x \tag{4.88}$$

where L is the length of an element. Alternatively, we can write

$$A = A_i \left(1 - \frac{x}{L}\right) + A_j \frac{x}{L}$$
$$= N_i A_i + N_j A_j \tag{4.89}$$

Similarly, $P = N_i P_i + N_j P_j$. The stiffness matrix is written as

$$[\mathbf{K}] = \int_\Omega \begin{bmatrix} -\dfrac{1}{l} \\ \dfrac{1}{l} \end{bmatrix} [k] \begin{bmatrix} -\dfrac{1}{l} & \dfrac{1}{l} \end{bmatrix} A \, dx + \int_\Omega h \begin{bmatrix} N_i \\ N_j \end{bmatrix} [N_i \;\; N_j] P \, dx \tag{4.90}$$

After integration and rearrangement, we have

$$[\mathbf{K}] = \frac{k}{l} \left(\frac{A_i + A_j}{2}\right) \begin{bmatrix} 1 & -1 \\ -1 & 1 \end{bmatrix} + \frac{hl}{12} \begin{bmatrix} 3P_i + P_j & P_i + P_j \\ P_i + P_j & P_i + 3P_j \end{bmatrix} \tag{4.91}$$

The forcing vector for this problem is

$$\{\mathbf{f}\} = \int_l G[\mathbf{N}]^T A \, \mathrm{d}x - \int_{A_s} q[\mathbf{N}]^T \, \mathrm{d}A_s + \int_{A_s} hT_a[\mathbf{N}]^T \, \mathrm{d}A_s \tag{4.92}$$

where G is the heat source per unit volume, q is the heat flux, h is the heat transfer coefficient and T_a is the atmospheric temperature. Integrating, we obtain

$$\{\mathbf{f}\} = \frac{Gl}{6} \begin{Bmatrix} 2A_i + A_j \\ A_i + 2A_j \end{Bmatrix} - \frac{ql}{6} \begin{Bmatrix} 2P_i + P_j \\ P_i + 2P_j \end{Bmatrix} + \frac{hT_a l}{6} \begin{Bmatrix} 2P_i + P_j \\ P_i + 2P_j \end{Bmatrix} + hT_a A \begin{Bmatrix} 0 \\ 1 \end{Bmatrix} \tag{4.93}$$

The last contribution is valid only for the element at the end face with area A. For all other elements, this last convective term is zero.

Example 4.4.1 *Let us consider an example with the fin tapering linearly from a thickness of 2 mm at the base to 1 mm at the tip (see Figure 4.14). Also, the tip loses heat to the ambient with convection, with a heat transfer coefficient, h, $= 120 \, W/m^2 \, °C$ and atmospheric temperature, T_a, $= 25 °C$. Determine the temperature distribution if the base temperature is maintained at $100 °C$. The total length of the fin, L, is 20 mm and the width, b is 3 mm. Assume the thermal conductivity of the material is equal to $200 \, W/m \, °C$.*

Let us divide the region into two elements of equal length, 10 mm each, as shown in Figure 4.15. Substituting the relevant data into Equation 4.91, we obtain the stiffness matrices for both elements as follows:

$$[\mathbf{K}]_1 = \begin{bmatrix} 0.109 & -0.103 \\ -0.103 & 0.108 \end{bmatrix} \tag{4.94}$$

and

$$[\mathbf{K}]_2 = \begin{bmatrix} 0.079 & -0.073 \\ -0.073 & 0.079 \end{bmatrix} \tag{4.95}$$

Similarly, the forcing vectors are calculated as

$$\{\mathbf{f}\}_1 = \begin{Bmatrix} 0.148 \\ 0.145 \end{Bmatrix} \tag{4.96}$$

and

$$\{\mathbf{f}\}_2 = \begin{Bmatrix} 0.130 \\ 0.137 \end{Bmatrix} \tag{4.97}$$

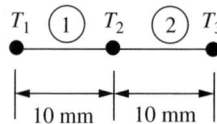

Figure 4.15   Tapered fin. Finite element discretization

Assembly of the above equations results in

$$\begin{bmatrix} 0.109 & -0.103 & 0.0 \\ -0.103 & 0.187 & -0.073 \\ 0.0 & -0.079 & 0.079 \end{bmatrix} \begin{Bmatrix} T_1 \\ T_2 \\ T_3 \end{Bmatrix} = \begin{Bmatrix} 0.148 \\ 0.145 + 0.13 \\ 0.137 \end{Bmatrix} \tag{4.98}$$

On applying the relevant boundary conditions and solving the above system, we obtain
$T_1 = 100\,^{\circ}C$, $T_2 = 85.39\,^{\circ}C$ and $T_3 = 83.52\,^{\circ}C$.

The heat dissipation can be calculated from the following relationship:

$$Q = \Sigma_{e=1}^{2} hP_e L_e \left(\frac{T_i + T_j}{2} - T_a \right) \tag{4.99}$$

Substituting the contribution from both elements results in a value of $Q = 1.38\,W$.

4.5 Summary

In this chapter, examples of one-dimensional problems have been discussed in detail. In most cases, analytical solutions were available as benchmarks for the finite element solutions. There are many other application problems, which can be studied in one dimension. However, the essential fundamentals of the finite element method for one-dimensional heat conduction problems have been given, which may easily be extended to other forms of one-dimensional heat conduction problems.

4.6 Exercise

Exercise 4.6.1 *A composite wall with three different layers, as shown in Figure 4.2 generates $0.25\,G\,W/m^3$ of heat. Using the relevant data given in Example 4.2.1, determine the temperature distribution across the wall using both linear and quadratic variations and compare the results.*

Exercise 4.6.2 *An insulation system around a cylindrical pipe consists of two different layers. The first layer immediately on the outer surface of the pipe is made of glass wool and the second one is constructed using plaster of Paris. The cylinder diameter is 10 cm and each insulating layer is 1 cm thick. The thermal conductivity of the glass wool is $0.04\,W/m\,^{\circ}C$ and that of the plaster is $0.06\,W/m\,^{\circ}C$. The cylinder carries hot oil at a temperature of $92\,^{\circ}C$, and the atmospheric temperature outside is $15\,^{\circ}C$. If the heat transfer coefficient from the outer surface of the insulation to the atmosphere is $15\,W/m^2\,^{\circ}C$, calculate the temperature at the interface between the two insulating materials and on the outer surface.*

Exercise 4.6.3 *A solid cylinder of 10 cm diameter generates $0.3\,G\,W/m^3$ of heat due to nuclear reaction. If the outside temperature is $40\,^{\circ}C$ and the heat transfer coefficient from the solid surface to the surrounding fluid is $30\,W/m^2\,^{\circ}C$, calculate the temperature distribution using quadratic elements. Assume a thermal conductivity of $15\,W/m\,^{\circ}C$.*

Exercise 4.6.4 *A circular fin of inner diameter 20 cm and outer diameter of 26 cm transfers heat from a small motorcycle engine. If the average engine surface temperature is 112 °C, determine the temperature distribution along the fin surface. The thermal conductivity of the fin material is 21 W/m °C and the convective heat transfer coefficient between the fin and the atmosphere is 120 W/m² °C. Assume an atmospheric temperature of 32 °C.*

Exercise 4.6.5 *Consider a composite wall consisting of four different materials as shown in Figure 4.16. Assuming a one-dimensional heat flow, determine the heat flow through the composite slab and the interfacial temperatures. $k_A = 200$ W/m °C, $k_B = 20$ W/m °C and $k_C = 40$ W/m °C and $k_D = 60$ W/m °C. Assume that the areas of the surfaces B and C are equal to 0.1 m².*

Exercise 4.6.6 *Consider a composite wall, which has one linearly varying cross-sectional area as shown in Figure 4.17. Determine the heat flow and interfacial temperatures. Thickness = 10 cm, $k_A = 200$ W/m °C, $k_B = 20$ W/m °C and $k_C = 40$ W/m °C.*

Exercise 4.6.7 *A plane wall ($k = 20$ W/m °C) of thickness 40 cm has its outer surfaces maintained at 30 °C. If there is uniform internal heat generation of 0.2 MW/m³ in the plane wall, determine the temperature distribution in the plane wall. Solve this problem using (a) four linear elements (b) one quadratic element and (c) one modified quadratic element with only two nodes. Compare the results with analytical solutions.*

Exercise 4.6.8 *A plane wall ($k = 10$ W/m °C) of thickness 50 cm has its exterior surface subjected to a convection environment of 30 °C with a surface heat transfer coefficient of 600 W/m² °C. Determine the temperature distribution in the plane wall using (a) four linear elements (b) one quadratic element and (c) one modified quadratic element with only two nodes. Compare the results with the analytical solution. If the heat transfer coefficient increases to 10,000 W/m² °C, what happens to the temperature of the exterior surface?*

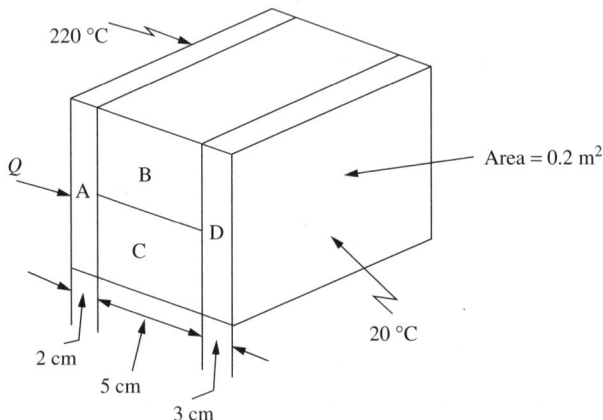

Figure 4.16   A composite wall

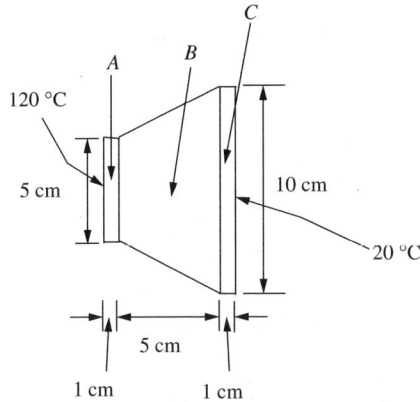

Figure 4.17   A composite wall

Exercise 4.6.9 *Calculate the outer wall surface temperature and the temperature distribution in a thick-walled hollow cylinder when the inner wall temperature is 120 °C and the outer wall is exposed to a convection environment of 25 °C with a surface heat transfer coefficient of 20 W/m² °C. The inner and outer radii of the hollow cylinder are 30 cm and 60 cm respectively. The thermal conductivity of the material of the hollow cylinder is 20 W/m °C. Use one linear element and two linear elements for the solution. Compare the results with the analytical solution.*

Exercise 4.6.10 *Calculate the surface temperature in a circular solid cylinder (k = 20 W/m² °C) of radius 30 mm with a volumetric heat generation of 25 MW/m³. The external surface of the cylinder is exposed to a liquid at 25 °C with a heat transfer coefficient of 5000 W/m² °C. Use (a) four linear elements and (b) two quadratic elements. Compare the solution with the analytical solution.*

Exercise 4.6.11 *Consider a tapered fin of length 5 cm dissipating heat to an ambient at 30 °C. The heat transfer coefficient on the surface and the tip is 100 W/m² °C. The fin tapers from a thickness of 5 mm to a thickness of 2 mm at the tip. The thermal conductivity of the material of the fin is 100 W/m °C. The width of the fin is constant along the length and equal to 2 mm. Determine the heat dissipation from the fin for a base temperature of 100 °C. Use (a) two linear elements and (b) one quadratic element. Also, calculate the fin efficiency.*

Bibliography

Bejan A 1993 *Heat Transfer*, John Wiley & Sons, New York.

Holman JP 1989 *Heat Transfer*, McGraw-Hill, Singapore.

Incropera FP and Dewitt DP 1990 *Fundamentals of Heat and Mass Transfer*, John Wiley & Sons, New York.

Ozisik MN 1968 *Boundary Value Problems of Heat Conduction*, International Text Book Company, Scranton, PA.

5

Steady State Heat Conduction in Multi-dimensions

5.1 Introduction

As seen in the previous chapters, a one-dimensional approximation is easy to implement and is also economical. However, the majority of heat transfer problems are multi-dimensional in nature (Bejan 1993; Holman 1989; Incropera and Dewitt 1990; Ozisik 1968). For such problems, the accuracy of the solution can be improved using either a two- or a three-dimensional approximation. For instance, conduction heat transfer in an infinitely long hollow rectangular tube, which is exposed to different boundary conditions inside and outside the tube (Figure 5.1(a)), and heat conduction in a thin plate, which has negligible heat transfer in the direction of the thickness may be approximated as two-dimensional problems.

In certain situations, it is often difficult to simplify the problem to two dimensions without sacrificing accuracy. Most complex industrial heat transfer problems are three-dimensional in nature because of the complicated geometries involved. Heat transfer in aircraft structures and heat shields used in space vehicles are examples of such problems. It is, however, important to note that even geometries that are simple but which have complex boundary conditions become three-dimensional in nature. For example, the same hollow, rectangular tube mentioned previously, but in this case having non-uniform conditions along the length, is a three-dimensional problem. Also, if the hollow rectangular tube is finite, again it may be necessary to treat it as a three-dimensional problem (Figure 5.1). One typical and simple example of three-dimensional heat conduction is that of a solid cube subjected to different boundary conditions on all six faces as shown in Figure 5.1(b).

Another approximation, commonly employed in heat conduction studies, is the *axisymmetric formulation*. This type of problem is often considered as a two-and-a-half-dimensional case as it has the features of both a two- and a three-dimensional approximation. If a geometry is generated by revolving a surface through $360°$ with reference to its axis then it

Fundamentals of the Finite Element Method for Heat and Fluid Flow   R. W. Lewis, P. Nithiarasu and K. N. Seetharamu
© 2004 John Wiley & Sons, Ltd   ISBNs: 0-470-84788-3 (HB); 0-470-84789-1 (PB)

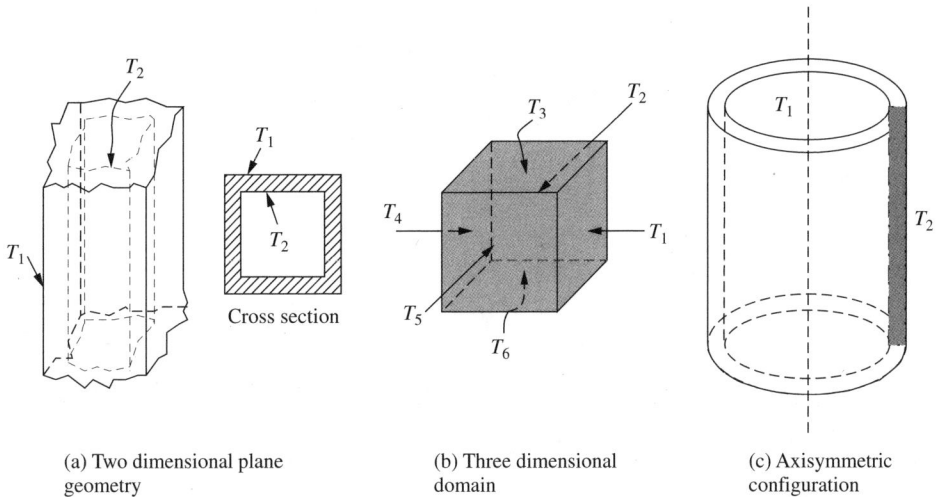

(a) Two dimensional plane geometry

(b) Three dimensional domain

(c) Axisymmetric configuration

Figure 5.1 Examples of heat conduction in two-dimensional, three-dimensional and axisymmetric geometries

is referred to as being axisymmetric. For instance, the revolution of a rectangular surface through 360°, with respect to a vertical axis, produces a vertical cylinder as shown in Figure 5.1(c). Therefore, the heat conduction equations need to be written in three-dimensional cylindrical coordinates for such a system. However, if no significant variation in temperature is expected in the circumferential direction (θ direction), which is often the case, the problem can be reduced to two dimensions, and a solution based on the shaded rectangular plane in Figure 5.1(c) is sufficient.

Unlike one-dimensional problems, two- and three-dimensional situations are usually geometrically complex and expensive to solve. The complexity of the problem is increased in multi-dimensions by the occurrence of irregular geometry shapes and the appropriate implementation of boundary conditions on their boundaries. In the case of complicated geometries, it is often necessary to use unstructured meshes (unstructured meshes are generated employing arbitrarily generated points in a domain, see Chapter 10) to divide the domain into finite elements. Fortunately, owing to present-day computing capabilities, even complex three-dimensional problems can be solved on a standard personal computer (PC). In the following sections, we demonstrate the solution of multi-dimensional steady state problems with relevant examples.

5.2 Two-dimensional Plane Problems

5.2.1 Triangular elements

The simplest finite element discretization that can be employed in two dimensions is by using linear triangular elements. In Chapter 3, we discussed the use of triangular elements

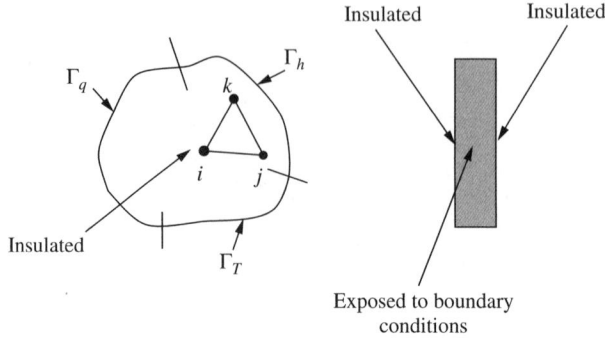

Figure 5.2   Typical two-dimensional plane geometry and triangular element

in detail. These principles are employed here to solve two-dimensional conduction heat transfer problems.

In order to demonstrate the use of linear triangular elements, let us consider a general problem as shown in Figure 5.2. As illustrated in the figure, the geometry is irregular and both the flat faces of the plate are insulated. The surface in the thickness direction is exposed to various boundary conditions. This is an ideal two-dimensional heat conduction problem with no temperature variation allowed in the thickness direction. The final matrix form of the finite element equations, as given in Chapter 3, is

$$[\mathbf{K}]\{\mathbf{T}\} = \{\mathbf{f}\} \tag{5.1}$$

where

$$[\mathbf{K}] = \int_{\Omega} [\mathbf{B}]^{\mathrm{T}}[\mathbf{D}][\mathbf{B}]\,\mathrm{d}\Omega + \int_{\Gamma} h[\mathbf{N}]^{\mathrm{T}}[\mathbf{N}]\,\mathrm{d}\Gamma \tag{5.2}$$

and

$$\{\mathbf{f}\} = \int_{\Omega} G[\mathbf{N}]^{\mathrm{T}}\,\mathrm{d}\Omega - \int_{\Gamma} q[\mathbf{N}]^{\mathrm{T}}\,\mathrm{d}\Gamma + \int_{\Gamma} hT_{\infty}[\mathbf{N}]^{\mathrm{T}}\,\mathrm{d}\Gamma \tag{5.3}$$

For a linear triangular element, the temperature distribution can be written as

$$T = N_i T_i + N_j T_j + N_k T_k \tag{5.4}$$

The gradient matrix is given as

$$\{\mathbf{g}\} = \left\{ \begin{array}{c} \dfrac{\partial T}{\partial x} \\[2mm] \dfrac{\partial T}{\partial y} \end{array} \right\} = \left[\begin{array}{ccc} \dfrac{\partial N_i}{\partial x} & \dfrac{\partial N_j}{\partial x} & \dfrac{\partial N_k}{\partial x} \\[3mm] \dfrac{\partial N_i}{\partial y} & \dfrac{\partial N_j}{\partial y} & \dfrac{\partial N_k}{\partial y} \end{array} \right] \left\{ \begin{array}{c} T_i \\ T_j \\ T_k \end{array} \right\} = [\mathbf{B}]\{\mathbf{T}\} \tag{5.5}$$

where

$$[\mathbf{B}] = \left[\begin{array}{ccc} \dfrac{\partial N_i}{\partial x} & \dfrac{\partial N_j}{\partial x} & \dfrac{\partial N_k}{\partial x} \\[3mm] \dfrac{\partial N_i}{\partial y} & \dfrac{\partial N_j}{\partial y} & \dfrac{\partial N_k}{\partial y} \end{array} \right] = \dfrac{1}{2A} \left[\begin{array}{ccc} b_i & b_j & b_k \\ c_i & c_j & c_k \end{array} \right] \tag{5.6}$$

Note that G in Equation 5.3 is a uniform heat source. Assuming an anisotropic material, we have

$$[\mathbf{D}] = \begin{bmatrix} k_x & 0 \\ 0 & k_y \end{bmatrix} \tag{5.7}$$

Note that the off-diagonal terms are neglected from the above equation for the sake of simplicity. Substituting [**D**] and [**B**] into Equation 5.2, we get, for a boundary element as shown in Figure 5.3

$$[\mathbf{K}]_e = \frac{t}{4A} \left\{ k_x \begin{bmatrix} b_i^2 & b_i b_j & b_i b_k \\ b_i b_j & b_j^2 & b_j b_k \\ b_i b_k & b_j b_k & b_k^2 \end{bmatrix} + k_y \begin{bmatrix} c_i^2 & c_i c_j & c_i c_k \\ c_i c_j & c_j^2 & c_j c_k \\ c_i c_k & c_j c_k & c_k^2 \end{bmatrix} \right\} + \frac{htl_{jk}}{6} \begin{bmatrix} 0 & 0 & 0 \\ 0 & 2 & 1 \\ 0 & 1 & 2 \end{bmatrix} \tag{5.8}$$

The subscript e in the above equation denotes a single element. It should be noted that in the above equation, $d\Omega$ is equal to $t\,dA$ and $d\Gamma$ is equal to $t\,dl$, where t is the thickness of the plate and l is the length of an element side on the domain boundary. In a similar fashion, the forcing vector can be written as

$$\{\mathbf{f}\}_e = \frac{GAt}{3} \begin{Bmatrix} 1 \\ 1 \\ 1 \end{Bmatrix} - \frac{qtl_{ij}}{2} \begin{Bmatrix} 1 \\ 1 \\ 0 \end{Bmatrix} + \frac{hT_a tl_{jk}}{2} \begin{Bmatrix} 0 \\ 1 \\ 1 \end{Bmatrix} \tag{5.9}$$

The integration formulae used for the above equations are simple, as indicated in Chapter 3. For convenience, we have listed the integration formulae in Appendix B.

As seen in the previous equations, the effect of uniform heat generation contributes to all three nodes of an element, irrespective of its position. However, the convection and flux boundary conditions are applicable only on the boundaries of the domain.

If we need to have a 'point source' G^* instead of a 'uniform source' G, the first term in Equation 5.9 is replaced with

$$\{\mathbf{f}\} = G^* t \begin{Bmatrix} N_i \\ N_j \\ N_k \end{Bmatrix}_{(x_o, y_o)} \tag{5.10}$$

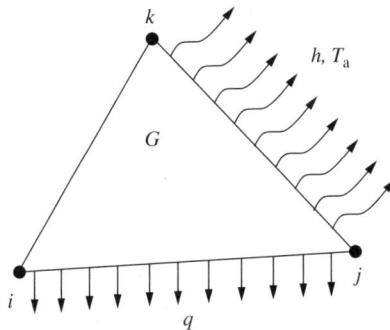

Figure 5.3   Typical two-dimensional triangular element with heat generation and heat flux and convection boundaries

where x_o and y_o are the coordinates of the point source. In the above equations, all the shape function values must be evaluated at (x_o, y_o) (note that although G^* is a point source, in two dimensions, it is a line source in the thickness direction and expressed in units of W/m). The contribution from the point source is then appropriately distributed to the three nodes of the element that contains the point source.

In order to demonstrate the characteristics of two-dimensional steady state heat transfer, the temperature distribution in a flat plate having constant temperature boundary conditions is considered in the following example.

Example 5.2.1 *A square plate of unit thickness, size 100 cm, as shown in Figure 5.4, is subjected to isothermal boundary conditions of $100\,^\circ C$ on all sides except the top side, which is subjected to $500\,^\circ C$. If the thermal conductivity of the material is constant and equal to $10\,W/m\,^\circ C$, determine the temperature distribution using linear triangular finite elements.*

The square domain is first divided into eight equal-sized linear triangular elements, as shown in Figure 5.5. Two sets of elemental [K] matrices exist because of the orientation of the triangles. For elements 1, 3, 5, and 7, we have the following elements of the [K] matrix:

$$b_1 = y_2 - y_4 = -0.50; \quad c_1 = x_4 - x_2 = -0.50$$

$$b_2 = y_4 - y_1 = 0.50; \quad c_2 = x_1 - x_4 = 0.00$$

$$b_4 = y_1 - y_2 = 0.00; \quad c_4 = x_2 - x_1 = 0.50 \tag{5.11}$$

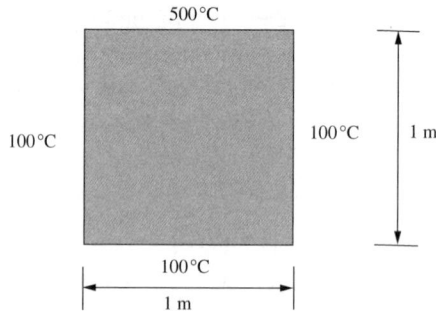

Figure 5.4 Square plate with different temperature boundary conditions

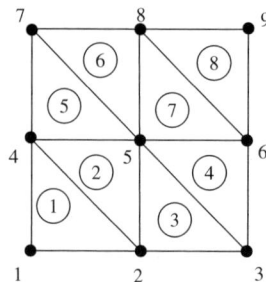

Figure 5.5 Discretization using triangular elements

The elemental [**K**] *matrices for elements 1, 3, 5 and 7 can be written as (refer to Equation 5.8)*

$$[\mathbf{K}]_1 = [\mathbf{K}]_3 = [\mathbf{K}]_5 = [\mathbf{K}]_7 = \frac{tk}{4A} \begin{bmatrix} b_1^2 + c_1^2 & b_1 b_2 + c_1 c_2 & b_1 b_4 + c_1 c_4 \\ b_1 b_2 + c_1 c_2 & b_2^2 + c_2^2 & b_2 b_4 + c_2 c_4 \\ b_1 b_4 + c_1 c_4 & b_2 b_4 + c_2 c_4 & b_4^2 + c_4^2 \end{bmatrix} \quad (5.12)$$

where the area of the elements can be written as

$$2A = \det \begin{vmatrix} 1.0 & 0.0 & 0.0 \\ 1.0 & 0.5 & 0.0 \\ 1.0 & 0.0 & 0.5 \end{vmatrix} = 0.25 \, \text{m}^2 \quad (5.13)$$

Substituting the area into Equation 5.12, we get the final form of the elemental equation as

$$[\mathbf{K}]_1 = [\mathbf{K}]_3 = [\mathbf{K}]_5 = [\mathbf{K}]_7 = \frac{tk}{2} \begin{bmatrix} 2.0 & -1.0 & -1.0 \\ -1.0 & 1.0 & 0.0 \\ -1.0 & 0.0 & 1.0 \end{bmatrix} \quad (5.14)$$

Similarly, we can calculate the elemental [**K**] *matrices for elements 2, 4, 6 and 8 as*

$$[\mathbf{K}]_2 = [\mathbf{K}]_4 = [\mathbf{K}]_6 = [\mathbf{K}]_8 = \frac{tk}{2} \begin{bmatrix} 1.0 & -1.0 & 0.0 \\ -1.0 & 2.0 & -1.0 \\ 0.0 & -1.0 & 1.0 \end{bmatrix} \quad (5.15)$$

The assembled equations are (see Appendix C)

$$\frac{tk}{2} \begin{bmatrix} 2.0 & -1.0 & 0.0 & -1.0 & 0.0 & 0.0 & 0.0 & 0.0 & 0.0 \\ -1.0 & 4.0 & -1.0 & 0.0 & -2.0 & 0.0 & 0.0 & 0.0 & 0.0 \\ 0.0 & -1.0 & 2.0 & 0.0 & 0.0 & -1.0 & 0.0 & 0.0 & 0.0 \\ -1.0 & 0.0 & 0.0 & 4.0 & -2.0 & 0.0 & -1.0 & 0.0 & 0.0 \\ 0.0 & -2.0 & 0.0 & -2.0 & 8.0 & -2.0 & 0.0 & -2.0 & 0.0 \\ 0.0 & 0.0 & -1.0 & 0.0 & -2.0 & 4.0 & 0.0 & 0.0 & -1.0 \\ 0.0 & 0.0 & 0.0 & -1.0 & 0.0 & 0.0 & 2.0 & -1.0 & 0.0 \\ 0.0 & 0.0 & 0.0 & 0.0 & -2.0 & 0.0 & -1.0 & 4.0 & -1.0 \\ 0.0 & 0.0 & 0.0 & 0.0 & 0.0 & -1.0 & 0.0 & -1.0 & 2.0 \end{bmatrix} \begin{bmatrix} T_1 \\ T_2 \\ T_3 \\ T_4 \\ T_5 \\ T_6 \\ T_7 \\ T_8 \\ T_9 \end{bmatrix} = \begin{Bmatrix} 0.0 \\ 0.0 \\ 0.0 \\ 0.0 \\ 0.0 \\ 0.0 \\ 0.0 \\ 0.0 \\ 0.0 \end{Bmatrix} \quad (5.16)$$

The only unknown quantity in the above equation is T_5, which can be calculated from the equation corresponding to the fifth node, that is, from

$$8T_5 = 2T_2 + 2T_4 + 2T_6 + 2T_8 \quad (5.17)$$

Substituting $T_2 = T_4 = T_6 = 100\,°C$ and $T_8 = 500\,°C$, we get $T_5 = 200\,°C$
The analytical solution to this problem is given by (Holman 1989)

$$T(x, y) = (T_{\text{top}} - T_{\text{side}}) \frac{2}{\pi} \sum_{n=1}^{\infty} \frac{(-1)^{n+1} + 1}{n} \sin\left(\frac{n\pi x}{w}\right) \frac{\sinh\left(\frac{n\pi y}{w}\right)}{\sinh\left(\frac{n\pi H}{w}\right)} + T_{\text{side}} \quad (5.18)$$

where w is the width, H is the height of the plate, T_{top} is the temperature at the top side and T_{side} is the temperature at the other sides of the plate. Therefore,

$$T(0.5, 0.5) = 200.11\,°C \tag{5.19}$$

As seen, the finite element solution is in close agreement with the analytical solution. It is interesting to note that the finite difference solution is given by

$$T_5 = \frac{T_2 + T_4 + T_6 + T_8}{4} = 200\,°C \tag{5.20}$$

which is identical to the finite element solution. Figure 5.6 shows an unstructured mesh and a computer-generated solution for this problem. As shown, the temperature at the centre is close to that obtained from the coarse mesh of Figure 5.5, and also to the analytical solution. However, the unstructured mesh solution is not as accurate as that of the regular mesh solution. This indicates that the accuracy of a regular structured mesh is superior to that of unstructured meshes. If a finer structured mesh as shown in Figure 5.7 is used, the temperature at the centre is $200\,°C$.

Using the nodal temperature values, the temperature at any other location within an element can be determined using linear interpolation. The calculation of the temperature at any arbitrary location has been demonstrated in Chapter 3. The following two-dimensional example is given in order to further illustrate this point.

Example 5.2.2 Calculate the temperature at point 4 (40, 40) shown in Figure 5.8. The temperature values at nodes 1, 2 and 3 are $100\,°C$, $200\,°C$ and $100\,°C$ respectively. The

(a) Finite element mesh

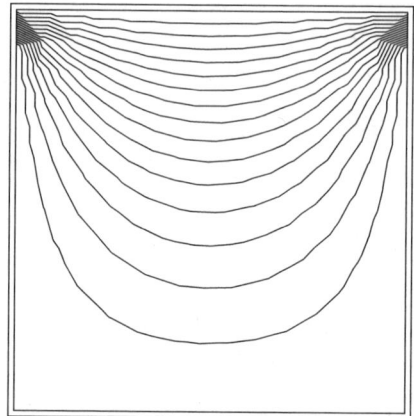

(b) Temperature contours. Temperature varies between 100 and 500°C. Interval between two contours is 25°C

Figure 5.6   Solution for Example 5.2.1 on an unstructured mesh. The temperature obtained at the centre of the plate is $200.42\,°C$

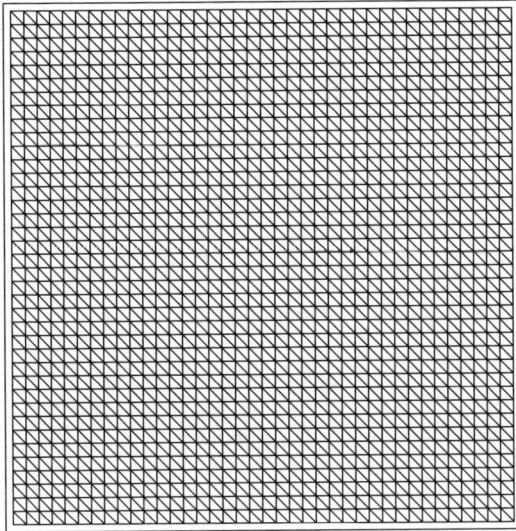

Figure 5.7   Fine structured mesh

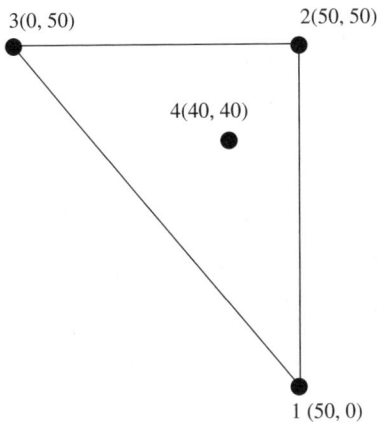

Figure 5.8   Interpolation into a triangular element

coordinates of these points are (50, 0), (50, 50) and (0, 50), respectively. All dimensions are in cm. Also, calculate the heat flux in both the x and y directions. Assume a thermal conductivity value of 10 W/m °C.

The following expression can be used to describe the linear variation of temperature within the element

$$T = N_1 T_1 + N_2 T_2 + N_3 T_3 \qquad (5.21)$$

In order to calculate the temperature at node 4, the shape functions N_1, N_2 and N_3 have to be calculated at node 4.

Therefore, for the first node

$$N_1 = \frac{1}{2A}(a_1 + b_1 x_4 + c_1 y_4) \tag{5.22}$$

where

$$a_1 = x_2 y_3 - x_3 y_2 = 2500.00$$

$$b_1 = y_2 - y_3 = 0.0$$

$$c_1 = x_3 - x_2 = -50.00 \tag{5.23}$$

At point 4, $(x = 40, y = 40)$, from Equation 5.22, we get $(2A = 2500)$

$$N_1 = \frac{1}{5} \tag{5.24}$$

Similarly, it can be verified that $N_2 = 1/5$ and $N_3 = 3/5$. Note that $N_1 + N_2 + N_3 = 1$. The substitution of these shape function values into Equation 5.21 results in a value of $T_4 = 160\,^{\circ}C$.

The heat flux in the x and y directions are calculated as

$$q_x = -k\frac{\partial T}{\partial x} = -\frac{10}{2500}(b_1 T_1 + b_2 T_2 + b_3 T_3) = -20\,\text{W}/\text{cm}^2 \tag{5.25}$$

Similarly, it can be shown that $q_y = -20\,W/cm^2$. It should be noted that the flux is constant over a linear triangular element.

From Examples 5.2.1 and 5.2.2, the demonstration of problems involving constant temperature boundary conditions is clear. It is therefore essential to move on to an example with more complicated boundary conditions. Thus, in the following example, a conduction problem is considered, which has mixed boundary conditions.

Example 5.2.3 *Determine the temperature distribution in a square plate of unit thickness size 5 cm as shown in Figure 5.9. The upper triangular half has an internal heat generation of 1.2 W/cm³, while the lower half has a point source of 5 W/cm in the thickness direction (point source on a two-dimensional plane) at the point (1, 1) cm. In addition to the above heat sources, the bottom side of the plate is insulated, the right vertical side is subjected to a temperature of 100°C, the top side is subjected to a convective heat transfer boundary condition with a heat transfer coefficient of h = 1.2 W/cm²K and $T_a = 30°C$ and the left vertical side is subjected to a uniform heat flux of 2 W/cm². Assume a thermal conductivity of 2 W/cm °C.*

To make the solution procedure simple, the plate is divided into two triangular elements as shown in Figure 5.10. The elemental equations of both elements can be set up separately using the formulation discussed (Equations 5.8 and 5.9). For the first element, $a_1 = 25.0$, $b_1 = -5.0$, $c_1 = -5.0$, $a_2 = 0.0$, $b_2 = 5.0$, $c_2 = 0.0$, $a_3 = 0.0$, $b_3 = 0.0$, $c_3 = 5.0$.

The stiffness matrix for element 1 is

$$[\mathbf{K}]_1 = \frac{t}{4A}\left\{ k_x \begin{bmatrix} b_1^2 & b_1 b_2 & b_1 b_3 \\ b_1 b_2 & b_2^2 & b_2 b_3 \\ b_1 b_3 & b_2 b_3 & b_3^2 \end{bmatrix} + k_y \begin{bmatrix} c_1^2 & c_1 c_2 & c_1 c_3 \\ c_1 c_2 & c_2^2 & c_2 c_3 \\ c_1 c_3 & c_2 c_3 & c_3^2 \end{bmatrix} \right\} \tag{5.26}$$

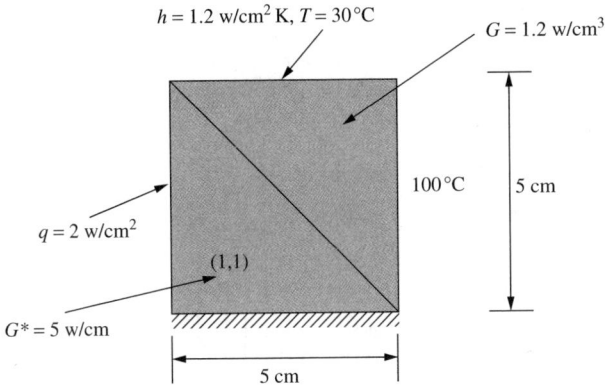

Figure 5.9 A square domain with mixed boundary conditions

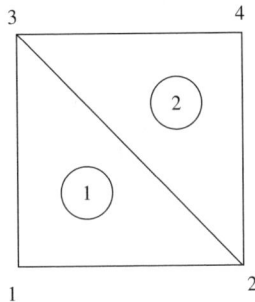

Figure 5.10 Discretization using two triangular elements

Substituting the values for a, b and c, we obtain

$$[\mathbf{K}]_1 = \begin{bmatrix} 2.0 & -1.0 & -1.0 \\ -1.0 & 1.0 & 0.0 \\ -1.0 & 0.0 & 1.0 \end{bmatrix} \tag{5.27}$$

The loading term for element 1 is given by

$$\{\mathbf{f}\}_1 = -\frac{ql_{31}}{2}\begin{Bmatrix} 1.0 \\ 0.0 \\ 1.0 \end{Bmatrix} + G^*t\begin{Bmatrix} N_1 \\ N_2 \\ N_3 \end{Bmatrix}_{(1,1)} = \begin{Bmatrix} -2.0 \\ 1.0 \\ -4.0 \end{Bmatrix} \tag{5.28}$$

Note that the shape functions evaluated at point (1, 1) are $N_1 = 3/5$, $N_2 = 1/5$ and $N_3 = 1/5$.

In a similar way, the stiffness matrix and loading terms for the second element can be calculated. They are

$$[\mathbf{K}]_2 = \begin{bmatrix} 1.0 & -1.0 & 0.0 \\ -1.0 & 4.0 & 0.0 \\ 0.0 & 0.0 & 3.0 \end{bmatrix} \tag{5.29}$$

and

$$\{f\}_2 = \begin{Bmatrix} 5.0 \\ 95.0 \\ 95.0 \end{Bmatrix} \tag{5.30}$$

On assembling the above contributions for the two elements, we obtain the following system of simultaneous equations, (see Appendix C) that is,

$$\begin{bmatrix} 2.0 & -1.0 & -1.0 & 0.0 \\ -1.0 & 2.0 & 0.0 & -1.0 \\ -1.0 & 0.0 & 4.0 & 0.0 \\ 0.0 & -1.0 & 0.0 & 4.0 \end{bmatrix} \begin{Bmatrix} T_1 \\ T_2 \\ T_3 \\ T_4 \end{Bmatrix} = \begin{Bmatrix} -2.0 \\ 6.0 \\ 91.0 \\ 95.0 \end{Bmatrix} \tag{5.31}$$

In the above set of equations, the temperature values T_2 and T_4 are known and are equal to $100\,^{\circ}C$.

The boundary conditions can be implemented as previously explained in Chapters 2 and 3.

Applying the boundary conditions, we get

$$\begin{bmatrix} 2.0 & -1.0 & -1.0 & 0.0 \\ 0.0 & 1.0 & 0.0 & 0.0 \\ -1.0 & 0.0 & 4.0 & 0.0 \\ 0.0 & 0.0 & 0.0 & 1.0 \end{bmatrix} \begin{Bmatrix} T_1 \\ T_2 \\ T_3 \\ T_4 \end{Bmatrix} = \begin{Bmatrix} -2.0 \\ 100.0 \\ 91.0 \\ 100.0 \end{Bmatrix} \tag{5.32}$$

Therefore, the simultaneous equations to be solved are $2T_1 - T_3 = 98$ and $-T_1 + 4T_3 = 91$. The solution to these equations results in $T_1 = 69\,^{\circ}C$ and $T_3 = 40\,^{\circ}C$.

If, in the above example, there is a uniform heat generation of $1.2\ W/cm^3$ throughout the domain, then the loading term for the first element changes to (in the absence of line source)

$$\{f\}_1 = -\frac{ql_{31}}{2} \begin{Bmatrix} 1 \\ 0 \\ 1 \end{Bmatrix} + \frac{GАt}{3} \begin{Bmatrix} 1 \\ 1 \\ 1 \end{Bmatrix} = \begin{Bmatrix} 0 \\ 5 \\ 0 \end{Bmatrix} \tag{5.33}$$

The resulting simultaneous equations become $2T_1 - T_3 = 100$ and $-T_1 + 4T_3 = 95$ and the solution becomes $T_1 = 70.71\,^{\circ}C$ and $T_3 = 40.42\,^{\circ}C$.

5.3 Rectangular Elements

A typical rectangular element is shown in Figure 5.11 with mixed boundary conditions. The temperature distribution in a rectangular element is written as

$$T = N_i T_i + N_j T_j + N_k T_k + N_l T_l \tag{5.34}$$

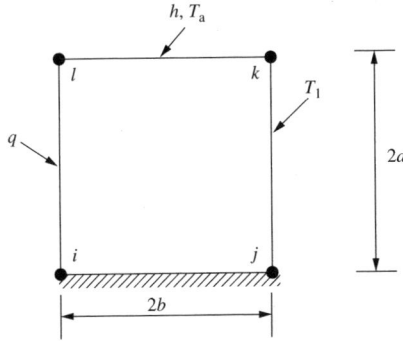

Figure 5.11   Rectangular element with different boundary conditions

From Equation 3.89, Chapter 3 (with origin at k), the shape functions for a rectangular element are given as

$$N_i = \left(1 - \frac{x}{2b}\right)\left(1 - \frac{y}{2a}\right)$$

$$N_j = \frac{x}{2b}\left(1 - \frac{y}{2a}\right)$$

$$N_k = \frac{xy}{4ab}$$

$$N_l = \frac{y}{2a}\left(1 - \frac{x}{2b}\right) \tag{5.35}$$

The gradient matrix of the shape functions is

$$[\mathbf{B}] = \begin{bmatrix} \dfrac{\partial N_i}{\partial x} & \dfrac{\partial N_j}{\partial x} & \dfrac{\partial N_k}{\partial x} & \dfrac{\partial N_l}{\partial x} \\[2mm] \dfrac{\partial N_i}{\partial y} & \dfrac{\partial N_j}{\partial y} & \dfrac{\partial N_k}{\partial y} & \dfrac{\partial N_l}{\partial y} \end{bmatrix} = \frac{1}{4ab}\begin{bmatrix} -(2a-y) & (2a-y) & y & -y \\ -(2b-x) & -x & x & (2b-x) \end{bmatrix} \tag{5.36}$$

The stiffness matrix is given by

$$[\mathbf{K}] = \int_\Omega [\mathbf{B}]^T[\mathbf{D}][\mathbf{B}]\,dV + \int_\Gamma h[\mathbf{N}]^T[\mathbf{N}]\,d\Gamma \tag{5.37}$$

where

$$[\mathbf{D}] = \begin{bmatrix} k_x & 0 \\ 0 & k_y \end{bmatrix} \tag{5.38}$$

Substituting, the [**B**] and [**D**] matrices into the above equation, results in a 4×4 matrix. We leave the algebra to the readers to work out. A typical term in the matrix is

$$\int_0^{2b}\int_0^{2a} \frac{k_x}{16a^2b^2}(2a-y)^2\,dx\,dy + \int_0^{2b}\int_0^{2a} \frac{k_y}{16a^2b^2}(2b-x)^2\,dx\,dy$$

$$+ \int_0^{2b}\int_0^{2a} \frac{xy}{4ab}\,dx\,dy \tag{5.39}$$

After integration, the matrix $[\mathbf{K}]$ becomes

$$[\mathbf{K}] = \frac{k_x a}{6b} \begin{bmatrix} 2.0 & -2.0 & -1.0 & 1.0 \\ -2.0 & 2.0 & 1.0 & -1.0 \\ -1.0 & 1.0 & 2.0 & -2.0 \\ 1.0 & -1.0 & -2.0 & 2.0 \end{bmatrix} + \frac{k_y b}{6a} \begin{bmatrix} 2.0 & -2.0 & -1.0 & 1.0 \\ -2.0 & 2.0 & 1.0 & -1.0 \\ -1.0 & 1.0 & 2.0 & -2.0 \\ 1.0 & -1.0 & -2.0 & 2.0 \end{bmatrix}$$

$$+ \frac{hl}{12} \begin{bmatrix} 0.0 & 0.0 & 0.0 & 0.0 \\ 0.0 & 0.0 & 0.0 & 0.0 \\ 0.0 & 0.0 & 4.0 & 2.0 \\ 0.0 & 0.0 & 2.0 & 4.0 \end{bmatrix} \tag{5.40}$$

The loading vector can be written as

$$\{\mathbf{f}\} = \int G[\mathbf{N}]^{\mathrm{T}} \, \mathrm{d}A = \int_0^{2b} \int_0^{2a} G \begin{Bmatrix} N_i \\ N_j \\ N_k \\ N_l \end{Bmatrix} \mathrm{d}x \, \mathrm{d}y = \frac{GAt}{4} \begin{Bmatrix} 1 \\ 1 \\ 1 \\ 1 \end{Bmatrix} \tag{5.41}$$

The heat flux and convective heat transfer boundary integrals are evaluated as for triangular elements. In order to demonstrate the application of such elements, Example 5.2.3 will now be reconsidered using a rectangular element.

Example 5.3.1 *Determine the temperature distribution in the square plate of Example 5.2.3, using a single rectangular element.*

Substituting the relevant data into Equation 5.40, we get (see Figure 5.12)

$$[\mathbf{K}] = \frac{5}{15} \begin{bmatrix} 2.0 & -2.0 & -1.0 & 1.0 \\ -2.0 & 2.0 & 1.0 & -1.0 \\ -1.0 & 1.0 & 2.0 & -2.0 \\ 1.0 & -1.0 & -2.0 & 2.0 \end{bmatrix} + \frac{5}{15} \begin{bmatrix} 2.0 & 1.0 & -1.0 & -2.0 \\ 1.0 & 2.0 & -2.0 & -1.0 \\ -1.0 & -2.0 & 2.0 & 1.0 \\ -2.0 & -1.0 & 1.0 & 2.0 \end{bmatrix}$$

$$+ \begin{bmatrix} 0.0 & 0.0 & 0.0 & 0.0 \\ 0.0 & 0.0 & 0.0 & 0.0 \\ 0.0 & 0.0 & 2.0 & 1.0 \\ 0.0 & 0.0 & 1.0 & 2.0 \end{bmatrix} \tag{5.42}$$

Simplifying, this becomes

$$[\mathbf{K}] = \frac{1}{6} \begin{bmatrix} 8.0 & -2.0 & -4.0 & -2.0 \\ -2.0 & 8.0 & -2.0 & -4.0 \\ -4.0 & -2.0 & 20.0 & 4.0 \\ -2.0 & -4.0 & 4.0 & 20.0 \end{bmatrix} \tag{5.43}$$

The forcing vector is

$$\{\mathbf{f}\} = \frac{6t}{4} \begin{Bmatrix} 1 \\ 1 \\ 1 \\ 1 \end{Bmatrix} + G^*t \begin{Bmatrix} N_1 \\ N_2 \\ N_3 \\ N_4 \end{Bmatrix} - \frac{qtl_{14}}{2} \begin{Bmatrix} 1 \\ 0 \\ 0 \\ 1 \end{Bmatrix} + \frac{hT_a tl_{31}}{2} \begin{Bmatrix} 0 \\ 0 \\ 1 \\ 1 \end{Bmatrix} \tag{5.44}$$

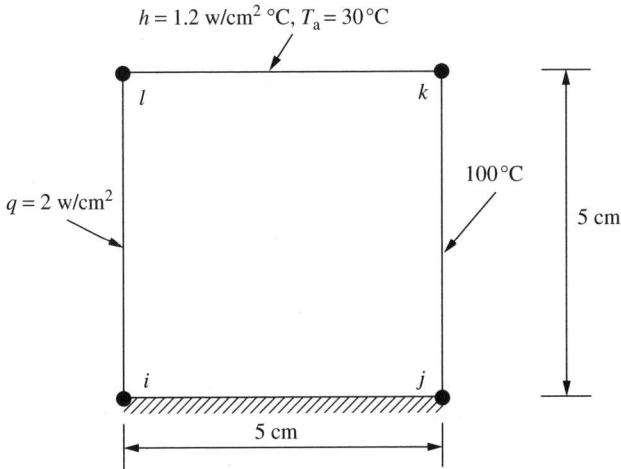

Figure 5.12   Heat conduction in a square plate. Approximated using a rectangular (square) element

again, on simplifying we obtain

$$\{\mathbf{f}\} = \begin{Bmatrix} 5.7 \\ 8.3 \\ 97.7 \\ 93.3 \end{Bmatrix} \tag{5.45}$$

Therefore, the final form of the set of simultaneous equations can be written as

$$\frac{1}{6} \begin{bmatrix} 8.0 & -2.0 & -4.0 & -2.0 \\ -2.0 & 8.0 & -2.0 & -4.0 \\ -4.0 & -2.0 & 20.0 & 4.0 \\ -2.0 & -4.0 & 4.0 & 20.0 \end{bmatrix} \begin{Bmatrix} T_1 \\ T_2 \\ T_3 \\ T_4 \end{Bmatrix} = \begin{Bmatrix} 5.7 \\ 8.3 \\ 97.7 \\ 93.3 \end{Bmatrix} \tag{5.46}$$

The temperatures at points 2 and 3 are known. Substitution into the above system results in the following simultaneous equations,

$$8T_1 - 2T_4 = 634.2$$

$$-2T_1 + 20T_4 = 559.8 \tag{5.47}$$

The solution of the above simultaneous equation gives $T_4 = 36.85\,°C$ and $T_1 = 88.48\,°C$.

5.4   Plate with Variable Thickness

The conduction heat transfer in a plate with variable thickness is essentially a three-dimensional problem. However, if the thickness variation is small, it is possible to express

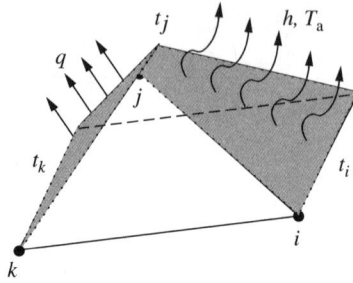

Figure 5.13   A triangular plate with linearly varying thickness

the thickness as a linear variation in the discretized triangular element as shown in Figure 5.13. If the thickness variation is assumed to be linear, we can write

$$t = N_i t_i + N_j t_j + N_k T_k \tag{5.48}$$

Therefore, the stiffness matrix can be rewritten as

$$
\begin{aligned}
[\mathbf{K}] &= \int_\Omega [\mathbf{B}]^{\mathrm{T}}[\mathbf{D}][\mathbf{B}] \, d\Omega + \int_S h[\mathbf{N}]^{\mathrm{T}}[\mathbf{N}] \, dS \\
&= \int_A [\mathbf{B}]^{\mathrm{T}}[\mathbf{D}][\mathbf{B}](N_i t_i + N_j t_j + N_k t_k) \, dA \\
&\quad + \int_l h[\mathbf{N}]^{\mathrm{T}}[\mathbf{N}](N_i t_i + N_j t_j + N_k t_k) \, dl_{ik}
\end{aligned}
\tag{5.49}
$$

On substitution of the various matrices and integrating (see Appendix B), we finally obtain

$$
\begin{aligned}
[\mathbf{K}] = \left(\frac{t_i + t_j + t_k}{12A}\right) &\left\{ k_x \begin{bmatrix} b_i^2 & b_i b_j & b_i b_k \\ b_i b_j & b_j^2 & b_j b_k \\ b_i b_k & b_j b_k & b_k^2 \end{bmatrix} + k_y \begin{bmatrix} c_i^2 & c_i c_j & c_i c_k \\ c_i c_j & c_j^2 & c_j c_k \\ c_i c_k & c_j c_k & c_k^2 \end{bmatrix} \right\} \\
&+ \frac{hl_{ij}}{12} \begin{bmatrix} 3t_i + t_j & t_i + t_j & 0.0 \\ t_i + t_j & t_i + 3t_j & 0.0 \\ 0.0 & 0.0 & 0.0 \end{bmatrix}
\end{aligned}
\tag{5.50}
$$

The load term is calculated as

$$
\begin{aligned}
\{\mathbf{f}\} &= \int_A G[\mathbf{N}]^{\mathrm{T}}(N_i t_i + N_j t_j + N_k t_k) \, dA - \int_{l_{jk}} q[\mathbf{N}]^{\mathrm{T}}(N_i t_i + N_j t_j + N_k t_k) \, dl_{jk} \\
&\quad + \int_{l_{ij}} hT_a[\mathbf{N}]^{\mathrm{T}}(N_i t_i + N_j t_j + N_k t_k) \, dl_{ij}
\end{aligned}
\tag{5.51}
$$

Again, on integration we obtain

$$
\frac{GA}{12} \left\{ \begin{matrix} 2t_i + t_j + t_k \\ t_i + 2t_j + t_k \\ t_i + t_j + 2t_k \end{matrix} \right\} - \frac{ql_{jk}}{6} \left\{ \begin{matrix} 0.0 \\ 2t_j + t_k \\ t_j + 2t_k \end{matrix} \right\} + \frac{hT_a l_{ij}}{6} \left\{ \begin{matrix} 2t_i + t_j \\ t_i + 2t_j \\ 0.0 \end{matrix} \right\}
\tag{5.52}
$$

If the thickness is constant, the above relations reduce to the same set of equations as in Section 5.2.

5.5 Three-dimensional Problems

The formulation of a three-dimensional problem follows a similar approach as explained previously for two-dimensional plane geometries but with an additional third dimension. The finite element equation is the same as in Equation 5.1, that is,

$$[\mathbf{K}]\{\mathbf{T}\} = \{\mathbf{f}\} \tag{5.53}$$

For a linear tetrahedral element, as shown in Figure 5.14, the temperature distribution can be written as

$$T = N_i T_i + N_j T_j + N_k T_k + N_l T_l \tag{5.54}$$

The gradient matrix is given as

$$\{\mathbf{g}\} = \begin{Bmatrix} \dfrac{\partial T}{\partial x} \\[2mm] \dfrac{\partial T}{\partial y} \\[2mm] \dfrac{\partial T}{\partial z} \end{Bmatrix} = \begin{bmatrix} \dfrac{\partial N_i}{\partial x} & \dfrac{\partial N_j}{\partial x} & \dfrac{\partial N_k}{\partial x} & \dfrac{\partial N_l}{\partial x} \\[2mm] \dfrac{\partial N_i}{\partial y} & \dfrac{\partial N_j}{\partial y} & \dfrac{\partial N_k}{\partial y} & \dfrac{\partial N_l}{\partial y} \\[2mm] \dfrac{\partial N_i}{\partial z} & \dfrac{\partial N_j}{\partial z} & \dfrac{\partial N_k}{\partial z} & \dfrac{\partial N_l}{\partial z} \end{bmatrix} \begin{Bmatrix} T_i \\ T_j \\ T_k \\ T_l \end{Bmatrix} = [\mathbf{B}]\{\mathbf{T}\} \tag{5.55}$$

The thermal conductivity matrix becomes

$$[\mathbf{D}] = \begin{bmatrix} k_x & 0 & 0 \\ 0 & k_y & 0 \\ 0 & 0 & k_z \end{bmatrix} \tag{5.56}$$

where the off-diagonal terms are assumed to be zero, for the sake of simplicity. On substituting [**D**] and [**B**] into Equation 5.2, we obtain the necessary elemental [**K**] equation

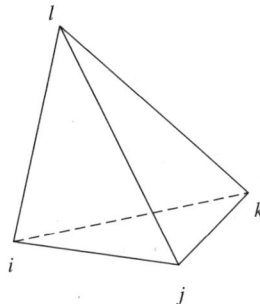

Figure 5.14 A linear tetrahedral element

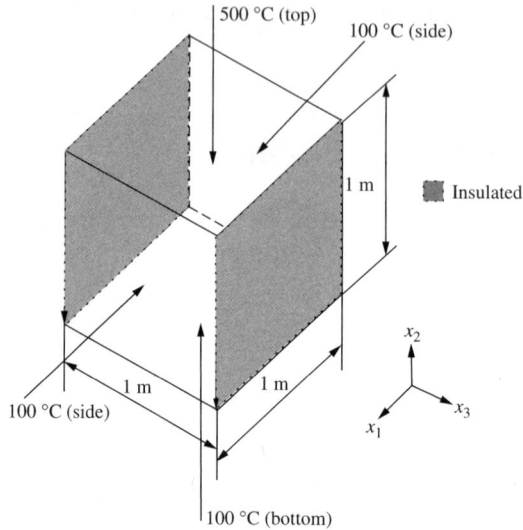

Figure 5.15   Representation of Example 5.2.1 in three dimensions

as for a two-dimensional plane problem. Similarly, the elemental equation for $\{\mathbf{f}\}$ can be derived.

In Figure 5.15, an extension of Example 5.2.1 to three dimensions is given for demonstration purpose only. As seen, the geometry is extended in the third dimension by 1 m. The corresponding boundary conditions are also given. The boundary conditions remain the same, but the boundary sides become boundary surfaces in 3D. Two extra surfaces, one in the front and another at the back, are also introduced when the problem is extended to three dimensions. These two extra surfaces are subjected to no heat flux conditions in order to preserve the two-dimensionality of the problem.

The mesh generated and the solution to this problem are shown in Figure 5.16. As seen, the solution in the plane perpendicular to the third dimension, x_3, is identical to that of the two-dimensional solution given in Figure 5.6(b). As mentioned previously, the variation of the temperature in the third dimension is suppressed by imposing a no heat flux condition on the front and back faces, perpendicular to x_3, as shown in Figure 5.15.

5.6 Axisymmetric Problems

In many three-dimensional problems, there is often a geometric symmetry about a reference axis, and such problems can be solved using two-dimensional elements, provided the boundary conditions and all field functions are independent of the circumferential direction (θ direction). The domain can then be represented by axisymmetric ring elements and analysed in a similar fashion to that of a two-dimensional problem. Figure 5.17 shows an axisymmetric ring element where the nodes of the finite element model lie in the $r - z$ plane.

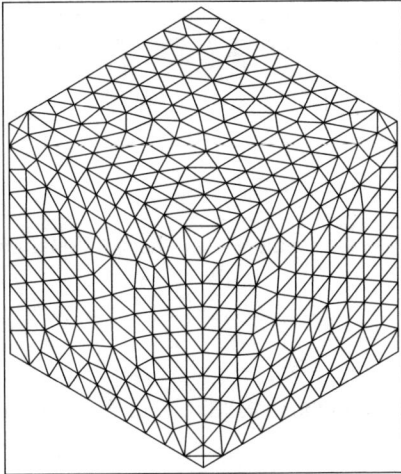

(a) Finite element mesh

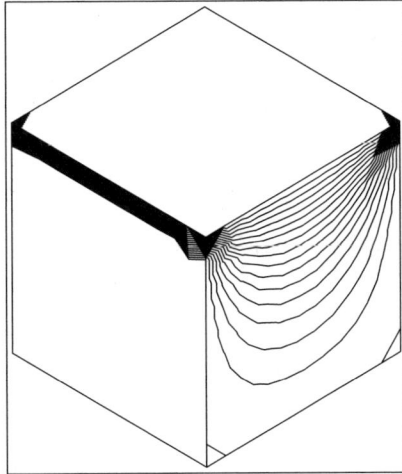

(b) Temperature contours.
Temperature varies between
100 and 500°C. Interval
between two contours is 25°C

Figure 5.16 Solution for Example 5.2.1 on a three-dimensional mesh, temperature at the centre point, (0.5, 0.5, 0.5), of the cube is 200.66 °C

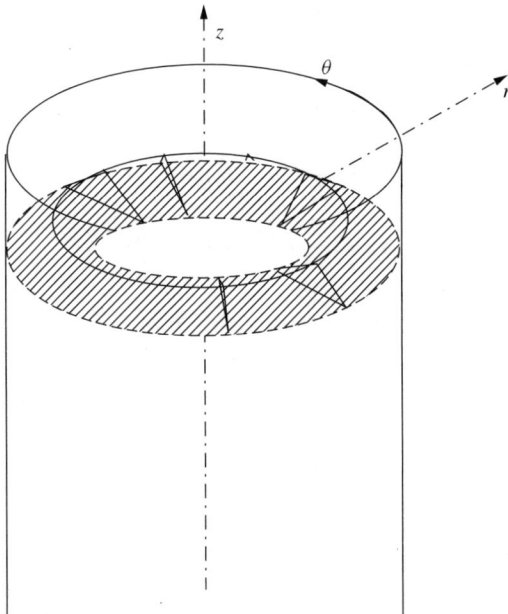

Figure 5.17 An axisymmetric problem

The Galerkin formulation and the element equations are similar to those for two-dimensional heat transfer problems, but are different owing to the ring nature of the elements.

The differential equation in a cylindrical coordinate system (r, z) for steady state is

$$k_r \frac{\partial^2 T}{\partial r^2} + \frac{k_r}{r} \frac{\partial T}{\partial r} + \frac{k_\theta}{r^2} \frac{\partial^2 T}{\partial \theta^2} + k_z \frac{\partial^2 T}{\partial z^2} + G = 0 \qquad (5.57)$$

An axisymmetric problem is independent of the angle θ and hence Equation 5.57 reduces to

$$k_r \frac{\partial T^2}{\partial r^2} + \frac{k_r}{r} \frac{\partial T}{\partial r} + k_z \frac{\partial^2 T}{\partial z^2} + G = 0 \qquad (5.58)$$

This can be rewritten, if the thermal conductivity in the radial direction, k_r is constant, as

$$\frac{1}{r} \left[k_r \frac{\partial}{\partial r} \left(r \frac{\partial T}{\partial r} \right) \right] + k_z \frac{\partial^2 T}{\partial z^2} + G = 0 \qquad (5.59)$$

The boundary conditions are

$$T = T_b \quad \text{on} \quad \Gamma_1$$

$$k_r \frac{\partial T}{\partial r} l + k_z \frac{\partial T}{\partial z} n + h(T - T_a) + q = 0 \quad \text{on} \quad \Gamma_2 \qquad (5.60)$$

The temperature distribution is described as follows:

$$T = N_i T_i + N_j T_j + N_k T_k \qquad (5.61)$$

which is similar in form to that of a linear triangular plane element, where

$$N_i = \frac{1}{2A}(a_i + b_i r + c_i z)$$

$$N_j = \frac{1}{2A}(a_j + b_j r + c_j z)$$

$$N_k = \frac{1}{2A}(a_k + b_k r + c_k z) \qquad (5.62)$$

The area, A, is calculated from

$$2A = \det \begin{vmatrix} 1 & r_i & z_i \\ 1 & r_j & z_j \\ 1 & r_k & z_k \end{vmatrix} \qquad (5.63)$$

Other constants in Equation 5.62 are defined as

$$a_i = r_j z_k - r_k z_j; \, b_i = z_j - z_k; \, c_i = r_k - r_j$$

$$a_j = r_k z_i - r_i z_k; \, b_j = z_k - z_i; \, c_j = r_i - r_k$$

$$a_k = r_i z_j - r_j z_i; \, b_k = z_i - z_j; \, c_k = r_j - r_i \qquad (5.64)$$

5.6.1   Galerkin's method for linear triangular axisymmetric elements

The Galerkin method for axisymmetric equations results in the following integral form

$$\int_{\Omega} N_i \left[\frac{k_r}{r} \frac{\partial}{\partial r} \left(r \frac{\partial T}{\partial r} \right) + k_z \frac{\partial^2 T}{\partial z^2} + G \right] d\Omega = 0 \tag{5.65}$$

The spatial approximation of temperature is given by Equation 5.61. As in the previous sections, the substitution of the spatial approximation will result in the familiar final form of the matrix equation as

$$[\mathbf{K}]\{\mathbf{T}\} = \{\mathbf{f}\} \tag{5.66}$$

where

$$[\mathbf{K}] = \int_{\Omega} [\mathbf{B}]^T [\mathbf{D}][\mathbf{B}] \, d\Omega + \int_{\Gamma} h[\mathbf{N}]^T [\mathbf{N}] \, d\Gamma \tag{5.67}$$

Here,

$$[\mathbf{B}] = \begin{Bmatrix} \dfrac{\partial T}{\partial x} \\ \dfrac{\partial T}{\partial y} \end{Bmatrix} = \begin{bmatrix} \dfrac{\partial N_i}{\partial r} & \dfrac{\partial N_j}{\partial r} & \dfrac{\partial N_k}{\partial r} \\ \dfrac{\partial N_i}{\partial z} & \dfrac{\partial N_j}{\partial z} & \dfrac{\partial N_k}{\partial z} \end{bmatrix} = \frac{1}{2A} \begin{bmatrix} b_i & b_j & b_k \\ c_i & c_j & c_k \end{bmatrix} \tag{5.68}$$

and

$$[\mathbf{D}] = \begin{bmatrix} k_r & 0 \\ 0 & k_z \end{bmatrix} \tag{5.69}$$

In Equation 5.67, the volume Ω is defined as

$$dV = 2\pi r \, dA \tag{5.70}$$

where r is the radius, which varies and can be approximated using linear shape functions as

$$r = N_i r_i + N_j r_j + N_k r_k \tag{5.71}$$

Substituting into Equation 5.67 and integrating, we obtain

$$[\mathbf{K}] = \frac{2\pi \bar{r} k_r}{4A} \begin{bmatrix} b_i^2 & b_i b_j & b_i b_k \\ b_i b_j & b_j^2 & b_j b_k \\ b_i b_k & b_j b_k & b_k^2 \end{bmatrix} + \frac{2\pi \bar{r} k_z}{4A} \begin{bmatrix} c_i^2 & c_i c_j & c_i c_k \\ c_i c_j & c_j^2 & c_j c_k \\ c_i c_k & c_j c_k & c_k^2 \end{bmatrix}$$

$$+ \frac{2\pi h l_{ij}}{12} \begin{bmatrix} 3r_i + r_j & r_i + r_j & 0.0 \\ r_i + r_j & r_i + 3r_j & 0.0 \\ 0.0 & 0.0 & 0.0 \end{bmatrix} \tag{5.72}$$

where

$$\bar{r} = \frac{r_i + r_j + r_k}{3} \tag{5.73}$$

Similarly,

$$\{\mathbf{f}\} = \int_{\Omega} G[\mathbf{N}]^T \, d\Omega - \int_{\Gamma} q[\mathbf{N}]^T \, d\Gamma + \int_{\Gamma} h T_a [\mathbf{N}]^T \, d\Gamma$$

$$= \frac{2\pi GA}{12} \begin{bmatrix} 2 & 1 & 1 \\ 1 & 2 & 1 \\ 1 & 1 & 2 \end{bmatrix} \begin{Bmatrix} r_i \\ r_j \\ r_k \end{Bmatrix} - \frac{2\pi q l_{jk}}{6} \begin{Bmatrix} 0 \\ 2r_j + r_k \\ r_j + 2r_k \end{Bmatrix} + \frac{2\pi h T_a l_{ij}}{6} \begin{Bmatrix} 2r_i + r_j \\ r_i + 2r_j \\ 0 \end{Bmatrix} \tag{5.74}$$

It is possible to approximately recover the two-dimensional plane problem by substituting a very large value for the radius r. In order to clarify the axisymmetric formulation, an example problem is solved as follows.

Example 5.6.1 *Calculate the stiffness matrix and loading vector for the axisymmetric element, shown in Figure 5.18, with heat generation of $G = 1.2\,W/cm^3$. The heat transfer coefficient on the side ij is 1.2 $W/cm^2\,K$ and the ambient temperature is $30\,°C$. The heat flux on the side jk is equal to 1 W/cm^2. Assume the thermal conductivities $k_r = k_z = 2\,W/cm\,°C$.*

The solution to this problem starts with the calculation of various terms in the stiffness matrix (Equation 5.72).

$$b_i = z_j - z_k = -2.0$$
$$b_j = z_k - z_i = 2.0$$
$$b_k = z_i - z_j = 0.0$$
$$c_i = x_k - x_j = -5.0$$
$$c_j = x_i - x_k = -5.0$$
$$c_k = x_j - x_i = 10.0 \tag{5.75}$$

From Equation 5.63, the value of 2A is $20\,cm^2$. Similarly, $\bar{r}$ from Equation 5.73 is calculated as being $20\,cm$ (a reference axis at $r = 0.0$ is assumed). The coefficients used in the stiffness matrix can also be calculated as

$$\frac{2\pi \bar{r} k_r}{4A} = \frac{2\pi \bar{r} k_z}{4A} = 2\pi \tag{5.76}$$

Similarly,

$$\frac{2\pi\, h l_{ij}}{12} = 2\pi \tag{5.77}$$

Note that the length of the convective side l_{ij} is calculated as

$$l_{ij} = \sqrt{(x_i - x_j)^2 + (y_i - y_j)^2} = 10\,cm \tag{5.78}$$

Substituting into Equation 5.72 gives

$$[\mathbf{K}] = 2\pi \begin{bmatrix} 99 & 61 & -50 \\ 61 & 119 & -50 \\ -50 & -50 & 100 \end{bmatrix} \tag{5.79}$$

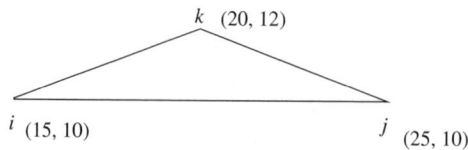

Figure 5.18   An axisymmetric problem

Now, to calculate the loading vector, we need to determine the relevant coefficients, that is,

$$\frac{2\pi h T_a l_{ij}}{6} = 120\pi \tag{5.80}$$

Similarly,

$$\frac{2\pi q l_{jk}}{6} = 1.8\pi \tag{5.81}$$

Substituting the coefficients and other values into Equation 5.74, we obtain

$$\{f\} = 2\pi \left\{ \begin{array}{c} 3337.5 \\ 3879.5 \\ -18.5 \end{array} \right\} \tag{5.82}$$

5.7 Summary

In this chapter, an extension of the steady state heat conduction analysis to multi-dimensions has been given. All commonly encountered approximations, namely, two-dimensional, three-dimensional and axisymmetric, have been discussed. Most of the boundary conditions have also been implemented and explained via examples. We trust the reader will appreciate the difficulties associated with such multi-dimensional calculations and that the exercises given in this chapter will prove useful for further understanding of multi-dimensional steady state heat conduction.

5.8 Exercise

Exercise 5.8.1 *A square plate of size 100 cm by 100 cm is subjected to an isothermal boundary condition of 500 °C on the top and to a convection environment on all the remaining three sides of 100 °C with a heat transfer coefficient of 10 W/m² K. The thermal conductivity of the plate is 10 W/m² K. Assume the thickness of the plate is 1 cm. Determine the temperature distribution in the plate using (a) two triangles and (b) eight triangles. Calculate the temperature and heat fluxes in the x and y directions at a location (x = 30 cm, y = 30 cm).*

Exercise 5.8.2 *If in Exercise 5.8.1, there is a uniform heat generation of 2 W/cm³, and a line source of 5 W/cm at a location of (x = 30 cm and y = 30 cm) then, calculate the new temperature distribution using (a) two triangles and (b) eight triangles. Calculate the temperature at the location (x = 40 cm, y = 40 cm) and the heat fluxes in both the x and y directions.*

Exercise 5.8.3 *Repeat Exercise 5.8.1 using (a) one rectangle (b) four rectangles.*

Exercise 5.8.4 *Repeat Exercise 5.8.2 using (a) one rectangle (b) four rectangles.*

Exercise 5.8.5 *In Exercise 5.8.1, if the thickness increases uniformly from 1 cm from the bottom edge to 3 cm at the top edge, re-solve the problem with (a) two triangles and (b) eight triangles.*

Exercise 5.8.6 *Calculate the stiffness matrix and loading vector for the axisymmetric element shown in Figure 5.19 with a heat generation of $G = 1\,W/cm^3$, the heat transfer coefficient on the side ij is $1.0\,W/cm^2K$ and the ambient temperature is $25\,°C$. The heat flux on the side jk is equal to $0.5\,W/cm^2$. Assume the thermal conductivities $k_r = k_z = 1.5W/m\,°C$.*

Exercise 5.8.7 *An internal combustion (IC) engine cylinder is exposed to hot gases of $1000\,°C$ on the inside wall with a heat transfer coefficient of $25\,W/m^2C$ as shown in Figure 5.20. The external surface is exposed to a coolant at $100\,°C$ with a heat transfer coefficient of $100\,W/m^2\,°C$ on the top half of the cylinder, while the bottom half of the cylinder is exposed to a coolant at $80\,°C$ with a heat transfer coefficient of $200\,W/m^2\,°C$. Calculate the temperature distribution in the cylinder wall with four axisymmetric elements.*

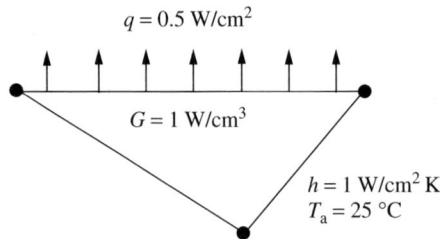

Figure 5.19   An axisymmetric element

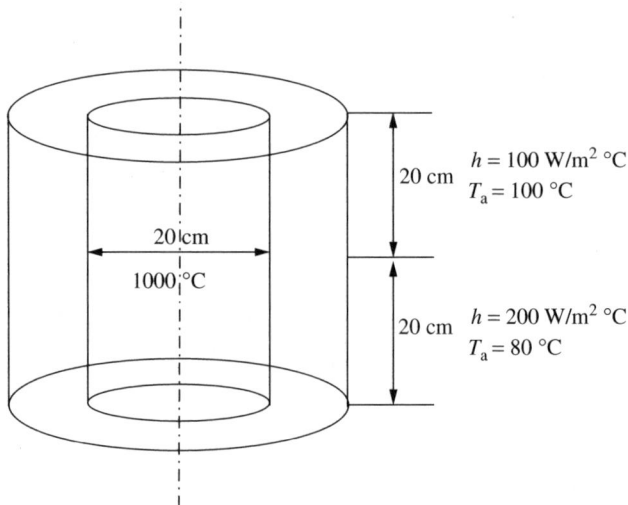

Figure 5.20   Cylinder of an IC engine

Bibliography

Bejan A 1993 *Heat Transfer*, John Wiley & Sons, New York.

Holman JP 1989 *Heat Transfer*, McGraw-Hill, Singapore.

Incropera FP and Dewitt DP 1990 *Fundamentals of Heat and Mass Transfer*, John Wiley & Sons, New York.

Ozisik MN 1968 *Boundary Value Problems of Heat Conduction*, International Text Book Company, Scranton, PA.

6

Transient Heat Conduction Analysis

6.1 Introduction

In the previous chapters, we have discussed steady state heat conduction in which the temperature in a solid body was assumed to be invariant with respect to time. However, many practical heat transfer applications are unsteady (transient) in nature and in such problems the temperature varies with respect to time. For instance, in many components of industrial plants such as boilers, refrigeration and air-conditioning equipment, the heat transfer process is transient during the initial stages of operation. Other transient processes include crystal growth, casting processes, drying, heat transfer associated with the earth's atmosphere, and many more. It is therefore obvious that the analysis of transient heat conduction is very important.

Analytical techniques such as variable separation, which are employed to solve transient heat conduction problems, are of limited use (Ozisik 1968), and a solution for practical heat transfer problems by these methods is difficult. Thus, it is essential to develop numerical solution procedures to solve transient heat conduction problems. In the following section, a simplified analytical method for the solution of transient problems is presented before discussing the finite element solution for such problems in Section 6.3.

6.2 Lumped Heat Capacity System

In this section, we consider the transient analysis of a body in which the temperature is assumed to be constant at any point within and on the surface of the body at any given instant of time. It is also assumed that the temperature of the whole body changes uniformly with time. Such an analysis is called a *lumped heat capacity* method and is a simple and approximate procedure in which no spatial variation in temperature is allowed. The change

Fundamentals of the Finite Element Method for Heat and Fluid Flow   R. W. Lewis, P. Nithiarasu and K. N. Seetharamu
© 2004 John Wiley & Sons, Ltd   ISBNs: 0-470-84788-3 (HB); 0-470-84789-1 (PB)

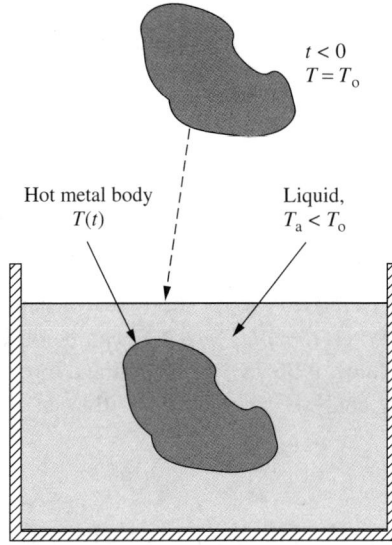

Figure 6.1 Lumped heat capacity system. A hot metal body is immersed in a liquid maintained at a constant temperature

in temperature in such systems varies only with respect to time. It is therefore obvious that the lumped heat capacity analysis is limited to small-sized bodies and/or high thermal conductivity materials.

Consider a body at an initial temperature T_o, immersed in a liquid maintained at a constant temperature T_a, as shown in Figure 6.1. At any instant in time, the convection heat loss from the surface of the body is at the expense of the internal energy of the body. Therefore, the internal energy of the body at any time will be equal to the heat convected to the surrounding medium, that is,

$$-\rho c_p V \frac{dT}{dt} = hA(T(t) - T_a) \tag{6.1}$$

where ρ is the density, c_p is the specific heat and V is the volume of the hot metal body; A is the surface area of the body; h is the heat transfer coefficient between the body surface and the surrounding medium; t is the time and $T(t)$ is the instantaneous temperature of the body.

Equation 6.1 is a first-order differential equation in time, which requires an initial condition to obtain a solution. As mentioned previously, the initial temperature of the body at time $t = 0$, is T_o. Applying the variable separation concept to Equation 6.1, we get

$$\frac{dT}{T(t) - T_a} = -\frac{hA}{\rho c_p V} dt \tag{6.2}$$

Integrating between temperatures T_o and $T(t)$, we obtain

$$\int_{T_o}^{T(t)} \frac{dT}{T(t) - T_a} = -\int_0^t \frac{hA}{\rho c_p V} dt \tag{6.3}$$

Note that the temperature changes from T_0 to $T(t)$ as the time changes from 0 to t. Integration of the above equation results in a transient temperature distribution as follows:

$$\ln\left(\frac{T - T_a}{T_0 - T_a}\right) = -\frac{hAt}{\rho c_p V} \tag{6.4}$$

or

$$\frac{T - T_a}{T_0 - T_a} = e^{\left[-\frac{hA}{\rho c_p V}\right]t} \tag{6.5}$$

The quantity $\rho C_p V / hA$ is referred to as the time constant of the system because it has the dimensions of time. When $t = \rho C_p V / hA$, it can be observed that the temperature difference $(T(t) - T_a)$ has a value of 36.78% of the initial temperature difference $(T_0 - T_a)$.

The lumped heat capacity analysis gives results within an accuracy of 5% when

$$\frac{h(V/A)}{k_s} < 0.1 \tag{6.6}$$

where k_s is the thermal conductivity of the solid. It should be observed that (V/A) represents a characteristic dimension of the body. The above non-dimensional parameter can thus be rewritten as hL/k_s, which is known as the *Biot number*. The Biot number represents a ratio between conduction resistance within the body to convection resistance at the surface of the hot body (Readers should consult Chapter 1 for the meaning of conduction and convection resistance).

Owing to the variability of the convection heat transfer coefficient, which can often vary as much as 25% in many heat transfer problems, a lumped system analysis is often considered as a realistic approximation even if the Biot number is slightly above 0.1. However, for higher Biot numbers, this method is certainly not valid. In such situations, numerical methods such as the finite element method are ideal in obtaining solutions with better accuracy.

6.3 Numerical Solution

Heat conduction solutions for many geometric shapes of practical interest cannot be found using the charts available for regular geometries (Holman 1989). Because of the time-dependent boundary, or interface conditions, prevalent in many transient heat conduction problems, analytical or lumped solutions are also difficult to obtain. In such complex situations, it is essential to develop approximate time-stepping procedures to determine the transient temperature distribution.

6.3.1 Transient governing equations and boundary and initial conditions

The transient heat conduction equation for a stationary medium is given by (Chapter 1)

$$\frac{\partial}{\partial x}\left(k_x(T)\frac{\partial T}{\partial x}\right) + \frac{\partial}{\partial y}\left(k_y(T)\frac{\partial T}{\partial y}\right) + \frac{\partial}{\partial z}\left(k_z(T)\frac{\partial T}{\partial z}\right) + G = \rho c_p \frac{\partial T}{\partial t} \tag{6.7}$$

where $k_x(T)$, $k_y(T)$ are $k_z(T)$ are the temperature-dependent thermal conductivities in the x, y and z directions respectively. The boundary conditions for this type of problem are

$$T = T_b \quad \text{on} \quad \Gamma_b \tag{6.8}$$

and

$$k_x(T)\frac{\partial T}{\partial x}l + k_y(T)\frac{\partial T}{\partial y}m + k_z(T)\frac{\partial T}{\partial z}n + q + h(T - T_a) = 0 \quad \text{on} \quad \Gamma_q \tag{6.9}$$

where, $\Gamma_b \cup \Gamma_q = \Gamma$ and $\Gamma_b \cap \Gamma_q = 0$. Γ represents the whole boundary. In the above equation, l, m and n are direction cosines, h is the heat transfer coefficient, T_a is the atmospheric temperature and q is the boundary heat flux. The initial condition for the problem is

$$T = T_o \quad \text{at} \quad t = 0.0 \tag{6.10}$$

It is now possible to solve the above system, provided that appropriate spatial and temporal discretizations are available. Before dealing with the temporal discretization, we introduce in the following subsection, the standard Galerkin weighted residual form for the transient equations.

6.3.2 The Galerkin method

In this subsection, the application of the Galerkin method for the transient equations subjected to appropriate boundary and initial conditions is addressed. The temperature is discretized over space as follows:

$$T(x, y, z, t) = \sum_{i=1}^{n} N_i(x, y, z)T_i(t) \tag{6.11}$$

where N_i are the shape functions, n is the number of nodes in an element, and $T_i(t)$ are the time-dependent nodal temperatures. The Galerkin representation of Equation 6.7 is

$$\int_{\Omega} N_i \left[\frac{\partial}{\partial x}\left(k_x(T)\frac{\partial T}{\partial x}\right) + \frac{\partial}{\partial y}\left(k_y(T)\frac{\partial T}{\partial y}\right) + \frac{\partial}{\partial z}\left(k_z(T)\frac{\partial T}{\partial z}\right) + G - \rho c_p \frac{\partial T}{\partial t} \right] d\Omega = 0 \tag{6.12}$$

Employing integration by parts on the first three terms of Equation 6.12, we get

$$-\int_{\Omega} \left[k_x(T)\frac{\partial N_i}{\partial x}\frac{\partial T}{\partial x} + k_y(T)\frac{\partial N_i}{\partial y}\frac{\partial T}{\partial y} + k_z(T)\frac{\partial N_i}{\partial z}\frac{\partial T}{\partial z} - N_i G + N_i \rho c_p \frac{\partial T}{\partial t} \right] d\Omega$$

$$+ \int_{\Gamma_q} N_i k_x(T)\frac{\partial T}{\partial x}l d\Gamma_q + \int_{\Gamma_q} N_i k_y(T)\frac{\partial T}{\partial y}m d\Gamma_q + \int_{\Gamma_q} N_i k_z(T)\frac{\partial T}{\partial z}n d\Gamma_q = 0 \tag{6.13}$$

Note that from Equation 6.9,

$$\int_{\Gamma_q} N_i k_x(T)\frac{\partial T}{\partial x}l d\Gamma_q + \int_{\Gamma_q} N_i k_y(T)\frac{\partial T}{\partial y}m d\Gamma_q + \int_{\Gamma_q} N_i k_z(T)\frac{\partial T}{\partial z}n d\Gamma_q$$

$$= -\int_{\Gamma_q} N_i q d\Gamma_q - \int_{\Gamma_q} N_i h(T - T_a)d\Gamma_q \tag{6.14}$$

On substituting the spatial approximation from Equation 6.11, Equation 6.13 finally becomes

$$-\int_{\Omega}\left[k_x(T)\frac{\partial N_i}{\partial x}\frac{\partial N_j}{\partial x}T_j(t) + k_y(T)\frac{\partial N_i}{\partial y}\frac{\partial N_j}{\partial y}T_j(t) + k_z(T)\frac{\partial N_i}{\partial z}\frac{\partial N_j}{\partial z}T_j(t)\right]d\Omega$$

$$+\int_{\Omega}\left[N_i G - N_i\rho c_p\frac{\partial N_j}{\partial t}T_j(t)\right]d\Omega - \int_{\Gamma_q}N_i q\,d\Gamma_q - \int_{\Gamma_q}N_i h(T - T_a)d\Gamma_q = 0 \quad (6.15)$$

where i and j represent the nodes. Equation 6.15 can be written in a more convenient form as

$$[\mathbf{C}]\left\{\frac{\partial \mathbf{T}}{\partial t}\right\} + [\mathbf{K}]\{\mathbf{T}\} = \{\mathbf{f}\} \quad (6.16)$$

or

$$[C_{ij}]\left\{\frac{\partial T_j}{\partial t}\right\} + [K_{ij}]\{T_j\} = \{f_i\} \quad (6.17)$$

where

$$[C_{ij}] = \int_{\Omega}\rho c_p N_i N_j d\Omega \quad (6.18)$$

$$[K_{ij}] = \int_{\Omega}\left[k_x(T)\frac{\partial N_i}{\partial x}\frac{\partial N_j}{\partial x}\{T_j\} + k_y(T)\frac{\partial N_i}{\partial y}\frac{\partial N_j}{\partial y}\{T_j\} + k_z(T)\frac{\partial N_i}{\partial z}\frac{\partial N_j}{\partial z}\{T_j\}\right]d\Omega$$

$$+\int_{\Gamma}h N_i N_j d\Gamma \quad (6.19)$$

and

$$\{f_i\} = \int_{\Omega}N_i G d\Omega - \int_{\Gamma_q}q N_i d\Gamma_q + \int_{\Gamma_q}N_i h T_a d\Gamma \quad (6.20)$$

In matrix form,

$$[\mathbf{C}] = \int_{\Omega}\rho c_p[\mathbf{N}]^{\mathrm{T}}[\mathbf{N}]\,d\Omega \quad (6.21)$$

$$[\mathbf{K}] = \int_{\Omega}[\mathbf{B}]^{\mathrm{T}}[\mathbf{D}][\mathbf{B}]d\Omega + \int_{\Gamma}h[\mathbf{N}]^{\mathrm{T}}[\mathbf{N}]\,d\Gamma \quad (6.22)$$

and

$$\{\mathbf{f}\} = \int_{\Omega}G[\mathbf{N}]^{\mathrm{T}}d\Omega - \int_{\Gamma_q}q[\mathbf{N}]^{\mathrm{T}}d\Gamma_q + \int_{\Gamma}h T_a[\mathbf{N}]^{\mathrm{T}}d\Gamma \quad (6.23)$$

Since $k_x(T)$, $k_y(T)$ and $k_z(T)$ are functions of temperature, Equation 6.16 is non-linear and requires an iterative solution. If k_x, k_y and k_z are independent of temperature, then Equation 6.16 is linear in form.

6.4 One-dimensional Transient State Problem

The relation derived in Equation 6.16 is employed here to illustrate the application to a one-dimensional transient problem using a linear element as shown in Figure 6.2

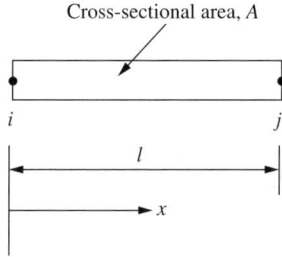

Figure 6.2   One-dimensional linear element

The temperature T is represented in the element by

$$T = N_i T_i + N_j T_j = [\mathbf{N}]\{\mathbf{T}\} \tag{6.24}$$

Note that i and j in the above equation represent the nodes i and j of the element shown in Figure 6.2. The shape functions in Equation 6.24 are defined as

$$N_i = 1 - \frac{x}{l}$$

$$N_j = \frac{x}{l} \tag{6.25}$$

The spatial derivative of temperature is given as

$$\frac{\partial T}{\partial x} = \frac{\partial N_i}{\partial x} T_i + \frac{\partial N_j}{\partial x} T_j = -\frac{1}{l} T_i + \frac{1}{l} T_j = [\mathbf{B}]\{\mathbf{T}\} \tag{6.26}$$

The relevant matrices, as discussed in the previous section (Equation 6.16), are

$$[\mathbf{C}] = \int_\Omega \rho c_p [\mathbf{N}]^T [\mathbf{N}] d\Omega = \int_l \rho c_p A \begin{bmatrix} N_i^2 & N_i N_j \\ N_i N_j & N_j^2 \end{bmatrix} dl \tag{6.27}$$

Note that $d\Omega$ is replaced by Adl in the above equation. Here, A is the uniform cross-sectional area of a one-dimensional body. The integration of Equation 6.27 results in (for details of the integration, refer to Chapter 3 and Appendix B)

$$[\mathbf{C}] = \frac{\rho c_p l A}{6} \begin{bmatrix} 2 & 1 \\ 1 & 2 \end{bmatrix} \tag{6.28}$$

Similarly, the $[\mathbf{K}]$ matrix and load vector $\{\mathbf{f}\}$ can be written as

$$[\mathbf{K}] = \frac{Ak_x}{l} \begin{bmatrix} 1 & -1 \\ -1 & 1 \end{bmatrix} + \frac{hPl}{6} \begin{bmatrix} 2 & 1 \\ 1 & 2 \end{bmatrix} \tag{6.29}$$

and

$$\{\mathbf{f}\} = \frac{GAl}{2} \begin{Bmatrix} 1 \\ 1 \end{Bmatrix} - \frac{qPl}{2} \begin{Bmatrix} 1 \\ 1 \end{Bmatrix} + \frac{hT_a Pl}{2} \begin{Bmatrix} 1 \\ 1 \end{Bmatrix} \tag{6.30}$$

where P is the perimeter of the one-dimensional body. Substituting Equations 6.28 to 6.30 into Equation 6.16, for a domain with only one element, gives

$$\frac{\rho c_p l A}{6} \begin{bmatrix} 2 & 1 \\ 1 & 2 \end{bmatrix} \begin{Bmatrix} \frac{\partial T_i}{\partial t} \\ \frac{\partial T_j}{\partial t} \end{Bmatrix} + \left(\frac{A k_x}{l} \begin{bmatrix} 1 & -1 \\ -1 & 1 \end{bmatrix} + \frac{h P l}{6} \begin{bmatrix} 2 & 1 \\ 1 & 2 \end{bmatrix} \right) \begin{Bmatrix} T_i \\ T_j \end{Bmatrix}$$

$$= \frac{G A l}{2} \begin{Bmatrix} 1 \\ 1 \end{Bmatrix} - \frac{q P l}{2} \begin{Bmatrix} 1 \\ 1 \end{Bmatrix} + \frac{h T_a P l}{2} \begin{Bmatrix} 1 \\ 1 \end{Bmatrix} \tag{6.31}$$

The above equation is a general representation of a one-dimensional problem with one linear element. All the terms are included irrespective of whether or not boundary fluxes and heat generation are present. We shall appropriately modify Equation 6.31, when solving the numerical problems.

Equation 6.31 is semi-discrete as it is discretized only in space. We now require a method of discretizing the transient terms of Equation 6.31. The following subsections give the details of how the transient terms will be discretized.

6.4.1 Time discretization using the Finite Difference Method (FDM)

As may be seen from the semi-discrete form of Equation 6.31 (or 6.16), the differential operator involving the time-dependent term still remains to be discretized. In this section, a numerical approximation of the transient terms, using the Finite Difference Method (FDM), is considered.

Figure 6.3 clarifies a typical temperature variation in the time domain between the n and $n + 1$ time levels. Using a Taylor series, we can write the temperature at the $n + 1$th level as

$$T^{n+1} = T^n + \Delta t \frac{\partial T^n}{\partial t} + \frac{\Delta t^2}{2} \frac{\partial^2 T^n}{\partial t^2} + \cdots \tag{6.32}$$

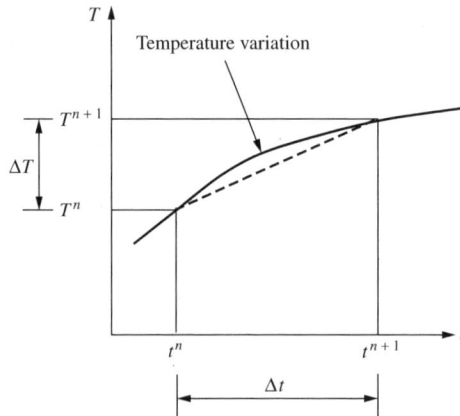

Figure 6.3   Temperature variation within a time step

If the second- and higher-order terms in the above equation are neglected, then

$$\frac{\partial T^n}{\partial t} \approx \frac{T^{n+1} - T^n}{\Delta t} + O(\Delta t) \tag{6.33}$$

which is first-order accurate in time. If we now introduce a parameter θ such that

$$T^{n+\theta} = \theta T^{n+1} + (1 - \theta)T^n \tag{6.34}$$

into Equation 6.16 then, along with Equation 6.33, we have

$$[\mathbf{C}] \left\{ \frac{\mathbf{T}^{n+1} - \mathbf{T}^n}{\Delta t} \right\} + [\mathbf{K}]\{\mathbf{T}\}^{n+\theta} = \{\mathbf{f}\}^{n+\theta} \tag{6.35}$$

or

$$[\mathbf{C}] \left\{ \frac{\mathbf{T}^{n+1} - \mathbf{T}^n}{\Delta t} \right\} + [\mathbf{K}] \left\{ \theta \mathbf{T}^{n+1} + (1 - \theta)\mathbf{T}^n \right\} = \theta\{\mathbf{f}\}^{n+1} + (1 - \theta)\{\mathbf{f}\}^n \tag{6.36}$$

The above equation can be rearranged as follows:

$$([\mathbf{C}] + \theta\Delta t[\mathbf{K}]) \{\mathbf{T}\}^{n+1} = ([\mathbf{C}] - (1 - \theta)\Delta t[\mathbf{K}]) \{\mathbf{T}\}^n + \Delta t \left(\theta\{\mathbf{f}\}^{n+1} + (1 - \theta)\{\mathbf{f}\}^n \right) \tag{6.37}$$

Equation 6.37 gives the nodal values of temperature at the $n + 1$ time level. These temperature values are calculated using the n time level values. However, both the $n + 1$ and n time level values of the forcing vector $\{\mathbf{f}\}$ must be known. By varying the parameter θ, different transient schemes can be constructed, which are shown in Table 6.1 for varying values of θ.

In the following numerical example, we demonstrate how the Crank–Nicolson time-stepping scheme can be used to solve a one-dimensional transient problem.

Example 6.4.1 *In Example 3.5.1, let us assume that the initial temperature of the fin is equal to the atmospheric temperature, 25°C. If the base temperature is suddenly raised to a temperature of 100°C, and maintained at that value, determine the temperature distribution in the fin with respect to time. Assume a heat capacity of 2.42×10^6 W/m³°C.*

Let us assume that the problem is to be solved using the Crank–Nicolson method, in which θ is equal to 0.5. Assume a time step, Δt, of 0.1 s. Equation 6.37 can be rewritten with the given value for θ and Δt as

$$([\mathbf{C}] + 0.5 \times 0.1[\mathbf{K}])\{\mathbf{T}\}^{n+1} = ([\mathbf{C}] - 0.5 \times 0.1[\mathbf{K}])\{\mathbf{T}\}^n + 0.1\{\mathbf{f}\} \tag{6.38}$$

Table 6.1 Different time-stepping schemes

θ	Name of the scheme	Comments
0.0	Fully explicit scheme	Forward difference method
1.0	Fully implicit scheme	Backward difference method
0.5	Semi-implicit scheme	Crank–Nicolson method

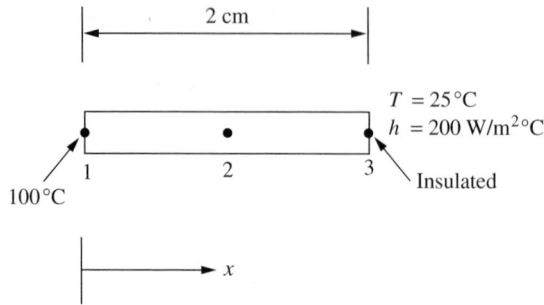

Figure 6.4 One-dimensional transient heat transfer. Two elements and three nodes

If we consider two elements, as shown in Figure 6.4, we have from Example 3.5.1,

$$[\mathbf{K}]_1 = [\mathbf{K}]_2 = \begin{bmatrix} 0.124 & -0.118 \\ -0.118 & 0.124 \end{bmatrix} \tag{6.39}$$

and

$$\{\mathbf{f}\}_1 = \{\mathbf{f}\}_2 = \begin{Bmatrix} 0.15 \\ 0.15 \end{Bmatrix} \tag{6.40}$$

The [**C**] *matrix can be calculated as*

$$[\mathbf{C}]_1 = [\mathbf{C}]_2 = \frac{\rho c_p AL}{6} \begin{bmatrix} 2 & 1 \\ 1 & 2 \end{bmatrix} = \begin{bmatrix} 0.0484 & 0.0242 \\ 0.0242 & 0.0484 \end{bmatrix} \tag{6.41}$$

On assembling the stiffness matrix and load vector, we obtain

$$[\mathbf{K}] = \begin{bmatrix} 0.124 & -0.118 & 0.00 \\ -0.118 & 0.248 & -0.118 \\ 0.00 & -0.118 & 0.124 \end{bmatrix} \tag{6.42}$$

and

$$\{\mathbf{f}\} = \begin{Bmatrix} 0.15 \\ 0.30 \\ 0.15 \end{Bmatrix} \tag{6.43}$$

The global capacitance matrix is

$$[\mathbf{C}] = \begin{bmatrix} 0.0484 & 0.0242 & 0.00 \\ 0.0242 & 0.0968 & 0.0242 \\ 0.00 & 0.0242 & 0.0484 \end{bmatrix} \tag{6.44}$$

Substituting into Equation 6.38, we get at $\Delta t = 0.1$ *s*

$$\begin{bmatrix} 0.0546 & 0.0183 & 0.0 \\ 0.0183 & 0.1092 & 0.0183 \\ 0.00 & 0.0183 & 0.0546 \end{bmatrix} \begin{Bmatrix} T_1 \\ T_2 \\ T_3 \end{Bmatrix} = \begin{bmatrix} 0.0422 & 0.0301 & 0.00 \\ 0.0301 & 0.0844 & 0.0301 \\ 0.00 & 0.0301 & 0.0422 \end{bmatrix} \begin{Bmatrix} 25.0 \\ 25.0 \\ 25.0 \end{Bmatrix} + \begin{Bmatrix} 0.015 \\ 0.030 \\ 0.015 \end{Bmatrix} \tag{6.45}$$

From the second and third equations of the above system, we calculate that $T_2 = 11.69°C$ and $T_3 = 29.45°C$.

Similarly at time $t = 0.2$ s, we arrive at the following values:

$$\begin{bmatrix} 0.0546 & 0.0183 & 0.0 \\ 0.0183 & 0.1092 & 0.0183 \\ 0.00 & 0.0183 & 0.0546 \end{bmatrix} \begin{Bmatrix} T_1 \\ T_2 \\ T_3 \end{Bmatrix} = \begin{bmatrix} 0.0422 & 0.0301 & 0.00 \\ 0.0301 & 0.0844 & 0.0301 \\ 0.00 & 0.0301 & 0.0422 \end{bmatrix} \begin{Bmatrix} 100.0 \\ 11.69 \\ 29.45 \end{Bmatrix} + \begin{Bmatrix} 0.015 \\ 0.030 \\ 0.015 \end{Bmatrix}$$

(6.46)

Solution of the above system results in $T_2 = 24.68°C$ and $T_3 = 21.22°C$. It is observed that the solution exhibits spatial and temporal oscillation at the start of the calculations. These oscillations can be eliminated via suitable mesh refinement.

In the above example, it has been demonstrated how the transient solution is calculated. In the following example, a similar case is considered using an explicit computer program (see Chapter 10).

Example 6.4.2 *A rod of 1 unit width and 20 units in length is initially assumed to be at $0°C$. The left-hand side of the domain is subjected to a uniform heat flux of 1 and all other sides are assumed to be insulated as shown in Figure 6.5. Assume all other properties are equal to unity and compute the temperature distribution and compare with a known analytical solution.*

The analytical solution for this problem is given by Carslaw and Jaeger (Carslaw and Jaeger 1959) as

$$T(x, t) = 2(t/\pi)^{1/2} \left[\exp\left(-x^2/4t\right) - (1/2)x\sqrt{\frac{\pi}{t}} erfc\left(\frac{x}{2\sqrt{t}}\right) \right] \qquad (6.47)$$

Figure 6.6 shows the two different meshes used in the calculations. Figure 6.6(a) is a coarse mesh with 122 nodes and 158 elements, and Figure 6.6(b) shows a mesh of 2349

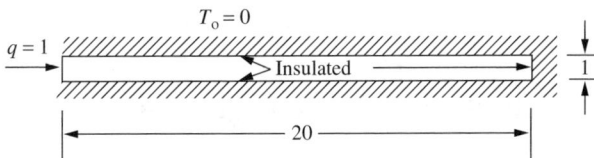

Figure 6.5 One-dimensional transient heat conduction analysis in a rod

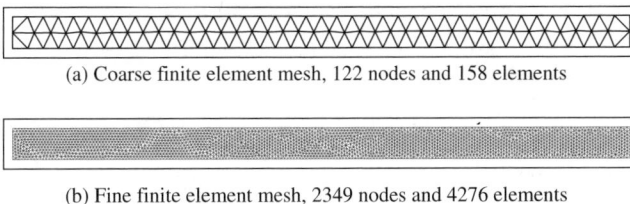

(a) Coarse finite element mesh, 122 nodes and 158 elements

(b) Fine finite element mesh, 2349 nodes and 4276 elements

Figure 6.6 Linear triangular element meshes

(a) Temperature distribution on the coarse mesh, $T_{max} = 1.12$ at the right-hand face

(b) Temperature distribution on the fine mesh, $T_{max} = 1.128$ at the left-hand face

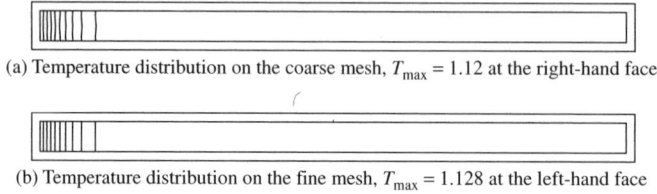

Figure 6.7   Temperature distribution at $t = 1$

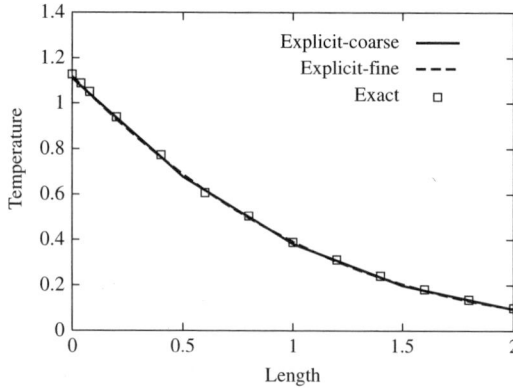

Figure 6.8   Temperature distribution along the length of the rod at $t = 1$

nodes and 4276 elements. This is a one-dimensional problem, which is solved using a two-dimensional forward difference (explicit) computer program.

Figure 6.7 shows the temperature contours at a time of unity. As seen, the results generated from both meshes are very similar. The temperature variation along the length of the rod is shown in Figure 6.8. The results of both meshes indicate excellent agreement with the analytical solution.

6.4.2   Time discretization using the Finite Element Method (FEM)

In the previous subsection, the temporal term in the transient heat conduction equation has been discretized using the finite difference method. Here, we concentrate on the use of the finite element method to discretize the equation in the time domain. In order to derive the appropriate transient relations using the FEM, let us rewrite the semi-discrete one-dimensional Equation 6.16. In this equation, the temperature is now discretized in the time domain as (refer to Figure 6.9).

$$T(t) = N_i(t)T_i(t) + N_j(t)T_j(T) \tag{6.48}$$

where the linear shape functions $N_i(t)$ and $N_j(t)$ are given as

$$N_i(t) = 1 - \frac{t}{\Delta t}; \quad N_j(t) = \frac{t}{\Delta t} \tag{6.49}$$

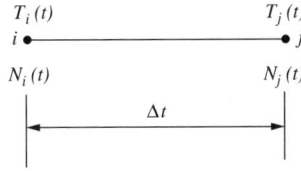

Figure 6.9   Time discretization between nth (i) and $n + 1$th (j) time levels

The time derivative of the temperature is thus written as

$$\frac{\mathrm{d}T(t)}{\mathrm{d}t} = \frac{\mathrm{d}N_i(t)}{\mathrm{d}t} T_i(t) + \frac{\mathrm{d}N_j(t)}{\mathrm{d}t} T_j(t) \qquad (6.50)$$

Substituting Equation 6.49 into Equation 6.50, we get

$$\frac{\mathrm{d}T(t)}{\mathrm{d}t} = -\frac{1}{\Delta t} T_i(t) + \frac{1}{\Delta t} T_j(t) \qquad (6.51)$$

Substituting Equations 6.48 and 6.51 into Equation 6.16 and applying the weighted residual principle (Galerkin method), we obtain for a time interval of Δt,

$$\int_{\Delta t} \begin{Bmatrix} N_i(t) \\ N_j(t) \end{Bmatrix} \left[[\mathbf{C}] \left(-\frac{T_i(t)}{\Delta t} + \frac{T_j(t)}{\Delta t} \right) + [\mathbf{K}] \left(N_i(t) T_i(t) + N_j(t) T_j(t) \right) - \{\mathbf{f}\} \right] \mathrm{d}t = 0$$

$$(6.52)$$

Employing (see Appendix B)

$$\int_{\Delta t} N_i(t)^a N_j(t)^b \mathrm{d}t = \frac{a! b!}{(a + b + 1)!} \Delta t \qquad (6.53)$$

we obtain the characteristic equation over the time interval Δt as

$$\frac{[\mathbf{C}]}{2\Delta t} \begin{bmatrix} -1 & 1 \\ -1 & 1 \end{bmatrix} \begin{Bmatrix} T_i(t) \\ T_j(t) \end{Bmatrix} + \frac{[\mathbf{K}]}{3} \begin{bmatrix} 2 & 1 \\ 1 & 2 \end{bmatrix} \begin{Bmatrix} T_i(t) \\ T_j(t) \end{Bmatrix} = \frac{1}{2} \begin{Bmatrix} f_1 \\ f_2 \end{Bmatrix} \qquad (6.54)$$

The above equation involves the temperature values at the nth and $n + 1$th level. A quadratic variation of temperature with respect to time may be derived in a similar fashion.

6.5   Stability

The stability of a numerical scheme may be obtained using a Fourier analysis (Hirsch 1988; Lewis *et al.* 1996). Here, we give a brief summary of the stability-related issues of the time-stepping schemes discussed in this chapter.

Backward Euler: This is an implicit scheme with a backward difference approximation for the time term. This scheme is unconditionally stable and the accuracy of the scheme is governed by the size of the time step.

Forward Euler: This is an explicit scheme with a forward difference approximation to the time term. The scheme is conditionally stable and the stability limit for the time step is given as

$$\Delta t \leq \frac{l^2}{b\alpha} \qquad (6.55)$$

where l is the element size and α is the thermal diffusivity.

Central Difference: The central difference approximation of the time term, with an explicit treatment for the other terms, is unconditionally unstable, and this scheme is not recommended.

Crank–Nicolson Scheme (semi-implicit): Owing to the oscillatory behaviour of this semi-implicit scheme at larger time steps, it is often termed as a *marginally stable scheme*.

6.6   Multi-dimensional Transient Heat Conduction

A finite element solution for multi-dimensional problems follows the same procedure as that for a one-dimensional case. However, the matrices [C], [K] and {f} are different because of their multi-dimensions. For more details on the matrices, the reader should refer to Chapter 3. A numerical problem, using a two- and three-dimensional approximation, is solved in the following example.

Example 6.6.1 *A square plate and a cube are subjected to different thermal boundary conditions as shown in Figure 6.10. If the initial temperature of both the domains is $0\,^\circ C$, calculate the transient temperature distribution within these two geometries. Also, plot the temperature change with respect to time at a point (0.5, 0.5) in the 2D geometry and at (0.5, 0.5, 0.5) in the three-dimensional geometry.*

The results from both the two- and three-dimensional geometries should be identical because of the insulated conditions on the two vertical sides of the cube.

Figure 6.11 shows the time evolution of the temperature contours. The first two figures, that is, Figure 6.11(a) and (b), show a zero temperature value at the centre of the plate. However, heat from the boundaries rapidly diffuses into the domain and the temperature reaches a steady value of $200.4\,^\circ C$ at the centre by the time $t = 0.5$ s. In Figure 6.12, we

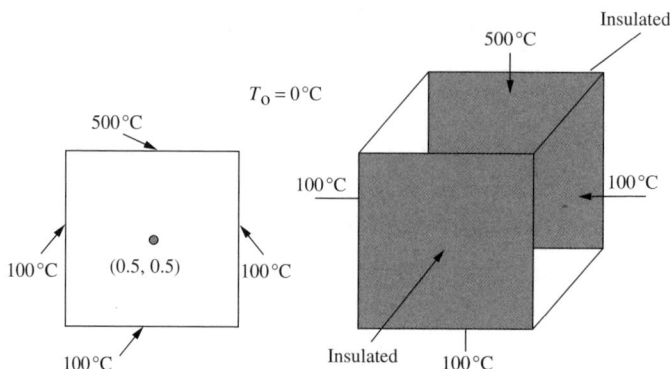

Figure 6.10   Square and cubical domains with thermal boundary conditions

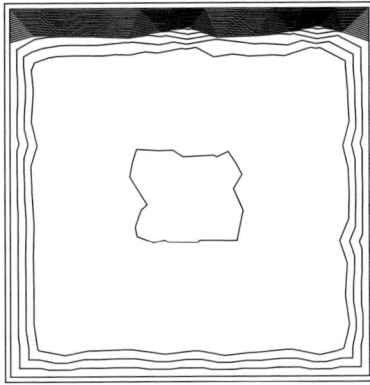

(a) Temperature distribution at $t = 0.001$ s,
$T(0.5, 0.5) = 0.0 °C$

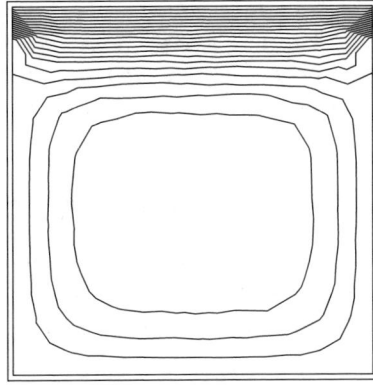

(b) Temperature distribution at $t = 0.01$ s,
$T(0.5, 0.5) = 0.0 °C$

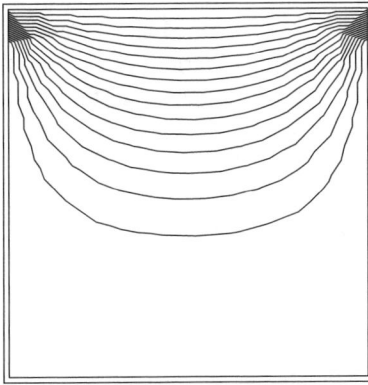

(c) Temperature distribution at $t = 0.1$ s,
$T(0.5, 0.5) = 155.38 °C$

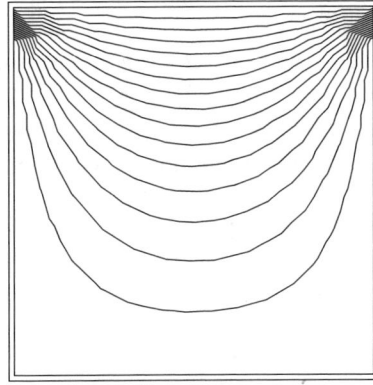

(d) Temperature distribution at $t = 0.5$ s,
$T(0.5, 0.5) = 200.40 °C$

Figure 6.11   Transient temperature distribution in a 2D plane geometry

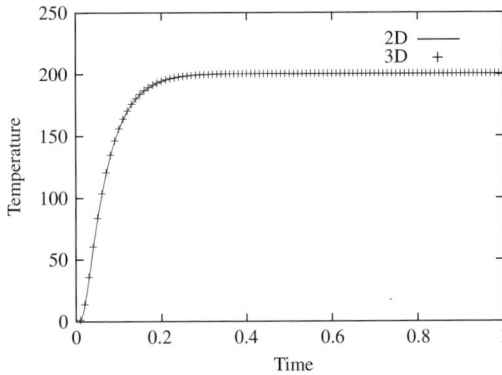

Figure 6.12   Temperature distribution at the centre of a square domain (cube in 3D) with respect to time

show the temperature variation at the centre point of both the two- and three-dimensional geometries with respect to time. It may be seen that both the results are identical. It should be noted that the temperature increases rapidly and reaches a value of 200.4 at about four seconds and thereafter remains constant.

6.7 Phase Change Problems—Solidification and Melting

Materials processing, metallurgy, purification of metals, growth of pure crystals from melts and solutions, solidification of casting and ingots, welding, electroslag melting, zone melting, thermal energy storage using phase change materials, and so forth, involve melting and solidification. These phase change processes are accompanied by either absorption or release of thermal energy. A moving boundary exists, which separates the two thermo-physical states in which the thermal energy is either absorbed or liberated. If we consider the solidification of a casting, or ingot, the super heat in the melt and the latent heat liberated at the solid–liquid interface are transferred across the solidified metal interface and the mould, encountering at each of these stages a certain thermal barrier. In addition, the metal shrinks as it solidifies and an air gap is formed between the metal and the mould. Thus, additional thermal resistance is encountered. The heat transfer processes that occur are complex. The cooling rates employed range from 10^{-5} to 10^{10} K/s and the corresponding solidification systems extend from depths of several metres to a few micrometres. These various cooling rates produce different microstructures and hence a variety of thermo-mechanical properties. During the solidification of binary and multi-component alloys, the physical phenomena become more complicated owing to phase transformation taking place over a range of temperatures. During the solidification of an alloy, the concentrations vary locally from the original mixture, as material may have been preferentially incorporated, or rejected, at the solidification front. This process is called *macro-segregation*. The material between the solidus and the liquidus temperatures is partly solid and partly liquid and resembles a porous medium and is referred to as a *mushy zone*.

A complete understanding of the phase change phenomenon involves an analysis of the various processes that accompany it. The most important of these processes, from a macroscopic point of view, is the heat transfer process. This is complicated by the release, or absorption, of the latent heat of fusion at the solid–liquid interface. Several methods have been used to take into account the liberation of latent heat. The following subsections give a brief account of commonly employed methods that deal with transient heat conduction during a phase change.

6.7.1   The governing equations

The classical problem involves considering the conservation of energy in the domain, Ω, by dividing this into two distinct domains, Ω_l (liquid) and Ω_s (solid), where $\Omega_l + \Omega_s = \Omega$. The energy conservation equation for the one-dimensional case is

$$\rho_l c_{pl} \frac{\partial T}{\partial t} = k_l \frac{\partial^2 T}{\partial x^2} \quad \text{in} \quad \Omega_l \tag{6.56}$$

where the subscript l denotes the liquid. Note that in the above equation, the convective motion is neglected. For details of convection, the reader is referred to Chapter 7. Similarly, the equation for the solid portion is written as

$$\rho_s c_{ps} \frac{\partial T}{\partial t} = k_s \frac{\partial^2 T}{\partial x^2} \quad \text{in} \quad \Omega_s \tag{6.57}$$

where the subscript s represents the solid. The problem will be complete only if the initial and boundary conditions and the interface conditions are given. The interface conditions are

$$T_{sl} = T_f \tag{6.58}$$

and

$$-k_s \left(\frac{\partial T}{\partial x} \right)_s = \rho_s L \frac{ds}{dt} - k_1 \left(\frac{\partial T}{\partial x} \right)_1 \quad \text{on} \quad \Gamma_{sl} \tag{6.59}$$

where sl represents the position of the interface, ds/dt represents the interface velocity and T_f is the phase change temperature. Equation 6.59 states that the heat transferred by conduction in the solidified portion is equal to the heat entering the interface by latent heat of liberation at the interface and the heat coming from the liquid by conduction. The main complication in solving this classical problem lies in tracking the interface and applying the interface conditions.

6.7.2 Enthalpy formulation

In the enthalpy method, one single equation is used to solve both the solid and liquid domains of the problem. A single energy conservation equation is written for the whole domain as

$$\frac{\partial H}{\partial t} = k \frac{\partial^2 T}{\partial x^2} \quad \text{in} \quad \Omega \tag{6.60}$$

where H is the enthalpy function, or the total heat content, which is defined for an isothermal phase change as

$$H(T) = \int_{T_r}^{T} \rho c_s(T) dT \quad \text{if} \quad (T \le T_f)$$

$$H(T) = \int_{T_r}^{T_f} \rho c_s(T) dT + \rho L + \int_{T_f}^{T} \rho c_1(T) dT \quad \text{if} \quad (T \ge T_l) \tag{6.61}$$

and, for a phase change over an interval of temperature T_s to T_l, that is, the solidus and the liquidus temperatures respectively, we have the following:

$$H(T) = \int_{T_r}^{T_s} \rho c_s(T) dT + \int_{T_s}^{T} \left[\rho \left(\frac{dL}{dT} \right) + \rho c_f(T) \right] dT \quad (T_s < T \le T_l)$$

$$H(T) = \int_{T_r}^{T_s} \rho c_s(T) dT + \rho L + \int_{T_s}^{T_l} \rho c_f(T) dT + \int_{T_l}^{T} \rho c_1(T) dT \quad (T \ge T_l) \tag{6.62}$$

where c_f is the specific heat in the freezing interval, L is the latent heat and T_r is a reference temperature that is below T_s.

One of the earliest and most commonly used methods for solving such problems has been the 'effective heat capacity' method. This method is derived from writing

$$\frac{\partial H}{\partial t} = \frac{\partial H}{\partial T}\frac{\partial T}{\partial t} = k\frac{\partial^2 T}{\partial x^2} \quad \text{in} \quad \Omega \tag{6.63}$$

We can rewrite the above equation as

$$c_{\text{eff}}\frac{\partial T}{\partial t} = k\frac{\partial^2 T}{\partial x^2} \tag{6.64}$$

where $c_{\text{eff}} = \partial H/\partial T$ is the effective heat capacity. This can be evaluated directly from Equation 6.62 as

$$c_{\text{eff}} = \rho c_s \quad (T < T_s)$$

$$c_{\text{eff}} = \rho c_f + \frac{L}{T_l - T_s} \quad (T_s < T < T_l)$$

$$c_{\text{eff}} = \rho c_l \quad (T > T_l) \tag{6.65}$$

Figure 6.13 shows the effective heat capacity variation with respect to temperature. As seen, the effective heat capacity will become infinitely high if the liquidus and solidus temperatures are close to each other.

In order to demonstrate the effective heat capacity method discussed above, a one-dimensional phase change problem is considered in the following example.

Example 6.7.1 *A phase change problem with an initial temperature of 0.0°C as shown in Figure 6.14 is subjected to a cooling temperature of −45.0°C at the left face and the right*

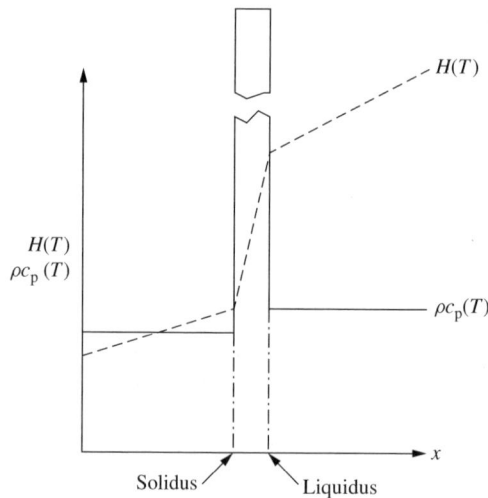

Figure 6.13　Variation of effective heat capacity and enthalpy across the solid–liquid interface

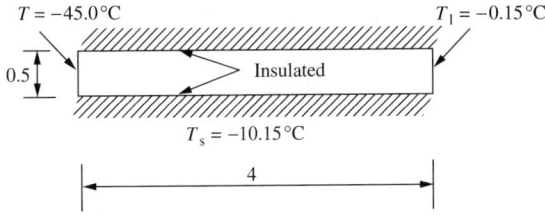

Figure 6.14 A one-dimensional solidification problem

side face is subjected to a liquidus temperature of $-0.15°C$. The solidus temperature is $-10.15°C$. Determine the temperature distribution with respect to time if the latent heat of solidification is 70.26, $\rho c_p = 1.0$ and $k = 1.0$. Draw the temperature variation at a distance of unity from the left side with respect to time.

The unstructured mesh used to solve this problem is shown in Figure 6.15(a). The temperature contours at a time of four units is shown in Figure 6.15(b) and the temperature variation at a point of unit length from the left face is shown in Figure 6.15(c). These results show a close agreement with existing results (Lewis et al. 1996).

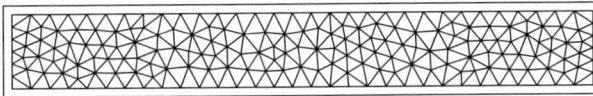

(a) Unstructured mesh, nodes: 202, elements: 328

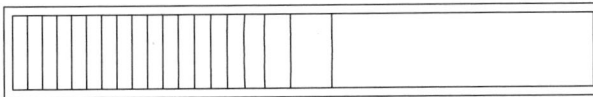

(b) Temperature distribution at $t = 4$

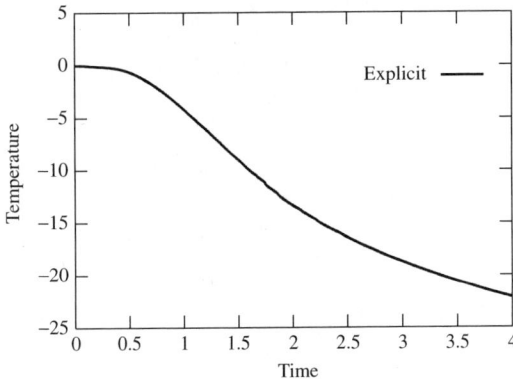

(c) Temperature distribution at a point
(1, 0.25) with respect to time

Figure 6.15 Solution for the phase change problem using the effective heat capacity method

6.8 Inverse Heat Conduction Problems

It is often difficult, or even impossible, to measure many quantities in certain heat transfer problems due to extreme conditions (Examples: heat flux on the surface of a heat shield of a re-entry vehicle, temperature inside a high temperature furnace, etc.). In some cases, obtaining experimental data is also very expensive. However, in order to accurately predict the temperature distribution using numerical methods, practical problems need appropriate information on the boundary. Even with a minimum of available data at any convenient location of the body, the finite element method can be constructed to determine the boundary conditions and the temperature distribution. This process is referred to as *inverse modelling* (Beck 1968; Ozisik 1968).

6.8.1 One-dimensional heat conduction

Consider a one-dimensional problem, as shown in Figure 6.16 (infinite wall), to demonstrate the concepts involved in an inverse heat conduction problem. The sensor is placed at the right hand surface of the insulated wall. The left side is assumed to be subjected to an unknown heat flux $q(t)$. The temperature measurements with respect to time are available at the sensor location. In addition to the temperature values at the sensor location, the known material properties are also valuable information.

The governing heat conduction equation for this type of problem is given as (for temperature-independent properties)

$$k\frac{\partial^2 T}{\partial x^2} = \rho c_p \frac{\partial T}{\partial t} \tag{6.66}$$

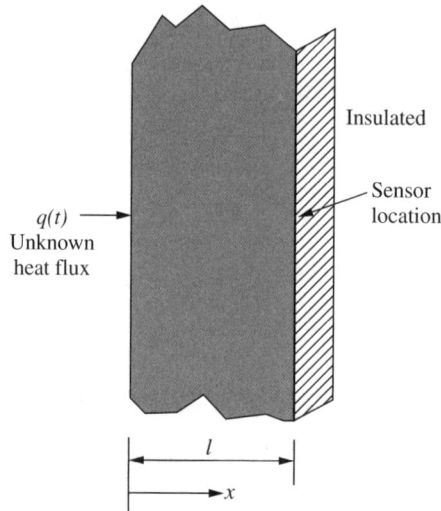

Figure 6.16   Heat conduction through a wall. Inverse problem

with

$$-k\frac{\partial T}{\partial x} = q(t) \quad \text{at} \quad x = 0 \tag{6.67}$$

$$k\frac{\partial T}{\partial x} = 0 \quad \text{at} \quad x = l \tag{6.68}$$

and

$$T = T_o(x) \quad \text{at} \quad t = 0 \tag{6.69}$$

where $q(t)$ is the unknown heat flux and $T_o(x)$ is the initial temperature of the body.
The known temperature values at the sensor location are given as

$$T(t_k, x_l) = U_{k,l} \tag{6.70}$$

where k varies between 1 and the total number of measured data at the sensor location (l) and t_k indicates the corresponding time. Introducing a sensitivity coefficient $Z_{k,i}^k$ as

$$T_{k,i} = T_{k,i}^* + Z_{k,i}^k(q_k - q_k^*) \tag{6.71}$$

where $T_{k,i}$ is the temperature at time t_k and location i, $T_{k,i}^*$ is the temperature calculated using $q(k) = q(k)^*$ in Equation 6.67 and $Z_{k,i}^k$ are the sensitivity coefficients. Note that we can write, using a Taylor series expansion,

$$T_{k,i} = T_{k,i}^* + \frac{\partial T_{k,i}}{\partial q_k}\bigg|_{q_k=q_k^*}(q_k - q_k^*) + \cdots \tag{6.72}$$

The above equation shows that

$$Z_{k,i}^k = \frac{\partial T_{k,i}}{\partial q_k} \tag{6.73}$$

In order to calculate the correct temperatures, the least squares error between the calculated and measured temperature values needs to be minimized, that is,

$$\sum_{i=1}^{I}(U_{k,i} - T_{k,i})^2 = 0 \tag{6.74}$$

where I is the number of sensors in the body. On substitution of Equation 6.71, into Equation 6.74, and rearranging, we get

$$q_k = q_k^* + \frac{\sum_{i=1}^{I}Z_{k,i}^k(U_{k,i} - T_{k,i}^*)}{\sum_{i=1}^{I}(Z_{k,i}^k)^2} \tag{6.75}$$

If we assume only one sensor in the field, the above equation is reduced to

$$q_k = q_k^* + \frac{Z_k^k(U_k - T_k^*)}{(Z_k^k)^2} \tag{6.76}$$

In practice, the above equation is difficult to use in order to obtain a smooth heat flux distribution. To arrive at such a smooth heat flux distribution, Beck (Beck 1968) suggested a procedure that has a certain number of future time steps (R) from the starting point, and for a one-sensor problem, this is given as follows:

$$q_k = q_k^* + \frac{\sum_{r=1}^{R}(U_{k+r-1} - T_{k+r-1}^*)Z_r^r}{\sum_{r=1}^{R}(Z_r^r)^2} \tag{6.77}$$

The calculation of the sensitivity coefficient is very important in the above equation. It is normally calculated by solving the following equation:

$$\rho c_p \frac{\partial Z}{\partial t} = k \frac{\partial^2 Z}{\partial x^2} \tag{6.78}$$

with

$$-k \frac{\partial Z}{\partial x} = 1 \quad \text{at} \quad x = 0 \tag{6.79}$$

$$k \frac{\partial Z}{\partial x} = 0 \quad \text{at} \quad x = l \tag{6.80}$$

and with an initial condition of $Z = 0$ at $t = 0$. Using the above procedure, the inverse heat conduction problem may be solved via the following steps.

(i) Assume $q_k^* = 0$ in the first time interval.

(ii) Calculate T_{k+r-1} for $r = 1, 2, \ldots, R$ (for all sensors) employing the finite element method and assumed heat flux at the left-hand side $q_k = q_k^*$ using Equations 6.66 to 6.69.

(iii) Calculate q_k from Equation 6.77.

(iv) Set $q_k^* = q_{k-1}$ and go to step (ii) and continue until convergence is achieved.

6.9   Summary

In this chapter, we have introduced the transient heat conduction problem and demonstrated solutions of such a problem via many numerical examples. However, the problems discussed in this chapter are only the 'tip of the iceberg'. We recommend that the readers formulate their own transient heat conduction problems and solve them using the transient computer programs available from the authors (see Chapter 10). For transient convection problems, the readers should refer to Chapters 7 and 9.

6.10   Exercise

Exercise 6.10.1 *A large block of steel with a thermal conductivity of 40 W/m°C and a thermal diffusivity of 1.5 × 10^{-5} m²/s is initially at a uniform temperature of 25°C. The surface* is exposed to (a) a heat flux of 3×10^5 W/m^2 and (b) a sudden rise in surface temperature of 200°C. Calculate the temperature at a depth of 1 cm after a time of 10 seconds for both cases. Verify the results with analytical results.

Exercise 6.10.2 A fin of length 1 cm is initially at the ambient temperature of 30°C. If the base temperature is suddenly raised to a temperature of 150°C and maintained at that value, determine the temperature distribution in the fin after 30 seconds if the thermal diffusivity of the fin material is 1×10^{-5} m^2/s. The heat transfer coefficient between the fin surface and the ambient is 100 W/m^2°C. The cross section of the fin is 6 mm by 5 mm.

Exercise 6.10.3 A short aluminium cylinder 2.5 cm in diameter and 5 cm long is initially at a uniform temperature of 100°C. It is suddenly subjected to a convection environment at 50°C and $h = 400$ W/m^2°C. Calculate the temperature at a radial position of 1 cm from outer surface and a distance of 0.5 cm from one end of the cylinder 10 seconds after exposure to the environment.

Exercise 6.10.4 A plane wall of thickness 4 mm has internal heat generation of 25 MW/m^3 with thermal properties of $k = 20$ W/m°C, $\rho = 8000$ kg/m^3 and specific heat $c_p = 500$ J/kg°C. It is initially at a uniform temperature of 50°C and is suddenly subjected to heat generation and a convective boundary condition as shown in Figure 6.17 Calculate the temperature at a location of 2 mm after 10 seconds.

Exercise 6.10.5 A stainless steel plate size 2 cm × 1 cm is surrounded by an insulating block as shown in Figure 6.18 and is initially at a uniform temperature of 40°C with a convection environment at 40°C. The plate is suddenly exposed to a radiant flux of 15 kW/m^2. Calculate the temperature at the centre of the top and bottom surfaces after 10 s. Take the properties of the stainless steel as $k = 18$ W/mK, $\rho = 8000$ kg/m^3, $c_p = 0.46$ kJ/kg°C, and $h = 30$ W/m^{2}K.

Figure 6.17   Plane wall discretization

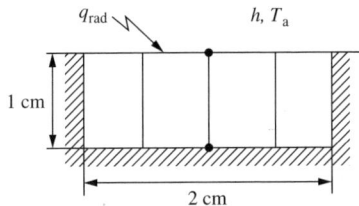

Figure 6.18   Stainless steel plate

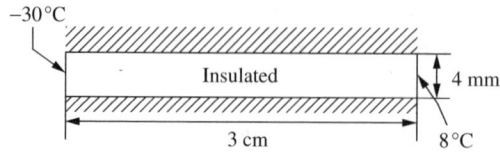

Figure 6.19   A phase change problem

Exercise 6.10.6 *A phase change problem with an initial temperature of $10°C$ is imposed with a cooling temperature of $-30°C$ at the left face, and the right face is subjected to a liquid temperature of $8°C$ as shown in Figure 6.19. The solidus temperature is $0°C$. Determine the temperature distribution with respect to time if the latent heat of solidification is 65.0, $\rho c_p = 1$ and $k = 1.0$. Draw the temperature variation at a distance of unity from the left side.*

Bibliography

Beck JV 1968 Surface heat flux determination using an integral method, *Nuclear Engineering Design*, **7**, 170–178.

Carslaw HS and Jaeger JC 1959 *Conduction of Heat in Solids*, Second Edition, Oxford University Press, Fairlawn, NJ.

Hirsch C 1988 *Numerical Computation of Internal and External Flows, Vol. 1, Fundamentals of Numerical Discretization*, Wiley & Sons, Chichester.

Holman JP 1989 *Heat Transfer*, McGraw-Hill, Singapore.

Lewis RW, Morgan K, Thomas HR and Seetharamu KN 1996 *Finite Element Methods in Heat Transfer Analysis*, John Wiley & Sons, Chichester.

Ozisik MN 1968 *Boundary Value Problems of Heat Conduction*, International Text Book Company, Scranton, PA.

7

Convection Heat Transfer

7.1 Introduction

In the previous six chapters, the conduction mode of heat transfer has been discussed in detail. Occasionally, convective heat transfer boundary conditions were discussed in these chapters whenever appropriate. However, little information on fluid flow characteristics was given in any of the previous chapters. In the present chapter, the heat transfer mechanism due to a fluid motion is discussed in detail. This method of heat transfer, which is caused by fluid motion, is referred to as *heat convection*.

The study of fluid motion (fluid dynamics) is an important subject that has wide application in many engineering disciplines. Several industries use computer-based fluid dynamics analysis (Computational Fluid Dynamics or CFD) tools for both design and analysis. For instance, aerospace applications, turbo-machines, weather forecasting, electronic cooling arrangements and flow in heat exchangers are merely a few examples. There has been a vast increase in the use of CFD tools in engineering industries in the last two decades, mainly because of an ever-increasing computing power. In the 1980s, a solution for a reasonably sized three-dimensional fluid dynamics problem was rarely possible on a personal computer (PC). However, now it is very common for researchers to solve reasonably sized fluid dynamics problems in three dimensions using such computers.

There are several books written on the topic of computational fluid dynamics, which include texts explaining the basic solution scheme underlying a successful CFD software (Cheung 2002; Donea and Huerta 2003; Fletcher 1988; Gresho and Sani 2000; Hirsch 1989; Lewis *et al.* 1996; Pironneau 1989; Zienkiewicz and Taylor 2000), or books on practical fluid dynamics calculations such as data structure and parallel computing (Löhner 2001). Several chapters could be written in the present text on the topic of CFD alone. However, our main interest is to give a practical introduction to the role of fluid dynamics in heat transport. It is intended that this chapter will give a good starting point to pursue a further education and/or research in fluid dynamics–assisted heat transport.

Fundamentals of the Finite Element Method for Heat and Fluid Flow   R. W. Lewis, P. Nithiarasu and K. N. Seetharamu
© 2004 John Wiley & Sons, Ltd   ISBNs: 0-470-84788-3 (HB); 0-470-84789-1 (PB)

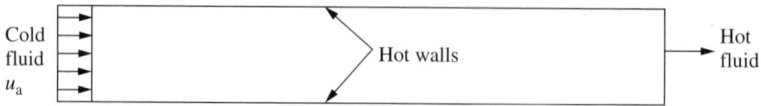

Figure 7.1   Flow and heat transport in a channel

7.1.1   Types of fluid-motion-assisted heat transport

The fluid-motion-assisted heat transfer (heat convection) may be classified into three different categories. In order to explain the different types, let us consider the fluid flow through
a two-dimensional channel as shown in Figure 7.1. The inlet to the channel is at the left
side and exit is at the right. Both the top and bottom walls of the channel are at higher
temperatures than the invading fluid. The mechanism here is that the fluid, which is at a
temperature lower than the wall temperature of the channel, comes into contact with the
wall and removes heat by convection. Although this process is termed as being convective,
there are aspects of the diffusion mode of heat transfer that dominate very close to the
hot walls.

It is obvious that flow with a higher incoming velocity will transport heat at a higher
rate. The flow rate is often characterized by a quantity called the *Reynolds number*, which
is defined as

$$Re = \frac{\rho_a u_a L}{\mu_a} \qquad (7.1)$$

where u_a is the average inlet velocity, L is a characteristic dimension, for example, the
width or height of the channel, ρ_a is a reference (inlet) density and μ_a is a reference (inlet)
dynamic viscosity of the fluid. If the Reynolds number is small and below a certain critical
value, the flow is laminar, and if it is above this critical number, then the flow becomes
turbulent. The critical Reynolds number for pipe and channel flows, based on the diameter
or height, is approximately 2000.

In Figure 7.1, if the flow is forced into the channel by means of an external device, for
example, a pump, then the convection process is referred to as *forced convection*, and the
Reynolds number is normally high (Jaluria 1986; Lewis *et al.* 1996, 1995b; Massarotti *et
al.* 1998; Minkowycz *et al.* 1988; Patnaik *et al.* 2001; Srinivas *et al.* 1994). In such situations, the fluid motion created by the density (or temperature) difference (buoyancy-driven
motion) is negligibly small as compared to the forced motion of the fluid. However, at low
and moderate Reynolds numbers, the motion created by the local density (or temperature)
differences in the fluid is comparable to that of the forced flow. A situation in which the
forced and density difference–driven motions are equally important is called *mixed convection* transport (Aung and Worku 1986a,b; Gowda *et al.* 1998). If the forced flow is
suddenly stopped and the fluid is stagnant inside the channel, then the fluid motion will
be entirely influenced by the local density (or temperature) differences until an equilibrium
state is reached, that is, no local differences in density or temperature are present. Such
a flow is often referred to as *natural, free or buoyancy-driven convection* (de Vahl Davis
1983; Jaluria 1986; Jaluria and Torrance 1986; Nithiarasu *et al.* 1998).

7.2 Navier–Stokes Equations

The mathematical model of any fundamental fluid dynamics problem is governed by the Navier–Stokes equations. These equations are important and represent the fluid as a continuum. The equations conserve mass, momentum and energy, and can be derived following either an integral or a differential approach. The integral form of the equations is derived using Reynolds Transport Theorem (RTT) and is discussed in many standard fluid mechanics texts (Shames 1982). The approach we follow in this book is the differential approach in which a differential control volume is considered in the fluid domain and a Taylor expansion is used to represent the variation of mass, momentum and energy.

7.2.1 Conservation of mass or continuity equation

The conservation of mass equation ensures that the total mass is conserved, or, in other words, the total mass of a fluid system is completely accounted for. In order to derive a general conservation of the mass equation, consider the differential control volume as shown in Figure 7.2. The reader can assume the control volume to be infinitesimal for a typical flow problem, such as flow in a channel (Figure 7.1), flow over a flat plate or the temperature (or density) difference driven circulation of air inside a room as shown in Figure 7.3.

Let us assume that the mass flux rate entering the control volume (Figure 7.2) is ρu_1 in the x_1 direction and ρu_2 in the x_2 direction. It is also assumed that there is no reaction or mass production within the fluid domain. The Taylor series expansion may be used to express the mass flux rate exiting the control volume as (refer to Figure 7.2)

$$(\rho u_1)_{x_1 + \Delta x_1} = (\rho u_1)_{x_1} + \frac{\Delta x_1}{1!} \frac{\partial (\rho u_1)}{\partial x_1} + \frac{\Delta x_1{}^2}{2!} \frac{\partial^2 (\rho u_1)}{\partial x_1^2} + \cdots. \qquad (7.2)$$

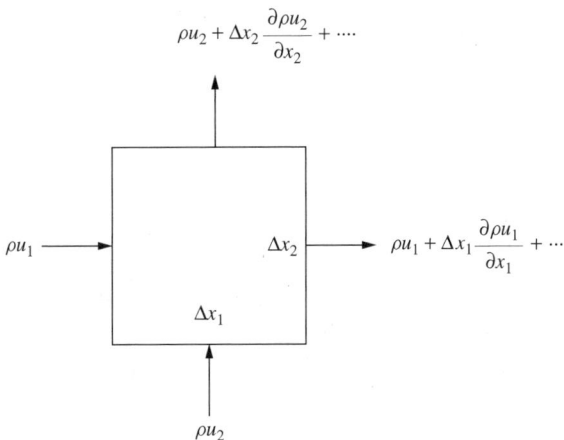

Figure 7.2   Infinitesimal control volume. Derivation of conservation of mass in a flow field

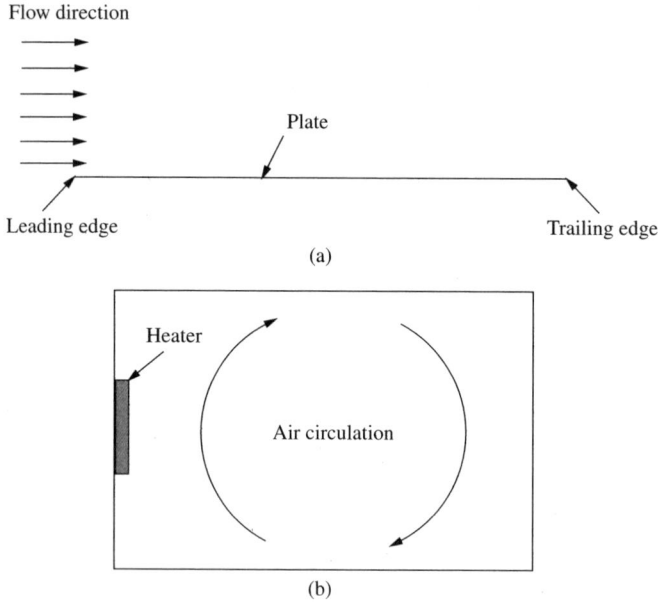

Figure 7.3   Forced flow over a flat plate and natural convection inside a room

in the x_1 direction and

$$(\rho u_2)_{x_2+\Delta x_2} = (\rho u_2)_{x_2} + \frac{\Delta x_2}{1!} \frac{\partial(\rho u_2)}{\partial x_2} + \frac{\Delta x_2{}^2}{2!} \frac{\partial^2(\rho u_2)}{\partial x_2^2} + \cdots . \tag{7.3}$$

in the x_2 direction. From an inspection of the control volume shown in Figure 7.2, we can write the difference between the total mass entering and exiting the control volume as

$$\Delta x_2 \left[(\rho u_1)_{x_1} - (\rho u_1)_{x_1+\Delta x_1} \right] = -\Delta x_2 \left[\frac{\Delta x_1}{1!} \frac{\partial(\rho u_1)}{\partial x_1} + \frac{\Delta x_1{}^2}{2!} \frac{\partial^2(\rho u_1)}{\partial x_1^2} + \cdots \right] \tag{7.4}$$

Similarly, in the x_2 direction

$$\Delta x_1 \left[(\rho u_2)_{x_2} - (\rho u_2)_{x_2+\Delta x_2} \right] = -\Delta x_1 \left[\frac{\Delta x_2}{1!} \frac{\partial(\rho u_2)}{\partial x_2} + \frac{\Delta x_2{}^2}{2!} \frac{\partial^2(\rho u_2)}{\partial x_2^2} + \cdots \right] \tag{7.5}$$

Note that the total mass is calculated as being the mass flux rate times the perpendicular area to the following regime. For instance, the total mass entering the control volume in the x_1 direction is $\Delta x_2 \times 1 \times \rho u_1$. A unit thickness is assumed in the x_3 direction.

Adding Equations 7.4 and 7.5 gives the total mass stored inside the control volume. Neglecting the second- and higher-order terms, the total mass stored inside the control volume is

$$-\Delta x_1 \Delta x_2 \left[\frac{\partial(\rho u_1)}{\partial x_1} + \frac{\partial(\rho u_2)}{\partial x_2} \right] \tag{7.6}$$

The above quantity, stored within the control volume, is equal to the rate of change of the total mass within the control volume, which is given as

$$\Delta x_1 \Delta x_2 \frac{\partial \rho}{\partial t} \tag{7.7}$$

We can therefore write

$$\Delta x_1 \Delta x_2 \frac{\partial \rho}{\partial t} = -\Delta x_1 \Delta x_2 \left[\frac{\partial(\rho u_1)}{\partial x_1} + \frac{\partial(\rho u_2)}{\partial x_2} \right] \tag{7.8}$$

or

$$\frac{\partial \rho}{\partial t} + \frac{\partial(\rho u_1)}{\partial x_1} + \frac{\partial(\rho u_2)}{\partial x_2} = 0 \tag{7.9}$$

The above equation is known as the equation of conservation of mass, or the continuity equation for two-dimensional flows. In three dimensions, the continuity equation is

$$\frac{\partial \rho}{\partial t} + \frac{\partial(\rho u_1)}{\partial x_1} + \frac{\partial(\rho u_2)}{\partial x_2} + \frac{\partial(\rho u_3)}{\partial x_3} = 0 \tag{7.10}$$

If the density is assumed to be constant, then the above equation is reduced to

$$\frac{\partial u_1}{\partial x_1} + \frac{\partial u_2}{\partial x_2} + \frac{\partial u_3}{\partial x_3} = 0 \tag{7.11}$$

Using vector notation, the above equation is written as (divergence-free velocity field)

$$\nabla . \mathbf{u} = 0 \tag{7.12}$$

or, using an indicial notation,

$$\frac{\partial u_i}{\partial x_i} = 0 \tag{7.13}$$

where $i = 1, 2$ for a two-dimensional case and $i = 1, 2, 3$ for three-dimensional flows.

7.2.2 Conservation of momentum

The conservation of momentum equation can be derived in a fashion similar to the conservation of mass equation. Here, the momentum equations are derived on the basis of the conservation of momentum principle, that is, the total force generated by the momentum transfer in each direction is balanced by the rate of change of momentum in each direction. The momentum equation has directional components and is therefore a vector equation. In order to derive the conservation of momentum equation, let us consider the control volume shown in Figure 7.4.

The momentum entering the control volume in the x_1 direction is given as

$$\rho u_1 \Delta x_2 u_1 = \rho u_1^2 \Delta x_2 \tag{7.14}$$

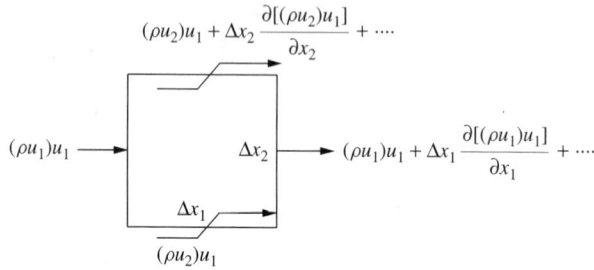

Figure 7.4 Infinitesimal control volume in a flow field. Derivation of conservation of momentum in x_1 direction. Rate of change of momentum

Since the momentum equation is a vector equation, the momentum in the x_1 direction will also have a contribution in the x_2 direction. The momentum entering the bottom face in the x_1 direction is

$$\rho u_2 \Delta x_2 u_1 = \rho u_1 u_2 \Delta x_1 \tag{7.15}$$

A Taylor expansion is employed to work out the x_1 momentum, leaving the control volume. In the x_1 direction, we have

$$\rho u_1^2 \Delta x_2 + \Delta x_2 \frac{\partial(\rho u_1^2)}{\partial x_1} \Delta x_1 \tag{7.16}$$

Similarly, the x_1 momentum leaving the x_2 direction (top surface) is

$$\rho u_1 u_2 \Delta x_1 + \Delta x_1 \frac{\partial(\rho u_1 u_2)}{\partial x_2} \Delta x_2 \tag{7.17}$$

Note that the second- and higher-order terms in the previous Taylor expansion are neglected. The rate of change of momentum within the control volume due to the x_1 component is written as

$$\Delta x_1 \Delta x_2 \frac{\partial(\rho u_1)}{\partial t} \tag{7.18}$$

The net momentum of the control volume is calculated as the 'momentum exiting the control volume − momentum entering the control volume + rate of change of the momentum, which is

$$\Delta x_1 \Delta x_2 \left[\frac{\partial(\rho u_1^2)}{\partial x_1} + \frac{\partial(\rho u_1 u_2)}{\partial x_2} + \frac{\partial(\rho u_1)}{\partial t} \right] \tag{7.19}$$

For equilibrium, the above net momentum should be balanced by the net force acting on the control volume. In order to derive the net force acting on the control volume, refer to Figure 7.5. From the figure, the total pressure force acting on the control volume in the x_1 direction is written as (positive in the positive x_1 direction and negative in the negative x_1 direction)

$$p \Delta x_2 - \left[p + \frac{\partial p}{\partial x_1} \Delta x_1 \right] \Delta x_2 = -\frac{\partial p}{\partial x_1} \Delta x_1 \Delta x_2 \tag{7.20}$$

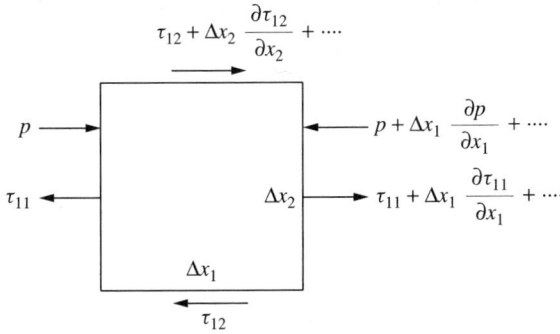

Figure 7.5   Infinitesimal control volume in a flow field. Derivation of conservation of momentum in x_1 direction. Viscous and pressure forces

Similarly, the total force due to the deviatoric stress (viscosity or friction) acting on the control volume in the x_1 direction is written as (see Figure 7.5)

$$\left[\tau_{11} + \frac{\partial \tau_{11}}{\partial x_1}\Delta x_1\right]\Delta x_2 - \tau_{11}\Delta x_2 + \left[\tau_{12} + \frac{\partial \tau_{12}}{\partial x_2}\Delta x_2\right]\Delta x_1 - \tau_{12}\Delta x_1 \tag{7.21}$$

Simplifying, we obtain the net force due to the deviatoric stress as

$$\frac{\partial \tau_{11}}{\partial x_1}\Delta x_1 \Delta x_2 + \frac{\partial \tau_{12}}{\partial x_2}\Delta x_2 \Delta x_2 \tag{7.22}$$

The total force acting on the control volume in the x_1 direction is

$$\Delta x_1 \Delta x_2 \left[-\frac{\partial p}{\partial x_1} + \frac{\partial \tau_{11}}{\partial x_1} + \frac{\partial \tau_{12}}{\partial x_2}\right] \tag{7.23}$$

As mentioned before, for equilibrium, the net momentum in the x_1 direction should be equal to the total force acting on the control volume in the x_1 direction, that is,

$$\Delta x_1 \Delta x_2 \left[\frac{\partial(\rho u_1^2)}{\partial x_1} + \frac{\partial(\rho u_1 u_2)}{\partial x_2} + \frac{\partial(\rho u_1)}{\partial t}\right] = \Delta x_1 \Delta x_2 \left[-\frac{\partial p}{\partial x_1} + \frac{\partial \tau_{11}}{\partial x_1} + \frac{\partial \tau_{12}}{\partial x_2}\right] \tag{7.24}$$

Simplifying, we obtain

$$\frac{\partial(\rho u_1)}{\partial t} + \frac{\partial(\rho u_1^2)}{\partial x_1} + \frac{\partial(\rho u_1 u_2)}{\partial x_2} = -\frac{\partial p}{\partial x_1} + \frac{\partial \tau_{11}}{\partial x_1} + \frac{\partial \tau_{12}}{\partial x_2} \tag{7.25}$$

Note that the external and body forces (buoyancy) are not included in the above force balance. In the above equations, the deviatoric stresses τ_{ij} are expressed in terms of the velocity gradients and dynamic viscosity as

$$\tau_{ij} = \mu \left(\frac{\partial u_i}{\partial x_j} + \frac{\partial u_j}{\partial x_i} - \frac{2}{3}\frac{\partial u_k}{\partial x_k}\delta_{ij}\right) \tag{7.26}$$

where δ_{ij} is the Kroneker delta, which is equal to unity if $i = j$ and equal to zero if $i \neq j$. From the previous expression, τ_{11} is expressed as

$$\tau_{11} = \mu \left(\frac{\partial u_1}{\partial x_1} + \frac{\partial u_1}{\partial x_1} - \frac{2}{3} \frac{\partial u_1}{\partial x_1} - \frac{2}{3} \frac{\partial u_2}{\partial x_2} \right) \tag{7.27}$$

Note that $i = j = 1$ in the above equation and $k = 1, 2$ for a two-dimensional flow. The above equation may be simplified as follows:

$$\tau_{11} = \mu \left(\frac{4}{3} \frac{\partial u_1}{\partial x_1} - \frac{2}{3} \frac{\partial u_2}{\partial x_2} \right) \tag{7.28}$$

Similarly, τ_{12} is

$$\tau_{12} = \mu \left(\frac{\partial u_1}{\partial x_2} + \frac{\partial u_2}{\partial x_1} \right) \tag{7.29}$$

Substituting Equations 7.28 and 7.29 into Equation 7.25, we obtain the x_1 component of the momentum equation as

$$\frac{\partial(\rho u_1)}{\partial t} + \frac{\partial(\rho u_1^2)}{\partial x_1} + \frac{\partial(\rho u_1 u_2)}{\partial x_2} =$$
$$- \frac{\partial p}{\partial x_1} + \frac{\partial}{\partial x} \left[\mu \left(\frac{4}{3} \frac{\partial u_1}{\partial x_1} - \frac{2}{3} \frac{\partial u_2}{\partial x_2} \right) \right]$$
$$+ \frac{\partial}{\partial x_2} \left[\mu \left(\frac{\partial u_2}{\partial x_1} + \frac{\partial u_1}{\partial x_2} \right) \right] \tag{7.30}$$

The momentum component in the x_2 direction can be derived by the following steps, which are similar to the derivation of the x_1 component of the momentum equation. The x_2 momentum equation is

$$\frac{\partial(\rho u_2)}{\partial t} + \frac{\partial(\rho u_1 u_2)}{\partial x_1} + \frac{\partial(\rho u_2^2)}{\partial x_2} =$$
$$- \frac{\partial p}{\partial x_2} + \frac{\partial}{\partial x_1} \left[\mu \left(\frac{\partial u_1}{\partial x_2} + \frac{\partial u_2}{\partial x_1} \right) \right]$$
$$+ \frac{\partial}{\partial x_2} \left[\mu \left(\frac{4}{3} \frac{\partial u_2}{\partial x_2} - \frac{2}{3} \frac{\partial u_1}{\partial x_1} \right) \right] \tag{7.31}$$

For a constant density flow (incompressible flow), the momentum equations can be further reduced by taking the density term out of the differential signs. In addition, substitution of the conservation of mass equation (Equation 7.11) into the momentum equation leads to a further simplification of the momentum equation. After simplification (see Appendix D for the detailed derivation), the momentum equations are

$$\rho \left(\frac{\partial u_1}{\partial t} + u_1 \frac{\partial u_1}{\partial x_1} + u_2 \frac{\partial u_1}{\partial x_2} \right) = - \frac{\partial p}{\partial x_1} + \mu \left[\frac{\partial^2 u_1}{\partial x_1^2} + \frac{\partial^2 u_1}{\partial x_2^2} \right] \tag{7.32}$$

in the x_1 direction and

$$\rho\left(\frac{\partial u_2}{\partial t} + u_1\frac{\partial u_2}{\partial x_1} + u_2\frac{\partial u_2}{\partial x_2}\right) = -\frac{\partial p}{\partial x_2} + \mu\left[\frac{\partial^2 u_2}{\partial x_1^2} + \frac{\partial^2 u_2}{\partial x_2^2}\right]$$ (7.33)

in the x_2 direction. In vector notation, the momentum equations can be written as

$$\rho\left[\frac{\partial \mathbf{u}}{\partial t} + \nabla.(\mathbf{u} \times \mathbf{u})\right] = \nabla.[-p\mathbf{I} + \tau]$$ (7.34)

or, in indicial form

$$\rho\left(\frac{\partial u_i}{\partial t} + u_j\frac{\partial u_i}{\partial x_j}\right) = -\frac{\partial p}{\partial x_i} + \mu\left(\frac{\partial^2 u_i}{\partial x_i^2}\right)$$ (7.35)

Note that the above equation is applicable in any dimension.

7.2.3 Energy equation

The energy equation can be derived by following a procedure similar to the momentum equation derivation. However, the difference here is that the temperature, or energy equation, is a scalar equation. In order to derive this equation, let us consider the control volume as shown in Figure 7.6. The energy convected into the control volume in the x_1 direction is

$$\rho c_p u_1 T \Delta x_2$$ (7.36)

Similarly, the energy convected into the control volume in the x_2 direction is

$$\rho c_p u_2 T \Delta x_1$$ (7.37)

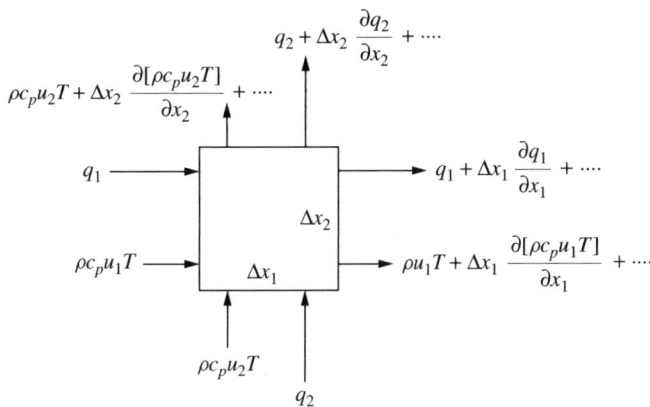

Figure 7.6 Infinitesimal control volume in a flow field. Derivation of conservation of energy

As before, a Taylor series expansion may be used to express the energy convected out of the control volume in both the x_1 and x_2 directions as

$$\rho c_p u_1 T \Delta x_2 + \rho c_p \frac{\partial (u_1 T)}{\partial x_1} \Delta x_1 \Delta x_2 \tag{7.38}$$

and

$$\rho c_p u_2 T \Delta x_1 + \rho c_p \frac{\partial (u_2 T)}{\partial x_2} \Delta x_2 \Delta x_1 \tag{7.39}$$

Note that the specific heat, c_p, and density, ρ, are assumed to be constants in deriving the above equation. The heat diffusion into and out of the control volume is also derived using the above approach. The heat diffusing into the domain in the x_1 direction (Fourier's law of heat conduction) is

$$\Delta x_2 q_1 = -k_{x_1} \frac{\partial T}{\partial x_1} \Delta x_2 \tag{7.40}$$

and the diffusion entering the control volume in the x_2 direction is

$$\Delta x_1 q_2 = -k_{x_2} \frac{\partial T}{\partial x_2} \Delta x_1 \tag{7.41}$$

Using a Taylor series expansion, the heat diffusing out of the control volume can be written as

$$-k_{x_1} \frac{\partial T}{\partial x_1} \Delta x_2 + \frac{\partial}{\partial x_1} \left(-k_{x_1} \frac{\partial T}{\partial x_1} \right) \Delta x_2 \Delta x_1 \tag{7.42}$$

in the x_1 direction and

$$-k_{x_2} \frac{\partial T}{\partial x_2} \Delta x_1 + \frac{\partial}{\partial x_2} \left(-k_{x_2} \frac{\partial T}{\partial x_2} \right) \Delta x_1 \Delta x_2 \tag{7.43}$$

in the x_2 direction. Finally, the rate of change of energy within the control volume is

$$\Delta x_1 \Delta x_2 \rho c_p \frac{\partial T}{\partial t} \tag{7.44}$$

Now, it is a simple matter of balancing the energy entering and exiting the control volume. The energy balance can be obtained as

'heat entering the control volume by convection + heat entering the control volume by diffusion = heat exiting the control volume by convection + heat exiting the control volume by diffusion + rate of change of energy within the control volume'.

Following the above heat balance approach and rearranging, we get

$$\frac{\partial T}{\partial t} + \frac{\partial (u_1 T)}{\partial x_1} + \frac{\partial (u_2 T)}{\partial x_2} = \frac{1}{\rho c_p} \left[\frac{\partial}{\partial x_1} \left(k_{x_1} \frac{\partial T}{\partial x_1} \right) + \frac{\partial}{\partial x_2} \left(k_{x_2} \frac{\partial T_2}{\partial x_2} \right) \right] \tag{7.45}$$

Differentiating the convection terms by parts and substituting Equation 7.11 (continuity) into Equation 7.45, we obtain the simplified energy equation in two dimensions as

$$\frac{\partial T}{\partial t} + u_1 \frac{\partial T}{\partial x_1} + u_2 \frac{\partial T}{\partial x_2} = \frac{1}{\rho c_p} \left[\frac{\partial}{\partial x_1} \left(k_{x_1} \frac{\partial T}{\partial x_1} \right) + \frac{\partial}{\partial x_2} \left(k_{x_2} \frac{\partial T}{\partial x_2} \right) \right] \qquad (7.46)$$

If the thermal conductivity is assumed to be constant and $k = k_{x_1} = k_{x_2}$, the energy equation is reduced to

$$\frac{\partial T}{\partial t} + u_1 \frac{\partial T}{\partial x_1} + u_2 \frac{\partial T}{\partial x_2} = \alpha \left(\frac{\partial^2 T}{\partial x_1^2} + \frac{\partial^2 T}{\partial x_2^2} \right) \qquad (7.47)$$

where $\alpha = k/\rho c_p$ is called the *thermal diffusivity*. The energy equation in vector form is

$$\frac{\partial T}{\partial t} + \mathbf{u}.\nabla T = \alpha \nabla^2 T \qquad (7.48)$$

and in indicial form

$$\frac{\partial T}{\partial t} + u_i \frac{\partial T}{\partial x_i} = \alpha \frac{\partial^2 T}{\partial x_i^2} \qquad (7.49)$$

The above equation is applicable in any space dimension.

7.3   Non-dimensional Form of the Governing Equations

In the previous section, we discussed the derivation of the Navier–Stokes equations for an incompressible fluid. In many heat transfer applications, it is often easy to generate data by non-dimensionalizing the equations using appropriate non-dimensional scales. To demonstrate the non-dimensional form of the governing equations, let us consider the following two-dimensional incompressible flow equations in dimensional form:

Continuity equation

$$\frac{\partial u_1}{\partial x_1} + \frac{\partial u_2}{\partial x_2} = 0 \qquad (7.50)$$

x_1 *momentum equation*

$$\frac{\partial u_1}{\partial t} + u_1 \frac{\partial u_1}{\partial x_1} + u_2 \frac{\partial u_1}{\partial x_2} = -\frac{1}{\rho} \frac{\partial p}{\partial x_1} + \nu \left(\frac{\partial^2 u_1}{\partial x_1^2} + \frac{\partial^2 u_1}{\partial x_2^2} \right) \qquad (7.51)$$

x_2 *momentum equation*

$$\frac{\partial u_2}{\partial t} + u_1 \frac{\partial u_2}{\partial x_1} + u_2 \frac{\partial u_2}{\partial x_2} = -\frac{1}{\rho} \frac{\partial p}{\partial x_2} + \nu \left(\frac{\partial^2 u_2}{\partial x_1^2} + \frac{\partial^2 u_2}{\partial x_2^2} \right) \qquad (7.52)$$

Energy equation

$$\frac{\partial T}{\partial t} + u_1 \frac{\partial T}{\partial x_1} + u_2 \frac{\partial T}{\partial x_2} = \alpha \left(\frac{\partial^2 T}{\partial x_1^2} + \frac{\partial^2 T}{\partial x_2^2} \right) \tag{7.53}$$

where $\nu = \mu/\rho$ is the kinematic viscosity. To obtain a set of non-dimensional equations, let us consider three different cases of convective heat transfer. We start with the forced convection problem followed by the 'natural' and 'mixed' convection problems. For each case, we discuss one set of non-dimensional scales. There are several other ways of scaling the equations. Some of these are discussed in the latter part of the chapter and others can be found in various other publications listed at the end of this chapter.

7.3.1 Forced convection

In forced convection problems, the following non-dimensional scales are normally employed:

$$x_1^* = \frac{x_1}{L}; \quad x_2^* = \frac{x_2}{L}; \quad t^* = \frac{t u_a}{L};$$

$$u_1^* = \frac{u_1}{u_a}; \quad u_2^* = \frac{u_2}{u_a}; \quad p^* = \frac{p}{\rho u_a^2};$$

$$T^* = \frac{T - T_a}{T_w - T_a} \tag{7.54}$$

Where $*$ indicates a non-dimensional quantity, L is a characteristic dimension, the subscript a indicates a constant reference value and T_w is a constant reference temperature, for example, wall temperature. The density ρ and viscosity μ of the fluid are assumed to be constant everywhere and equal to the inlet value.

Substitution of the above scales into the dimensional Equations 7.50 to 7.53 leads to the following non-dimensional form of the equations:

Continuity equation

$$\frac{\partial u_1^*}{\partial x_1^*} + \frac{\partial u_2^*}{\partial x_2^*} = 0 \tag{7.55}$$

x_1 momentum equation

$$\frac{\partial u_1^*}{\partial t^*} + u_1^* \frac{\partial u_1^*}{\partial x_1^*} + u_2^* \frac{\partial u_1^*}{\partial x_2^*} = -\frac{\partial p^*}{\partial x_1^*} + \frac{1}{Re} \left(\frac{\partial^2 u_1^*}{\partial x_1^{*2}} + \frac{\partial^2 u_1^*}{\partial x_2^{*2}} \right) \tag{7.56}$$

x_2 momentum equation

$$\frac{\partial u_2^*}{\partial t^*} + u_1^* \frac{\partial u_2^*}{\partial x_1^*} + u_2^* \frac{\partial u_2^*}{\partial x_2^*} = -\frac{\partial p^*}{\partial x_2^*} + \frac{1}{Re} \left(\frac{\partial^2 u_2^*}{\partial x_1^{*2}} + \frac{\partial^2 u_2^*}{\partial x_2^{*2}} \right) \tag{7.57}$$

Energy equation

$$\frac{\partial T^*}{\partial t^*} + u_1^* \frac{\partial T^*}{\partial x_1^*} + u_2^* \frac{\partial T^*}{\partial x_2^*} = \frac{1}{Re\,Pr} \left(\frac{\partial^2 T^*}{\partial x_1^{*2}} + \frac{\partial^2 T^*}{\partial x_2^{*2}} \right) \tag{7.58}$$

Where Re is the Reynolds number defined as

$$Re = \frac{u_a L}{v} \tag{7.59}$$

and Pr is the Prandtl number given as

$$Pr = \frac{v}{\alpha} \tag{7.60}$$

Once again, note that the density, kinematic viscosity and thermal conductivity are assumed to be constant in deriving the above non-dimensional equations. Appropriate changes will be necessary if an appreciable variation in these quantities occurs in a flow field. Another non-dimensional number, which is often employed in forced convection heat transfer calculations is the Peclet number and is given as $Pe = RePr = u_a L/\alpha$. For buoyancy-driven natural convection problems, a different type of non-dimensional scale is necessary if there are no reference velocity values available. The following subsection gives the natural convection scales:

7.3.2   Natural convection (Buoyancy-driven convection)

Natural convection is generated by the density difference induced by the temperature differences within a fluid system. Because of the small density variations present in these types of flows, a general incompressible flow approximation is adopted. In most buoyancy-driven convection problems, flow is generated by either a temperature variation or a concentration variation in the fluid system, which leads to local density differences. Therefore, in such flows, a body force term needs to be added to the momentum equations to include the effect of local density differences. For temperature-driven flows, the Boussinesq approximation is often employed, that is,

$$g(\rho - \rho_a) = g\beta(T - T_a) \tag{7.61}$$

where g is the acceleration due to gravity ($9.81 \, \text{m/s}^2$) and β is the coefficient of thermal expansion. The above body force term is added to the momentum equation in the gravity direction. In a normal situation (refer to Figure 7.7), the body force is added to the x_2 momentum (if the gravity direction is negative x_2), that is,

$$\frac{\partial u_2}{\partial t} + u_1 \frac{\partial u_2}{\partial x_1} + u_2 \frac{\partial u_2}{\partial x_2} = -\frac{1}{\rho}\frac{\partial p}{\partial x_2} + v\left(\frac{\partial^2 u_2}{\partial x_1^2} + \frac{\partial^2 u_2}{\partial x_2^2}\right) + g\beta(T - T_\infty) \tag{7.62}$$

In practice, the following non-dimensional scales are adopted for natural convection in the absence of a reference velocity value:

$$x_1^* = \frac{x_1}{L}; \quad x_2^* = \frac{x_2}{L}; \quad t^* = \frac{t\alpha}{L^2};$$

$$u_1^* = \frac{u_1 L}{\alpha}; \quad u_2^* = \frac{u_2 L}{\alpha}; \quad p^* = \frac{pL^2}{\rho\alpha^2};$$

$$T^* = \frac{T - T_a}{T_w - T_a} \tag{7.63}$$

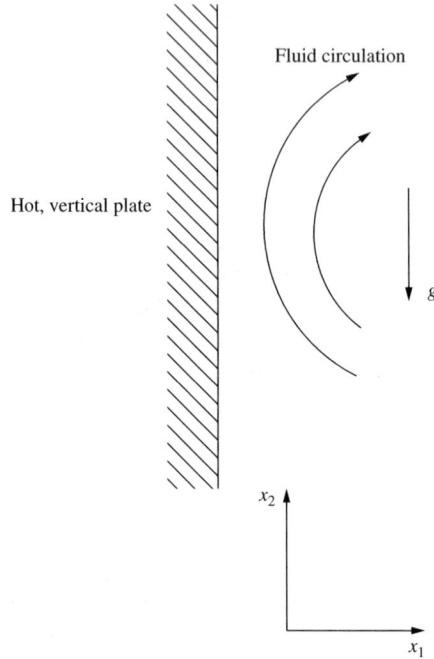

Figure 7.7   Natural convective flow near a hot, vertical plate

On introducing the above non-dimensional scales into the governing equations, we obtain the non-dimensional form of the equations as follows:

Continuity equation

$$\frac{\partial u_1^*}{\partial x_1^*} + \frac{\partial u_2^*}{\partial x_2^*} = 0 \tag{7.64}$$

x_1 *momentum equation*

$$\frac{\partial u_1^*}{\partial t^*} + u_1^* \frac{\partial u_1^*}{\partial x_1^*} + u_2^* \frac{\partial u_1^*}{\partial x_2^*} = -\frac{\partial p^*}{\partial x_1^*} + Pr \left(\frac{\partial^2 u_1^*}{\partial x_1^{*2}} + \frac{\partial^2 u_1^*}{\partial x_2^{*2}} \right) \tag{7.65}$$

x_2 *momentum equation*

$$\frac{\partial u_2^*}{\partial t^*} + u_1^* \frac{\partial u_2^*}{\partial x_1^*} + u_2^* \frac{\partial u_2^*}{\partial x_2^*} = -\frac{\partial p^*}{\partial x_2^*} + Pr \left(\frac{\partial^2 u_2^*}{\partial x_1^{*2}} + \frac{\partial^2 u_2^*}{\partial x_2^{*2}} \right) + Gr\, Pr^2 T^* \tag{7.66}$$

Energy equation

$$\frac{\partial T^*}{\partial t^*} + u_1^* \frac{\partial T^*}{\partial x_1^*} + u_2^* \frac{\partial T^*}{\partial x_2^*} = \left(\frac{\partial^2 T^*}{\partial x_1^{*2}} + \frac{\partial^2 T^*}{\partial x_2^{*2}} \right) \tag{7.67}$$

Where Gr is the Grashof number given as

$$Gr = \frac{g\beta \Delta T L^3}{\nu^2} \tag{7.68}$$

Often, another non-dimensional number called the *Rayleigh number* is used in the calculations. This is given as

$$Ra = Gr\,Pr = \frac{g\beta \Delta T L^3}{\nu\alpha} \tag{7.69}$$

On comparing the non-dimensional equations of natural and forced convection, it is easy to identify the differences. If we substitute $1/Pr$ in place of the Reynolds number for the forced convection equations, we revert to a natural convection scaling. Obviously, the extra buoyancy term needs to be added to appropriate component(s) of the momentum equation for natural convection flows.

7.3.3 Mixed convection

Mixed convection involves features from both forced and natural flow conditions. The buoyancy effects become comparable to the forced flow effects at small and moderate Reynolds numbers. Since the flow is partly forced, a reference velocity value is normally known (Example: velocity at the inlet of a channel). Therefore, non-dimensional scales of forced convection can be adopted here. However, in mixed convection problems, the buoyancy term needs to be added to the appropriate component of the momentum equation. If we replace $1/Pr$ with Re in the non-dimensional natural convection equations of the previous subsection, we obtain the non-dimensional equations for mixed convection flows. These equations are the same as for the forced convection flow problem except for the body force term, which will be added to the momentum equation in the gravity direction. The body force term is

$$\frac{Gr}{Re^2}T^* \tag{7.70}$$

Note that sometimes a non-dimensional parameter referred to as the *Richardson number* (Gr/Re^2) is also used in the literature.

7.4 The Transient Convection–diffusion Problem

An understanding of the fundamentals of the convection–diffusion equations is crucial in studying fluid-dynamics-assisted heat transfer. The equations governing the combined fluid flow and heat transfer mainly involve the convection and diffusion components. A typical scalar convection–diffusion equation may be written as

$$\frac{\partial \phi}{\partial t} + u_i \frac{\partial \phi}{\partial x_i} + \phi \frac{\partial u_i}{\partial x_i} - \frac{\partial}{\partial x_i}\left(k \frac{\partial \phi}{\partial x_i}\right) + Q = 0 \tag{7.71}$$

where ϕ is a scalar variable, k is a diffusion coefficient (thermal conductivity if $\phi = T$), u_i are the convection velocity components and Q is a source term. In the above equation, the first term is a transient term, the second and third terms are convection terms and the fourth term is the diffusion term. For a one-dimensional problem, the above equation is reduced to

$$\frac{\partial \phi}{\partial t} + u_1 \frac{\partial \phi}{\partial x_1} + \phi \frac{\partial u_1}{\partial x_1} - \frac{\partial}{\partial x_1} \left(k \frac{\partial \phi}{\partial x_1} \right) + Q = 0 \qquad (7.72)$$

If the convection velocity u_1 is assumed to be constant, we can rewrite Equation 7.72 as follows:

$$\frac{\partial \phi}{\partial t} + u_1 \frac{\partial \phi}{\partial x_1} - \frac{\partial}{\partial x_1} \left(k \frac{\partial \phi}{\partial x_1} \right) + Q = 0 \qquad (7.73)$$

A one-dimensional convection equation without a source term is obtained by neglecting the diffusion and source terms as follows:

$$\frac{\partial \phi}{\partial t} + u_1 \frac{\partial \phi}{\partial x_1} = 0 \qquad (7.74)$$

Note that an appropriate solution for the above equation is valid for any similar equations such as the energy equation.

7.4.1   Finite element solution to convection–diffusion equation

Unlike the conduction equation, a numerical solution for the convection equation has to deal with the convection part of the governing equation in addition to diffusion. For most conduction equations, the finite element solution is straightforward, as discussed in the previous chapters. However, if a similar Galerkin type approximation was used in the solution of convection equations, the results will be marked with spurious oscillations in space (see the example discussed later in this section) if certain parameters exceed a critical value (element Peclet number). This problem is not unique to finite elements as all other spatial discretization techniques have the same difficulties. In a finite difference formulation, the spatial oscillations are reduced, or suppressed, by a family of discretization methods called *upwinding schemes* (Fletcher 1988; Spalding 1972). In the finite element method, procedures such as Petrov–Galerkin (Zienkiewicz and Taylor 2000) and Streamline Upwind Petrov Galerkin (SUPG) (Brooks and Hughes 1982) are equivalent upwinding schemes with the specific purpose of eliminating spatial oscillations. In these methods, the basic shape function is modified to obtain the upwinding effect.

For time-dependent equations, however, a different kind of approach is followed. The finite difference Lax–Wendroff (Hirsch 1989) scheme has an equivalent in the finite element method, which is referred to as the *Taylor–Galerkin (TG) scheme* (Donea 1984). Another similar method, which is widely used, is known as the *Characteristic Galerkin (CG) scheme* (Zienkiewicz and Taylor 2000). For scalar variables, the CG and TG methods are identical (Löhner *et al.* 1984). In this book, we follow the Characteristic Galerkin (CG) approach to deal with spatial oscillations due to the discretization of the convection transport terms.

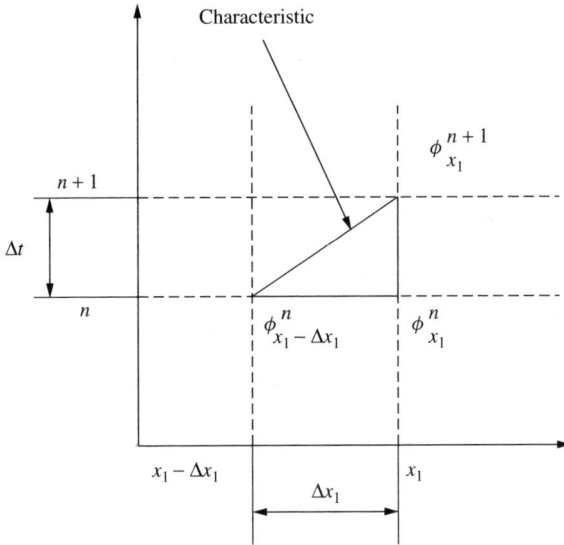

Figure 7.8 Characteristic in a space–time domain

In order to demonstrate the CG method, let us reconsider the simple convection–diffusion equation in one dimension, namely,

$$\frac{\partial \phi}{\partial t} + u_1 \frac{\partial \phi}{\partial x_1} - \frac{\partial}{\partial x_1}\left(k \frac{\partial \phi}{\partial x_1} \right) = 0 \qquad (7.75)$$

Let us consider a characteristic of the flow as shown in Figure 7.8 in the time–space domain. The incremental time period covered by the flow is Δt from the nth time level to the $n + 1$th time level and the incremental distance covered during this time period is Δx_1, that is, from $(x_1 - \Delta x_1)$ to x_1. If a moving coordinate is assumed along the path of the characteristic wave with a speed of u_1, the convection terms of Equation 7.75 disappear (as in a Lagrangian fluid dynamics approach). Although this approach eliminates the convection term responsible for spatial oscillation when discretized in space, the complication of a moving coordinate system x_1' is introduced, that is, Equation 7.75 becomes

$$\frac{\partial \phi}{\partial t}(x_1', t) - \frac{\partial}{\partial x_1'}\left(k \frac{\partial \phi}{\partial x_1'} \right) = 0 \qquad (7.76)$$

The semi-discrete form of the above equation can be written as

$$\frac{\phi^{n+1}|_{x_1} - \phi^n|_{x_1 - \Delta x_1}}{\Delta t} - \frac{\partial}{\partial x_1'}\left(k \frac{\partial \phi}{\partial x_1'} \right)^n \Big|_{x_1 - \Delta x_1} = 0 \qquad (7.77)$$

Note that the diffusion term is treated explicitly (a definition of explicit schemes has been given in Chapter 6 and later on in this chapter). It is possible to solve the above equation by adapting a moving coordinate strategy. However, a simple spatial Taylor series expansion in space avoids such a moving coordinate approach. With reference to Figure 7.8, we can write using a Taylor series expansion as follows:

$$\phi^n|_{x_1-\Delta x_1} = \phi^n|_{x_1} - \frac{\partial \phi}{\partial x_1}^n \frac{\Delta x_1}{1!} + \frac{\partial^2 \phi}{\partial x_1^2} \frac{\Delta x_1^2}{2!} - \cdots \tag{7.78}$$

Similarly, the diffusion term is expanded as

$$\frac{\partial}{\partial x_1'} \left(k \frac{\partial \phi}{\partial x_1'} \right)^n \Big|_{x_1-\Delta x_1} = \frac{\partial}{\partial x_1} \left(k \frac{\partial \phi}{\partial x_1} \right)^n \Big|_{x_1} - \frac{\partial}{\partial x_1} \left[\frac{\partial}{\partial x_1} \left(k \frac{\partial \phi}{\partial x_1} \right)^n \right] \Delta x \tag{7.79}$$

On substituting Equations 7.78 and 7.79 into Equation 7.77, we obtain (higher-order terms being neglected) the following expression:

$$\frac{\phi^{n+1} - \phi^n}{\Delta t} = -\frac{\Delta x}{\Delta t} \frac{\partial \phi}{\partial x_1}^n + \frac{\Delta x^2}{2\Delta t} \frac{\partial^2 \phi}{\partial x_1^2}^n + \frac{\partial}{\partial x_1} \left(k \frac{\partial \phi}{\partial x_1} \right)^n \tag{7.80}$$

In this case, all the terms are evaluated at the position x_1, and not at two positions as in Equation 7.77. If the flow velocity is u_1, we can write $\Delta x = u_1 \Delta t$. Substituting into Equation 7.80, we obtain the semi-discrete form as

$$\frac{\phi^{n+1} - \phi^n}{\Delta t} = -u_1 \frac{\partial \phi}{\partial x_1}^n + u_1^2 \frac{\Delta t}{2} \frac{\partial^2 \phi}{\partial x_1^2}^n + \frac{\partial}{\partial x_1} \left(k \frac{\partial \phi}{\partial x_1} \right)^n \tag{7.81}$$

By carrying out a Taylor series expansion (see Figure 7.8), the convection term reappears in the equation along with an additional second-order term. This second-order term acts as a smoothing operator that reduces the oscillations arising from the spatial discretization of the convection terms. The equation is now ready for spatial approximation.

The following linear spatial approximation of the scalar variable ϕ in space is used to approximate Equation 7.81:

$$\phi = N_i \phi_i + N_j \phi_j = [\mathbf{N}]\{\boldsymbol{\phi}\} \tag{7.82}$$

where $[\mathbf{N}]$ are the shape functions and subscripts i and j indicate the nodes of a linear element as shown in Figure 7.9. On employing the Galerkin weighting to Equation 7.81, we obtain

$$\int_\Omega [\mathbf{N}]^T \frac{\phi^{n+1} - \phi^n}{\Delta t} \, d\Omega + \int_\Omega [\mathbf{N}]^T \left(u_1 \frac{\partial \phi}{\partial x_1} \right)^n d\Omega$$

$$- \frac{\Delta t}{2} \int_\Omega [\mathbf{N}]^T \left(u_1^2 \frac{\partial^2 \phi}{\partial x_1^2} \right)^n d\Omega$$

$$- \int_\Omega [\mathbf{N}]^T \frac{\partial}{\partial x_1} \left(k \frac{\partial \phi}{\partial x_1} \right) d\Omega = 0 \tag{7.83}$$

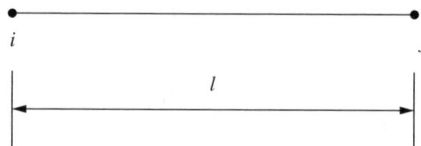

Figure 7.9   One-dimensional linear element

The above equation is equal to zero only if all the element contributions are assembled. For a domain with only one element, we can substitute

$$[\mathbf{N}]^T = \begin{bmatrix} N_i \\ N_j \end{bmatrix} \tag{7.84}$$

On substituting a linear spatial approximation for the variable ϕ, over elements as typified in Figure 7.9, into Equation 7.83, we get

$$\int_\Omega [\mathbf{N}]^T [\mathbf{N}] \frac{\{\phi^{n+1} - \phi^n\}}{\Delta t} \, d\Omega = -u_1 \int_\Omega [\mathbf{N}]^T \frac{\partial}{\partial x_1} ([\mathbf{N}]\{\phi\})^n \, d\Omega$$
$$+ \frac{\Delta t}{2} u_1^2 \int_\Omega [\mathbf{N}]^T \frac{\partial^2}{\partial x_1^2} ([\mathbf{N}]\{\phi\})^n \, d\Omega$$
$$+ \int_\Omega [\mathbf{N}]^T \frac{\partial^2}{\partial x_1^2} ([\mathbf{N}]\{\phi\})^n \, d\Omega \tag{7.85}$$

Before utilizing the linear integration formulae, we apply Green's lemma to some of the integrals in the above equation. Green's lemma is given as follows:

$$\int_\Omega \alpha \frac{\partial \beta}{\partial x_1} \, d\Omega = -\int_\Omega \frac{\partial \alpha}{\partial x_1} \beta \, d\Omega + \int_\Gamma \alpha \beta n_1 \, d\Gamma$$
$$\int_\Omega \alpha \frac{\partial \beta}{\partial x_2} \, d\Omega = -\int_\Omega \frac{\partial \alpha}{\partial x_2} \beta \, d\Omega + \int_\Gamma \alpha \beta n_2 \, d\Gamma \tag{7.86}$$

where n_1 and n_2 are the direction cosines of the outward normal $\mathbf{n}$, Ω is the domain and Γ is the domain boundary. The second-order derivatives can also be similarly expressed (see Appendix A). Applying Green's lemma to the second-order terms of Equation 7.85, we obtain

$$\int_\Omega [\mathbf{N}]^T [\mathbf{N}] \frac{\{\phi^{n+1}\} - \{\phi^n\}}{\Delta t} \, d\Omega = -u_1 \int_\Omega [\mathbf{N}]^T \frac{\partial}{\partial x_1} ([\mathbf{N}]\{\phi\})^n \, d\Omega$$
$$- \frac{\Delta t}{2} u_1^2 \int_\Omega \frac{\partial [\mathbf{N}]^T}{\partial x_1} \frac{\partial [\mathbf{N}]}{\partial x_1} \{\phi\} \, d\Omega$$
$$+ \frac{\Delta t}{2} u_1^2 \int_\Gamma [\mathbf{N}]^T \frac{\partial [\mathbf{N}]}{\partial x_1} \{\phi\} n_1 \, d\Gamma$$
$$- \int_\Omega \frac{\partial [\mathbf{N}]^T}{\partial x_1} k \frac{\partial [\mathbf{N}]}{\partial x_1} \{\phi\} \, d\Omega$$
$$+ \int_\Gamma [\mathbf{N}]^T k \frac{\partial [\mathbf{N}]}{\partial x_1} \{\phi\} n_1 \, d\Gamma \tag{7.87}$$

The first-order convection term can be integrated either directly or via Green's lemma. In this section, the convection term is integrated directly without applying Green's lemma. However, integration of the first derivatives by parts is useful for the solution of Navier–Stokes equations, as demonstrated in Section 7.6. It is now possible to apply a shortcut for the integration using the following formula:

$$\int_\Omega N_i^a N_j^b \, d\Omega = \frac{a!b!l}{(a+b+1)!} \tag{7.88}$$

and therefore derive the element matrices for all the terms in Equation 7.87. The term on the left-hand side for a single element is

$$\int_\Omega [\mathbf{N}]^T [\mathbf{N}] \frac{\{\phi^{n+1}\} - \{\phi^n\}}{\Delta t} \, d\Omega = \int_\Omega \begin{bmatrix} N_i \\ N_j \end{bmatrix} \begin{bmatrix} N_i & N_j \end{bmatrix} \left\{ \begin{array}{c} \dfrac{\phi_i^{n+1} - \phi_i^n}{\Delta t} \\ \dfrac{\phi_j^{n+1} - \phi_j^n}{\Delta t} \end{array} \right\} d\Omega$$

$$= \int_\Omega \begin{bmatrix} N_i^2 & N_i N_j \\ N_j N_i & N_j^2 \end{bmatrix} \left\{ \begin{array}{c} \dfrac{\phi_i^{n+1} - \phi_i^n}{\Delta t} \\ \dfrac{\phi_j^{n+1} - \phi_j^n}{\Delta t} \end{array} \right\} d\Omega$$

$$= \frac{l}{6} \begin{bmatrix} 2 & 1 \\ 1 & 2 \end{bmatrix} \left\{ \begin{array}{c} \dfrac{\phi_i^{n+1} - \phi_i^n}{\Delta t} \\ \dfrac{\phi_j^{n+1} - \phi_j^n}{\Delta t} \end{array} \right\}$$

$$= [\mathbf{M_e}] \frac{\Delta\{\phi\}}{\Delta t} \tag{7.89}$$

where $[\mathbf{M_e}]$ is the mass matrix. For a single element, the mass matrix is given as

$$[\mathbf{M_e}] = \frac{l}{6} \begin{bmatrix} 2 & 1 \\ 1 & 2 \end{bmatrix} \tag{7.90}$$

The above mass matrix for a single element will have to be utilized in an assembly procedure for a fluid domain containing many elements. In Equation 7.89

$$\frac{\Delta\{\phi\}}{\Delta t} = \left\{ \begin{array}{c} \dfrac{\phi_i^{n+1} - \phi_i^n}{\Delta t} \\ \dfrac{\phi_j^{n+1} - \phi_j^n}{\Delta t} \end{array} \right\} \tag{7.91}$$

In a similar fashion, all other terms can be integrated; for example, the convection term is given by

$$u_1 \int_\Omega [\mathbf{N}]^T \frac{\partial[\mathbf{N}]}{\partial x_1} \{\phi\}^n \, d\Omega = u_1 \int_\Omega \begin{bmatrix} N_i \\ N_j \end{bmatrix} \begin{bmatrix} \dfrac{\partial N_i}{\partial x_1} & \dfrac{\partial N_j}{\partial x_1} \end{bmatrix} \left\{ \begin{array}{c} \phi_i \\ \phi_j \end{array} \right\}^n d\Omega$$

$$= u_1 \begin{bmatrix} \dfrac{l}{2}\dfrac{\partial N_i}{\partial x_1} & \dfrac{l}{2}\dfrac{\partial N_j}{\partial x_1} \\ \dfrac{l}{2}\dfrac{\partial N_i}{\partial x_1} & \dfrac{l}{2}\dfrac{\partial N_j}{\partial x_1} \end{bmatrix} \left\{ \begin{array}{c} \phi_i \\ \phi_j \end{array} \right\}^n$$

$$= \frac{u_1}{2} \begin{bmatrix} -1 & 1 \\ -1 & 1 \end{bmatrix} \left\{ \begin{array}{c} \phi_i \\ \phi_j \end{array} \right\}^n$$

$$= [\mathbf{C_e}]\{\phi\}^n \tag{7.92}$$

where $[\mathbf{C_e}]$ is the elemental convection matrix, that is,

$$[\mathbf{C_e}] = \frac{u_1}{2}\begin{bmatrix} -1 & 1 \\ -1 & 1 \end{bmatrix} \tag{7.93}$$

The values of the derivatives of the shape functions are substituted in order to derive the above matrix. The diffusion term within the domain Ω is integrated as

$$\int_\Omega \frac{\partial[\mathbf{N}]^T}{\partial x_1} k \frac{\partial[\mathbf{N}]}{\partial x_1} d\Omega \{\phi\}^n = \int_\Omega \begin{bmatrix} \dfrac{\partial N_i}{\partial x_1} \\[2mm] \dfrac{\partial N_j}{\partial x_1} \end{bmatrix} k \begin{bmatrix} \dfrac{\partial N_i}{\partial x_1} & \dfrac{\partial N_j}{\partial x_1} \end{bmatrix} \begin{Bmatrix} \phi_i \\ \phi_j \end{Bmatrix}^n d\Omega$$

$$= \int_\Omega k \begin{bmatrix} \dfrac{\partial N_i}{\partial x_1}\dfrac{\partial N_i}{\partial x_1} & \dfrac{\partial N_i}{\partial x_1}\dfrac{\partial N_j}{\partial x_1} \\[3mm] \dfrac{\partial N_j}{\partial x_1}\dfrac{\partial N_i}{\partial x_1} & \dfrac{\partial N_j}{\partial x_1}\dfrac{\partial N_j}{\partial x_1} \end{bmatrix} \begin{Bmatrix} \phi_i \\ \phi_j \end{Bmatrix}^n d\Omega$$

$$= \frac{k}{l}\begin{bmatrix} 1 & -1 \\ -1 & 1 \end{bmatrix}\begin{Bmatrix} \phi_i \\ \phi_j \end{Bmatrix}^n$$

$$= [\mathbf{K_{1e}}]\{\phi\}^n \tag{7.94}$$

where $[\mathbf{K_{1e}}]$ is the elemental diffusion matrix, that is,

$$[\mathbf{K_{1e}}] = \frac{k}{l}\begin{bmatrix} 1 & -1 \\ -1 & 1 \end{bmatrix} \tag{7.95}$$

The characteristic Galerkin term within the domain Ω is integrated as

$$u_1^2 \frac{\Delta t}{2}\int_\Omega \frac{\partial[\mathbf{N}]^T}{\partial x_1}\frac{\partial[\mathbf{N}]}{\partial x_1}\{\phi\}^n d\Omega = u_1^2 \frac{\Delta t}{2}\int_\Omega \begin{bmatrix} \dfrac{\partial N_i}{\partial x_1} \\[2mm] \dfrac{\partial N_j}{\partial x_1} \end{bmatrix}\begin{bmatrix} \dfrac{\partial N_i}{\partial x_1} & \dfrac{\partial N_j}{\partial x_1} \end{bmatrix}\begin{Bmatrix} \phi_i \\ \phi_j \end{Bmatrix}^n d\Omega$$

$$= u_1^2 \frac{\Delta t}{2}\int_\Omega \begin{bmatrix} \dfrac{\partial N_i}{\partial x_1}\dfrac{\partial N_i}{\partial x_1} & \dfrac{\partial N_i}{\partial x_1}\dfrac{\partial N_j}{\partial x_1} \\[3mm] \dfrac{\partial N_j}{\partial x_1}\dfrac{\partial N_i}{\partial x_1} & \dfrac{\partial N_j}{\partial x_1}\dfrac{\partial N_j}{\partial x_1} \end{bmatrix}\begin{Bmatrix} \phi_i \\ \phi_j \end{Bmatrix} d\Omega$$

$$= u_1^2 \frac{\Delta t}{2}\frac{1}{l}\begin{bmatrix} 1 & -1 \\ -1 & 1 \end{bmatrix}\begin{Bmatrix} \phi_i \\ \phi_j \end{Bmatrix}^n$$

$$= [\mathbf{K_{2e}}]\{\phi\}^n \tag{7.96}$$

where $[\mathbf{K_{2e}}]$ is a stabilization matrix,

$$[\mathbf{K_{2e}}] = u_1^2 \frac{\Delta t}{2}\frac{1}{l}\begin{bmatrix} 1 & -1 \\ -1 & 1 \end{bmatrix} \tag{7.97}$$

The boundary term from the diffusion operator is integrated by assuming that i is a boundary node, as follows:

$$\int_\Gamma [N]^T k \frac{\partial [N]}{\partial x_1} \{\phi\}^n \, d\Gamma = \int_\Gamma \begin{bmatrix} N_i \\ 0 \end{bmatrix} k \begin{bmatrix} \frac{\partial N_i}{\partial x_1} & \frac{\partial N_j}{\partial x_1} \end{bmatrix} \begin{Bmatrix} \phi_i \\ \phi_j \end{Bmatrix}^n \, d\Gamma$$

$$= \int_\Gamma k \begin{bmatrix} N_i \frac{\partial N_i}{\partial x_1} & N_i \frac{\partial N_j}{\partial x_1} \\ 0 & 0 \end{bmatrix} \begin{Bmatrix} \phi_i \\ \phi_j \end{Bmatrix}^n \, d\Gamma$$

$$= k \begin{bmatrix} -\frac{1}{l} & \frac{1}{l} \\ 0 & 0 \end{bmatrix} \begin{Bmatrix} \phi_i \\ \phi_j \end{Bmatrix}^n$$

$$= \{f_{1e}\} \tag{7.98}$$

where $\{f_{1e}\}$ is the forcing vector due to the diffusion term, that is,

$$\{f_{1e}\} = k \begin{Bmatrix} -\dfrac{\phi_i}{l} + \dfrac{\phi_j}{l} \\ 0 \end{Bmatrix}^n \tag{7.99}$$

The boundary integral from the characteristic Galerkin term is integrated, again by assuming that i is a boundary node, as

$$\int_\Gamma u_1^2 \frac{\Delta t}{2} [N]^T \frac{\partial [N]}{\partial x_1} \{\phi\}^n \, d\Gamma = u_1^2 \frac{\Delta t}{2} \int_\Gamma \begin{bmatrix} N_i \\ 0 \end{bmatrix} \begin{bmatrix} \frac{\partial N_i}{\partial x_1} & \frac{\partial N_j}{\partial x_1} \end{bmatrix} \begin{Bmatrix} \phi_i \\ \phi_j \end{Bmatrix}^n \, d\Gamma$$

$$= u_1^2 \frac{\Delta t}{2} \int_\Gamma \begin{bmatrix} N_i \frac{\partial N_i}{\partial x_1} & N_i \frac{\partial N_j}{\partial x_1} \\ 0 & 0 \end{bmatrix} \begin{Bmatrix} \phi_i \\ \phi_j \end{Bmatrix}^n \, d\Gamma$$

$$= u_1^2 \frac{\Delta t}{2} \begin{bmatrix} -\frac{1}{l} & \frac{1}{l} \\ 0 & 0 \end{bmatrix} \begin{Bmatrix} \phi_i \\ \phi_j \end{Bmatrix}^n$$

$$= \{f_{2e}\} \tag{7.100}$$

where $\{f_{2e}\}$ is the forcing vector due to the stabilization term

$$\{f_{2e}\} = u_1^2 \frac{\Delta t}{2} \begin{Bmatrix} -\dfrac{\phi_i}{l} + \dfrac{\phi_j}{l} \\ 0 \end{Bmatrix}^n \tag{7.101}$$

The forcing vectors are formulated by assuming that the node i is a boundary node. Because of the opposite signs of the outward normals at the interface between any two elements within the domain, these forcing vector terms vanish for all nodes other than the boundary nodes. The remaining terms will have a value only at the domain boundaries. Also, the boundary terms due to the CG stabilizing operator (Equation 7.101) can be neglected during the calculations without any loss in accuracy.

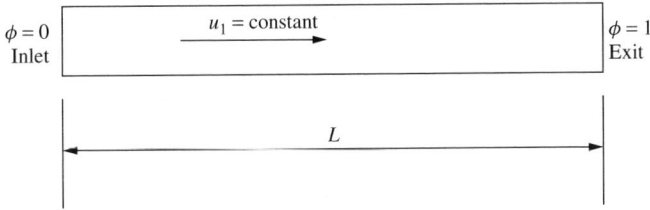

Figure 7.10   One-dimensional convection–diffusion problems

For a one-dimensional domain with more than one element, all the matrices and vectors need to be assembled in order to obtain the global matrices. Once assembled, the discretized one-dimensional equation becomes

$$[\mathbf{M}]\frac{\Delta\{\boldsymbol{\phi}\}}{\Delta t} = -[\mathbf{C}]\{\phi\}^n - [\mathbf{K}_1]\{\phi\}^n - [\mathbf{K}_2]\{\phi\}^n + \{\mathbf{f}_1\}^n + \{\mathbf{f}_2\}^n \qquad (7.102)$$

Let us now consider a simple one-dimensional convection problem, as given in Figure 7.10, to demonstrate the effect of a discretization with and without the CG scheme.

The scalar variable value at the inlet is $\phi = 0$, and at the exit its value is 1.0. This scalar variable is transported in the direction of the velocity as shown in Figure 7.10. Note that the convection velocity u_1 is constant. The element Peclet number for this problem is defined as

$$Pe = \frac{u_1 h}{2k} \qquad (7.103)$$

where h is the element size in the flow direction, which, in one dimension is the local element length. Figure 7.11 shows the comparison between a solution with the CG discretization scheme and one without it. Only two Peclet numbers are shown in these diagrams to demonstrate the spatial oscillations without the CG discretization. As seen, both discretizations give no spatial oscillations at a Pe value of unity. However, at a Pe value of 1.5, the CG discretization is accurate and stable, while the discretization without the CG term becomes oscillatory. The exact solution to this problem is given as follows (Brooks and Hughes 1982):

$$\phi = \frac{1 - e^{\frac{u_1 x_1}{k}}}{1 - e^{\frac{u_1 L}{k}}} \qquad (7.104)$$

In this equation, L is the total length of the domain and x_1 is the local length of the domain.

7.4.2   Extension to multi-dimensions

The extension of the characteristic Galerkin scheme to a multi-dimensional scalar convection-diffusion equation is straightforward and follows the previous procedure as discussed for a one-dimensional case. The two-dimensional convection–diffusion equation

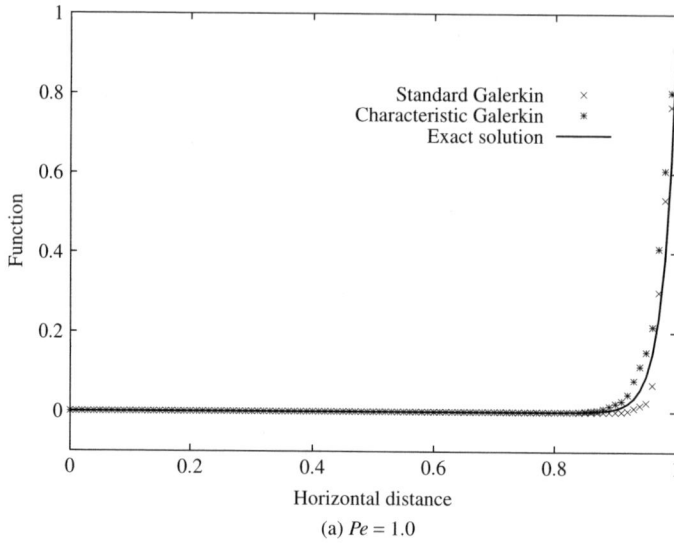

(a) $Pe = 1.0$

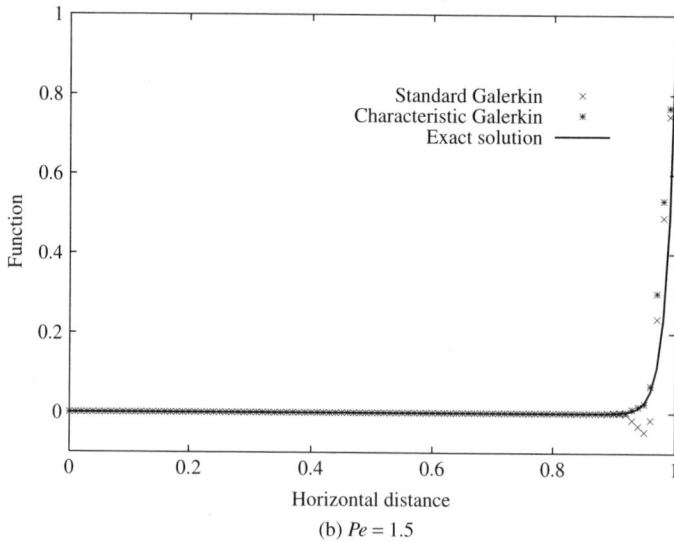

(b) $Pe = 1.5$

Figure 7.11 Spatial variation of a function, ϕ, in one-dimensional space for different element Peclet numbers

without the source term is

$$\frac{\partial \phi}{\partial t} + u_1 \frac{\partial \phi}{\partial x_1} + u_2 \frac{\partial \phi}{\partial x_2} = \frac{\partial}{\partial x_1}\left(k\frac{\partial \phi}{\partial x_1}\right) + \frac{\partial}{\partial x_1}\left(k\frac{\partial \phi}{\partial x_2}\right) \tag{7.105}$$

The convection velocity components u_1 and u_2 are assumed to be constant in deriving this equation. Applying the characteristic Galerkin procedure to the above equation, we obtain

$$\frac{\phi^{n+1} - \phi^n}{\Delta t} = -u_1 \frac{\partial \phi}{\partial x_1}^n - u_2 \frac{\partial \phi}{\partial x_2}^n$$

$$+ \frac{\partial}{\partial x_1} \left(k \frac{\partial \phi}{\partial x_1} \right)^n + \frac{\partial}{\partial x_1} \left(k \frac{\partial \phi}{\partial x_2} \right)^n$$

$$+ u_1 \frac{\Delta t}{2} \frac{\partial}{\partial x_1} \left[u_1 \frac{\partial \phi}{\partial x_1} + u_2 \frac{\partial \phi}{\partial x_2} \right]^n$$

$$+ u_2 \frac{\Delta t}{2} \frac{\partial}{\partial x_2} \left[u_1 \frac{\partial \phi}{\partial x_1} + u_2 \frac{\partial \phi}{\partial x_2} \right]^n \qquad (7.106)$$

The standard Galerkin approximation can now be employed for solving the above equation. Assuming a linear variation of ϕ within an element as indicated in Figure 7.12, we can express the variation of ϕ as

$$\phi = N_i \phi_1 + N_j \phi_j + N_k \phi_k = [\mathbf{N}]\{\boldsymbol{\phi}\} \qquad (7.107)$$

Employing the Galerkin weighting, we obtain

$$\int_\Omega [\mathbf{N}]^T \frac{\phi^{n+1} - \phi^n}{\Delta t} \, d\Omega = - \int_\Omega [\mathbf{N}]^T u_1 \frac{\partial \phi}{\partial x_1}^n \, d\Omega - \int_\Omega [\mathbf{N}]^T u_2 \frac{\partial \phi}{\partial x_2}^n \, d\Omega$$

$$+ \int_\Omega [\mathbf{N}]^T \frac{\partial}{\partial x_1} \left(k \frac{\partial \phi}{\partial x_1} \right)^n \, d\Omega$$

$$+ \int_\Omega [\mathbf{N}]^T \frac{\partial}{\partial x_2} \left(\frac{\partial \phi}{\partial x_2} \right)^n \, d\Omega$$

$$+ \frac{\Delta t}{2} u_1 \int_\Omega [\mathbf{N}]^T \frac{\partial}{\partial x_1} \left[u_1 \frac{\partial \phi}{\partial x_1} + u_2 \frac{\partial \phi}{\partial x_2} \right]^n \, d\Omega$$

$$+ \frac{\Delta t}{2} u_2 \int_\Omega [\mathbf{N}]^T \frac{\partial}{\partial x_2} \left[u_1 \frac{\partial \phi}{\partial x_1} + u_2 \frac{\partial \phi}{\partial x_2} \right]^n \, d\Omega \quad (7.108)$$

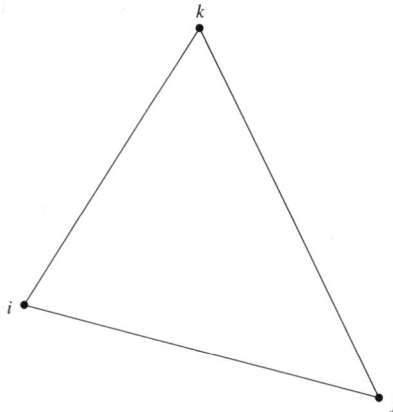

Figure 7.12   Two-dimensional linear triangular element

The above equation is valid globally. On substituting the global spatial approximation for the scalar variable ϕ into the above equation, we obtain

$$\int_\Omega [\mathbf{N}]^T [\mathbf{N}] \frac{\{\phi\}^{n+1} - \{\phi\}^n}{\Delta t} \, d\Omega = -u_1 \int_\Omega [\mathbf{N}]^T \frac{\partial [\mathbf{N}]}{\partial x_1} \{\phi\}^n \, d\Omega - u_2 \int_\Omega [\mathbf{N}]^T \frac{\partial [\mathbf{N}]}{\partial x_2} \{\phi\}^n \, d\Omega$$

$$+ \int_\Omega [\mathbf{N}]^T \frac{\partial}{\partial x_1} \left(k \frac{\partial [\mathbf{N}]}{\partial x_1} \right) \{\phi\}^n \, d\Omega$$

$$+ \int_\Omega [\mathbf{N}]^T \frac{\partial}{\partial x_2} \left(k \frac{\partial [\mathbf{N}]}{\partial x_2} \right) \{\phi\}^n \, d\Omega$$

$$+ \frac{\Delta t}{2} u_1 \int_\Omega \left[\frac{\partial}{\partial x_1} \left(u_1 \frac{\partial [\mathbf{N}]}{\partial x_1} \{\phi\}^n + u_2 \frac{\partial [\mathbf{N}]}{\partial x_2} \{\phi\}^n \right) \right] d\Omega$$

$$+ \frac{\Delta t}{2} u_2 \int_\Omega \left[\frac{\partial}{\partial x_2} \left(u_1 \frac{\partial [\mathbf{N}]}{\partial x_1} \{\phi\}^n + u_2 \frac{\partial [\mathbf{N}]}{\partial x_2} \{\phi\}^n \right) \right] d\Omega$$

$$\tag{7.109}$$

The above equation is valid only if all the element contributions in a finite element domain are assembled. The elemental matrices are derived by applying the following formula for integration over linear triangular elements:

$$\int_\Omega N_i^a N_j^b N_k^c \, d\Omega = \frac{a! \, b! \, c! \, 2A}{(a+b+c+2)!} \tag{7.110}$$

and for the line integral

$$\int_\Gamma N_i^a N_i^b N_k^c \, d\Gamma = \frac{a! \, b! \, c! \, \Gamma}{(a+b+c+1)!} \tag{7.111}$$

where A is the area of a triangular element and Γ is the length of a boundary edge. Applying the above formulae, we obtain the element characteristic equations as follows:

The mass matrix is

$$[\mathbf{M_e}] = \int_\Omega [\mathbf{N}]^T [\mathbf{N}] \, d\Omega = \frac{A}{12} \begin{bmatrix} 2 & 1 & 1 \\ 1 & 2 & 1 \\ 1 & 1 & 2 \end{bmatrix} \tag{7.112}$$

The convection matrix is

$$[\mathbf{C_e}] = \int_\Omega [\mathbf{N}]^T \left(u_1 \frac{\partial [\mathbf{N}]}{\partial x_1} + u_2 \frac{\partial [\mathbf{N}]}{\partial x_2} \right) d\Omega$$

$$= \frac{u_1}{6} \begin{bmatrix} b_i & b_j & b_k \\ b_i & b_j & b_k \\ b_i & b_j & b_k \end{bmatrix} + \frac{u_2}{6} \begin{bmatrix} c_i & c_j & c_k \\ c_i & c_j & c_k \\ c_i & c_j & c_k \end{bmatrix} \tag{7.113}$$

where

$$b_i = y_j - y_k; \quad c_i = x_k - x_j$$

$$b_j = y_k - y_i; \quad c_j = x_i - x_k$$

$$b_k = y_i - y_j; \quad c_k = x_j - x_i \tag{7.114}$$

As before, the diffusion term can be integrated after applying Green's lemma. The diffusion matrix for the elements inside the domain is

$$[\mathbf{K_{1e}}] = \int_{\Omega} \left(\frac{\partial [\mathbf{N}]^T}{\partial x_1} k \frac{\partial [\mathbf{N}]}{\partial x_1} + \frac{\partial [\mathbf{N}]^T}{\partial x_2} k \frac{\partial [\mathbf{N}]}{\partial x_2} \right) d\Omega$$

$$= \frac{k}{4A} \begin{bmatrix} b_i^2 & b_i b_j & b_i b_k \\ b_j b_i & b_j^2 & b_j b_k \\ b_k b_i & b_k b_j & b_k^2 \end{bmatrix} + \frac{k}{4A} \begin{bmatrix} c_i^2 & c_i c_j & c_i c_k \\ c_j c_i & c_j^2 & c_j c_k \\ c_k c_i & c_k c_j & c_k^2 \end{bmatrix} \qquad (7.115)$$

The stabilization matrix is

$$[\mathbf{K_{2e}}] = u_1 \frac{\Delta t}{2} \left[\int_{\Omega} u_1 \frac{\partial [\mathbf{N}]^T}{\partial x_1} \frac{\partial [\mathbf{N}]}{\partial x_1} d\Omega + \int_{\Omega} u_2 \frac{\partial [\mathbf{N}]^T}{\partial x_1} \frac{\partial [\mathbf{N}]}{\partial x_2} d\Omega \right]$$

$$+ u_2 \frac{\Delta t}{2} \left[\int_{\Omega} u_1 \frac{\partial [\mathbf{N}]^T}{\partial x_2} \frac{\partial [\mathbf{N}]}{\partial x_1} d\Omega + \int_{\Omega} u_2 \frac{\partial [\mathbf{N}]^T}{\partial x_2} \frac{\partial [\mathbf{N}]}{\partial x_2} d\Omega \right]$$

$$= \frac{u_1}{4A} \frac{\Delta t}{2} \begin{bmatrix} u_1 b_i^2 + u_2 b_i c_i & u_1 b_i b_j + u_2 b_i c_j & u_1 b_i b_k + u_2 b_i c_k \\ u_1 b_j b_i + u_2 b_j c_i & u_1 b_j^2 + u_2 b_j c_j & u_1 b_j b_k + u_2 b_j c_k \\ u_1 b_k b_i + u_2 b_k c_i & u_1 b_k b_j + u_2 b_k c_j & u_1 b_k^2 + u_2 b_k c_k \end{bmatrix}$$

$$+ \frac{u_2}{4A} \frac{\Delta t}{2} \begin{bmatrix} u_1 c_i b_i + u_2 c_i^2 & u_1 c_i b_j + u_2 c_i c_j & u_1 c_i b_k + u_2 c_i c_k \\ u_1 c_j b_i + u_2 c_j c_i & u_1 c_j b_j + u_2 c_j^2 & u_1 c_j b_k + u_2 c_j c_k \\ u_1 c_k b_i + u_2 c_k c_i & u_1 c_k b_j + u_2 c_k c_j & u_1 c_k b_k + u_2 c_k^3 \end{bmatrix} \quad (7.116)$$

The forcing vectors along the boundary edges are (assuming ij as the boundary edge)

$$[\mathbf{f_{1e}}] = k \int_{\Gamma} \begin{bmatrix} N_i \\ N_j \\ 0 \end{bmatrix} \begin{bmatrix} \frac{\partial N_i}{\partial x_1} & \frac{\partial N_j}{\partial x_1} & \frac{\partial N_k}{\partial x_1} \end{bmatrix} \{\phi\}^n d\Gamma n_1$$

$$+ k \int_{\Gamma} \begin{bmatrix} N_i \\ N_j \\ 0 \end{bmatrix} \begin{bmatrix} \frac{\partial N_i}{\partial x_2} & \frac{\partial N_j}{\partial x_2} & \frac{\partial N_k}{\partial x_2} \end{bmatrix} \{\phi\} d\Gamma n_2$$

$$= \frac{\Gamma}{4A} k \begin{bmatrix} b_i \phi_i + b_j \phi_j + b_k \phi_k \\ b_i \phi_i + b_j \phi_j + b_k \phi_k \\ 0 \end{bmatrix} n_1$$

$$+ \frac{\Gamma}{4A} k \begin{bmatrix} c_i \phi_i + c_j \phi_j + c_k \phi_k \\ c_i \phi_i + c_j \phi_j + c_k \phi_k \\ 0 \end{bmatrix} n_2 \qquad (7.117)$$

$$[\mathbf{f_{2e}}] = u_1 \frac{\Delta t}{2} \int_{\Gamma} u_1 \begin{bmatrix} N_i \\ N_j \\ 0 \end{bmatrix} \begin{bmatrix} \frac{\partial N_i}{\partial x_2} & \frac{\partial N_j}{\partial x_2} & \frac{\partial N_k}{\partial x_2} \end{bmatrix} \{\phi\}^n$$

$$+ u_1 \frac{\Delta t}{2} \int_{\Gamma} u_2 \begin{bmatrix} N_i \\ N_j \\ 0 \end{bmatrix} \begin{bmatrix} \frac{\partial N_i}{\partial x_2} & \frac{\partial N_j}{\partial x_2} & \frac{\partial N_k}{\partial x_2} \end{bmatrix} \{\phi\}^n d\Gamma n_1$$

$$+ u_2 \frac{\Delta t}{2} \int_\Gamma u_1 \begin{bmatrix} N_i \\ N_j \\ 0 \end{bmatrix} \begin{bmatrix} \dfrac{\partial N_i}{\partial x_1} & \dfrac{\partial N_j}{\partial x_1} & \dfrac{\partial N_k}{\partial x_1} \end{bmatrix} \{\phi\}^n \, d\Gamma n_2$$

$$+ u_2 \frac{\Delta t}{2} \int_\Gamma u_2 \begin{bmatrix} N_i \\ N_j \\ 0 \end{bmatrix} \begin{bmatrix} \dfrac{\partial N_i}{\partial x_2} & \dfrac{\partial N_j}{\partial x_2} & \dfrac{\partial N_k}{\partial x_2} \end{bmatrix} \{\phi\}^n \, d\Gamma n_2$$

$$= \frac{u_1}{2A} \frac{\Delta t}{2} \frac{\Gamma}{2} \begin{bmatrix} u_1(b_i\phi_i + b_j\phi_j + b_k\phi_k) + u_2(c_i\phi_i + c_j\phi_j + c_k\phi_k) \\ u_1(b_i\phi_i + b_j\phi_j + b_k\phi_k) + u_2(c_i\phi + c_j\phi_j + c_k\phi_k) \\ 0 \end{bmatrix}^n n_1$$

$$+ \frac{u_2}{2A} \frac{\Delta t}{2} \frac{\Gamma}{2} \begin{bmatrix} u_1(b_i\phi_i + b_j\phi_j + b_k\phi_k) + u_2(c_i\phi_i + c_j\phi_j + c_k\phi_k) \\ u_1(b_i\phi_i + b_j\phi_j + b_k\phi_k) + u_2(c_i\phi + c_j\phi_j + c_k\phi_k) \\ 0 \end{bmatrix}^n n_2$$

$$(7.118)$$

The assembled equation for a two-dimensional analysis takes a form similar to the one-dimensional Equation 7.102. Once again, the boundary terms from Equation 7.118 may be neglected in the calculations.

7.5 Stability Conditions

The stability conditions for a given time discretization may be derived using a Von Neumann or Fourier analysis for either the convection- or the convection–diffusion equations. However, for more complicated equations such as the Navier–Stokes equations, the derivation of the stability limit is not straightforward. A detailed discussion on stability criteria is not within the scope of this book and readers are asked to refer to the relevant text books and papers for details (Hirsch 1989; Zienkiewicz and Codina 1995). A stability analysis will give some idea about the time-step restrictions of any numerical scheme.

In general, for fluid dynamics problems, the time-step magnitude is controlled by two wave speeds. The first one is due to the convection velocity and the second to the real diffusion introduced by the equations. In the case of a convection–diffusion equation, the convection velocity is $\sqrt{u_i u_i}$, which is $\sqrt{u_1^2 + u_2^2} = |\mathbf{u}|$. The diffusion velocity is $2k/h$ where h is the local element size. The time-step restrictions are calculated as the ratio of the local element size and the local wave speed. It is therefore correct to write that the time step is calculated as

$$\Delta t = \min(\Delta t_c, \Delta t_d) \qquad (7.119)$$

where Δt_c and Δt_d are the convection and diffusion time-step limits respectively, which are

$$\Delta t_c = \frac{h}{|\mathbf{u}|}$$

$$\Delta t_d = \frac{h^2}{2k} \qquad (7.120)$$

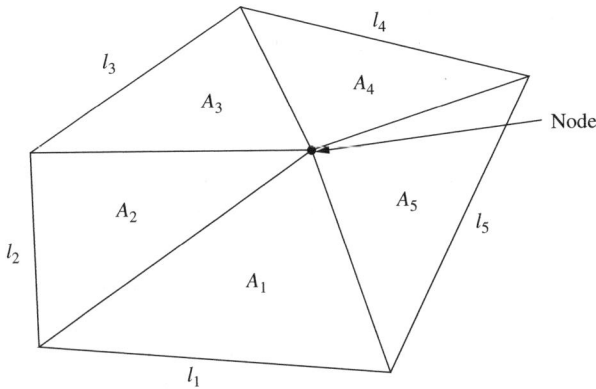

Figure 7.13   Two-dimensional linear triangular element

Often, it may be necessary to multiply the time-step Δt by a safety factor due to different methods of element size calculations. A simple procedure to calculate the element size in two dimensions is

$$h = \min\left(\frac{2Area_i}{l_i}\right), i = 1, \text{number of elements connected to the node} \qquad (7.121)$$

where $Area_i$ are the area of the elements connected to the node and l_i are the length of the opposite sides as shown in Figure 7.13. For the node shown in this figure, the local element size is calculated as

$$h = \min(A_1/l_1, A_2/l_2, A_3/l_3, A_4/l_4, A_5/l_5) \qquad (7.122)$$

In three dimensions, the term $2Area_i$ is replaced by $3Volume_i$ and l_i is replaced by the area opposite the node in question.

7.6   Characteristic-based Split (CBS) Scheme

It is essential to understand the characteristic Galerkin procedure, discussed in the previous section for the convection–diffusion equation, in order to apply the concept to solve the real convection equations. Unlike the convection–diffusion equation, the momentum equation, which is part of a set of heat convection equations, is a vector equation. A direct extension of the CG scheme to solve the momentum equation is difficult. In order to apply the characteristic Galerkin approach to the momentum equations, we have to introduce two steps. In the first step, the pressure term from the momentum equation will be dropped and an intermediate velocity field will be calculated. In the second step, the intermediate velocities will be corrected. This two-step procedure for the treatment of the momentum equations has two advantages. The first advantage is that without the pressure terms, each component of the momentum equation is similar to that of a convection–diffusion equation and the CG procedure can be readily applied. The second advantage is that removing the pressure term from the momentum equations enhances the pressure stability and allows the use of arbitrary interpolation functions for both velocity and pressure. In other words, the well-known Babuska–Brezzi condition is satisfied. Owing to the split introduced in the equations, the method is referred to as the *Characteristic Based Split* (CBS) scheme.

The CG procedure may be applied to the individual momentum components without removing the pressure term, provided the pressure term is treated as a source term. However, such a procedure will lose the advantages mentioned in the previous paragraph.

For more mathematical details, readers are directed to earlier publications on the method (Zienkiewicz and Codina 1995; Zienkiewicz and Taylor 2000) and for recent developments, references (Nithiarasu 2003; Zienkiewicz et al. 1999) are recommended. In order to apply the CG procedure, the governing equations in two dimensions (note that body forces are not included for simplicity) may be written as follows:

Continuity equation

$$\frac{\partial u_1}{\partial x_1} + \frac{\partial u_2}{\partial x_2} = 0 \tag{7.123}$$

x_1 *momentum equation*

$$\frac{\partial u_1}{\partial t} + u_1 \frac{\partial u_1}{\partial x_1} + u_2 \frac{\partial u_1}{\partial x_2} = -\frac{1}{\rho} \frac{\partial p}{\partial x_1} + \nu \left(\frac{\partial^2 u_1}{\partial x_1^2} + \frac{\partial^2 u_1}{\partial x_2^2} \right) \tag{7.124}$$

x_2 *momentum equation*

$$\frac{\partial u_2}{\partial t} + u_1 \frac{\partial u_2}{\partial x_1} + u_2 \frac{\partial u_2}{\partial x_2} = -\frac{1}{\rho} \frac{\partial p}{\partial x_2} + \nu \left(\frac{\partial^2 u_2}{\partial x_1^2} + \frac{\partial^2 u_2}{\partial x_2^2} \right) \tag{7.125}$$

Energy equation

$$\frac{\partial T}{\partial t} + u_1 \frac{\partial T}{\partial x_1} + u_2 \frac{\partial T}{\partial x_2} = \alpha \left(\frac{\partial^2 T}{\partial x_1^2} + \frac{\partial^2 T}{\partial x_2^2} \right) \tag{7.126}$$

From the governing equations, it is obvious that the application of the CG scheme is not straightforward. However, by implementing the following steps, it is possible to obtain a solution to the convection heat transfer equation.

Step 1 Intermediate velocity or momentum field: This step is carried out by removing the pressure terms from Equations 7.124 and 7.125. The intermediate velocity component equations, in their semi-discrete form, are

intermediate x_1 momentum equation

$$\frac{\tilde{u}_1 - u_1^n}{\Delta t} + u_1 \frac{\partial u_1}{\partial x_1}^n + u_2 \frac{\partial u_1}{\partial x_2}^n = \nu \left(\frac{\partial^2 u_1}{\partial x_1^2} + \frac{\partial^2 u_1}{\partial x_2^2} \right)^n \tag{7.127}$$

intermediate x_2 momentum equation

$$\frac{\tilde{u}_2 - u_2^n}{\Delta t} + u_1 \frac{\partial u_2}{\partial x_1}^n + u_2 \frac{\partial u_2}{\partial x_2}^n = \nu \left(\frac{\partial^2 u_2}{\partial x_1^2} + \frac{\partial^2 u_2}{\partial x_2^2} \right)^n \tag{7.128}$$

where $\tilde{u}_1$ and $\tilde{u}_2$ are the intermediate momentum variables. It is obvious that the CG scheme can now be applied, as the above equations are very similar to the convection–diffusion equations of the previous section. If the CG procedure is applied to the above equations, a semi-discrete from of the equations is obtained, namely,

intermediate x_1 momentum equation

$$\frac{\tilde{u}_1 - u_1{}^n}{\Delta t} = -u_1 \frac{\partial u_1}{\partial x_1}{}^n - u_2 \frac{\partial u_1}{\partial x_2}{}^n + v \left(\frac{\partial^2 u_1}{\partial x_1^2} + \frac{\partial^2 u_1}{\partial x_2^2} \right)^n$$

$$+ u_1 \frac{\Delta t}{2} \frac{\partial}{\partial x_1} \left[u_1 \frac{\partial u_1}{\partial x_1}{}^n + u_2 \frac{\partial u_1}{\partial x_2}{}^n \right]$$

$$+ u_2 \frac{\Delta t}{2} \frac{\partial}{\partial x_2} \left[u_1 \frac{\partial u_1}{\partial x_1}{}^n + u_2 \frac{\partial u_1}{\partial x_2}{}^n \right] \tag{7.129}$$

intermediate x_2 momentum equation

$$\frac{\tilde{u}_2 - u_2{}^n}{\Delta t} = -u_1 \frac{\partial u_2}{\partial x_1}{}^n - u_2 \frac{\partial u_2}{\partial x_2}{}^n + v \left(\frac{\partial^2 u_2}{\partial x_1^2} + \frac{\partial^2 u_2}{\partial x_2^2} \right)^n$$

$$+ u_1 \frac{\Delta t}{2} \frac{\partial}{\partial x_1} \left[u_1 \frac{\partial u_2}{\partial x_1}{}^n + u_2 \frac{\partial u_2}{\partial x_2}{}^n \right]$$

$$+ u_2 \frac{\Delta t}{2} \frac{\partial}{\partial x_2} \left[u_1 \frac{\partial u_2}{\partial x_1}{}^n + u_2 \frac{\partial u_2}{\partial x_2}{}^n \right] \tag{7.130}$$

Step 2 Pressure calculation: The pressure field is calculated from a pressure equation of the Poisson type. The pressure equation is derived from the fact that the intermediate velocities at the first step need to be corrected. If the pressure terms are not removed from the momentum equations, then the correct velocities are obtained, but with the loss of some advantages. If the semi-discrete form of the momentum equations are written without removing the pressure terms, then

semi-discrete x_1 momentum equation

$$\frac{u_1{}^{n+1} - u_1{}^n}{\Delta t} = -u_1 \frac{\partial u_1}{\partial x_1}{}^n - u_2 \frac{\partial u_1}{\partial x_2}{}^n + v \left(\frac{\partial^2 u_1}{\partial x_1^2} + \frac{\partial^2 u_1}{\partial x_2^2} \right)^n - \frac{1}{\rho} \frac{\partial p}{\partial x_1}{}^n$$

$$+ u_1 \frac{\Delta t}{2} \frac{\partial}{\partial x_1} \left[u_1 \frac{\partial u_1}{\partial x_1}{}^n + u_2 \frac{\partial u_1}{\partial x_2}{}^n + \frac{1}{\rho} \frac{\partial p}{\partial x_1}{}^n \right]$$

$$+ u_2 \frac{\Delta t}{2} \frac{\partial}{\partial x_2} \left[u_1 \frac{\partial u_1}{\partial x_1}{}^n + u_2 \frac{\partial u_1}{\partial x_2}{}^n + \frac{1}{\rho} \frac{\partial p}{\partial x_1}{}^n \right] \tag{7.131}$$

semi-discrete x_2 momentum equation

$$\frac{u_2{}^{n+1} - u_2{}^n}{\Delta t} = -u_1 \frac{\partial u_2}{\partial x_1}{}^n - u_2 \frac{\partial u_2}{\partial x_2}{}^n + \nu \left(\frac{\partial^2 u_2}{\partial x_1^2} + \frac{\partial^2 u_2}{\partial x_2^2} \right)^n - \frac{1}{\rho} \frac{\partial p}{\partial x_2}{}^n$$

$$+ u_1 \frac{\Delta t}{2} \frac{\partial}{\partial x_1} \left[u_1 \frac{\partial u_2}{\partial x_1}{}^n + u_2 \frac{\partial u_2}{\partial x_2}{}^n + \frac{1}{\rho} \frac{\partial p}{\partial x_2}{}^n \right]$$

$$+ u_2 \frac{\Delta t}{2} \frac{\partial}{\partial x_2} \left[u_1 \frac{\partial u_2}{\partial x_1}{}^n + u_2 \frac{\partial u_2}{\partial x_2}{}^n + \frac{1}{\rho} \frac{\partial p}{\partial x_2}{}^n \right] \qquad (7.132)$$

The real velocity field may be directly obtained if the above equations are utilized. Subtracting Equation 7.129 from 7.131 and 7.130 from 7.132 results in the following two equations:

$$\frac{u_1^{n+1} - \tilde{u}_1}{\Delta t} = -\frac{1}{\rho} \frac{\partial p}{\partial x_1}{}^n + u_1 \frac{\Delta t}{2} \frac{\partial}{\partial x_1} \left(\frac{1}{\rho} \frac{\partial p}{\partial x_1} \right)^n + u_2 \frac{\Delta t}{2} \frac{\partial}{\partial x_2} \left(\frac{1}{\rho} \frac{\partial p}{\partial x_1} \right)^n$$

$$\frac{u_2^{n+1} - \tilde{u}_2}{\Delta t} = -\frac{1}{\rho} \frac{\partial p}{\partial x_2}{}^n + u_1 \frac{\Delta t}{2} \frac{\partial}{\partial x_1} \left(\frac{1}{\rho} \frac{\partial p}{\partial x_1} \right)^n + u_2 \frac{\Delta t}{2} \frac{\partial}{\partial x_2} \left(\frac{1}{\rho} \frac{\partial p}{\partial x_2} \right)^n \qquad (7.133)$$

It is obvious that if the pressure terms can be calculated from another source, the intermediate velocities of Step 1 can be corrected using Equation 7.133. However, an independent pressure equation is required in order to substitute the pressure values into the above equation. In order to do this, u_i^{n+1} terms have to be eliminated from the above equation. This can be done via the continuity equation if we differentiate the first equation with respect to x_1 and the second equation with respect to x_2 and adding these together, that is, (neglecting third-order terms)

$$\frac{\partial u_1^{n+1}}{\partial x_1} + \frac{\partial u_2^{n+1}}{\partial x_2} - \frac{\partial \tilde{u}_1}{\partial x_1} - \frac{\partial \tilde{u}_2}{\partial x_2} = -\frac{\Delta t}{\rho} \left(\frac{\partial^2 p}{\partial x_1^2} + \frac{\partial^2 p}{\partial x_2^2} \right)^n \qquad (7.134)$$

Note that from the continuity equation

$$\frac{\partial u_1^{n+1}}{\partial x_1} + \frac{\partial u_2^{n+1}}{\partial x_2} = 0 \qquad (7.135)$$

On substituting the above equation into Equation 7.134, we obtain the pressure equation as follows:

$$\frac{1}{\rho} \left(\frac{\partial^2 p}{\partial x_1^2} + \frac{\partial^2 p}{\partial x_2^2} \right)^n = \frac{1}{\Delta t} \left(\frac{\partial \tilde{u}_1}{\partial x_1} + \frac{\partial \tilde{u}_2}{\partial x_2} \right) \qquad (7.136)$$

It should be noted that there are no transient or convection terms present in the above equation. Although this equation does not require any special treatment in order to stabilize the oscillations, the absence of a transient term leads to a compulsory implicit treatment solution procedure. In other words, a matrix solution method is necessary in order to obtain a solution for the above equation. However, it is possible to introduce an artificial compressibility formulation to avoid the implicit treatment of pressure. This will be discussed in a later section.

It has been stated in the literature that, even though the pressure terms in Equation 7.136 need to be treated implicitly, the scheme is really an explicit one. However, in our own publications, the scheme is referred to as being semi-implicit because the implicit solution to the pressure equation is used in the second step.

Step 3 Velocity or momentum correction: The velocity correction has already been derived in the previous step (Equation 7.133). This involves the pressure and intermediate velocity field, and is written as

$$\frac{u_1^{n+1} - \tilde{u}_1}{\Delta t} = -\frac{1}{\rho}\frac{\partial p}{\partial x_1}^n + u_1 \frac{\partial}{\partial x_1}\left(\frac{1}{\rho}\frac{\partial p}{\partial x_1}\right)^n + u_2 \frac{\partial}{\partial x_2}\left(\frac{1}{\rho}\frac{\partial p}{\partial x_1}\right)^n$$

$$\frac{u_2^{n+1} - \tilde{u}_2}{\Delta t} = -\frac{1}{\rho}\frac{\partial p}{\partial x_2}^n + u_1 \frac{\partial}{\partial x_1}\left(\frac{1}{\rho}\frac{\partial p}{\partial x_1}\right)^n + u_2 \frac{\partial}{\partial x_2}\left(\frac{1}{\rho}\frac{\partial p}{\partial x_2}\right)^n \qquad (7.137)$$

The higher-order terms in the above equations may be neglected as these terms have very little influence on the velocity correction.

Step 4 Temperature calculation: Applying the CG procedure to the temperature equation, we get

$$\frac{T^{n+1} - T^n}{\Delta t} = -u_1 \frac{\partial T}{\partial x_1}^n - u_2 \frac{\partial T}{\partial x_2}^n + \alpha \left(\frac{\partial^2 T}{\partial x_1^2} + \frac{\partial^2 T}{\partial x_2^2}\right)^n$$

$$+ u_1 \frac{\Delta t}{2}\frac{\partial}{\partial x_1}\left[u_1\frac{\partial T}{\partial x_1}^n + u_2\frac{\partial T}{\partial x_2}^n\right]$$

$$+ u_2 \frac{\Delta t}{2}\frac{\partial}{\partial x_2}\left[u_1\frac{\partial T}{\partial x_1}^n + u_2\frac{\partial T}{\partial x_2}^n\right] \qquad (7.138)$$

All four preceding steps will now be summarized.

Step 1: Intermediate velocity

intermediate x_1 momentum equation

$$\frac{\tilde{u}_1 - \tilde{u}_1^n}{\Delta t} = -u_1 \frac{\partial u_1}{\partial x_1}^n - u_2 \frac{\partial u_1}{\partial x_2}^n + v \left(\frac{\partial^2 u_1}{\partial x_1^2} + \frac{\partial^2 u_1}{\partial x_2^2}\right)^n$$

$$+ u_1 \frac{\Delta t}{2}\frac{\partial}{\partial x_1}\left[u_1\frac{\partial u_1}{\partial x_1} + u_2\frac{\partial u_1}{\partial x_2}\right]^n$$

$$+ u_2 \frac{\Delta t}{2}\frac{\partial}{\partial x_2}\left[u_1\frac{\partial u_1}{\partial x_1} + u_2\frac{\partial u_1}{\partial x_2}\right]^n \qquad (7.139)$$

intermediate x_2 momentum equation

$$\frac{\tilde{u}_2 - \tilde{u}_2^n}{\Delta t} = -u_1 \frac{\partial u_2}{\partial x_1}^n - u_2 \frac{\partial u_2}{\partial x_2}^n + v \left(\frac{\partial^2 u_2}{\partial x_1^2} + \frac{\partial^2 u_2}{\partial x_2^2} \right)^n$$

$$+ u_1 \frac{\Delta t}{2} \frac{\partial}{\partial x_1} \left[u_1 \frac{\partial u_2}{\partial x_1} + u_2 \frac{\partial u_2}{\partial x_2} \right]^n$$

$$+ u_2 \frac{\Delta t}{2} \frac{\partial}{\partial x_2} \left[u_1 \frac{\partial u_2}{\partial x_1} + u_2 \frac{\partial u_2}{\partial x_2} \right]^n \tag{7.140}$$

Step 2: Pressure calculation

$$\frac{1}{\rho} \left(\frac{\partial^2 p}{\partial x_1^2} + \frac{\partial^2 p}{\partial x_2^2} \right)^n = \frac{1}{\Delta t} \left(\frac{\partial \tilde{u}_1}{\partial x_1} + \frac{\partial \tilde{u}_2}{\partial x_2} \right) \tag{7.141}$$

Step 3: Velocity correction

$$\frac{u_1^{n+1} - \tilde{u}_1}{\Delta t} = -\frac{1}{\rho} \frac{\partial p}{\partial x_1}^n + u_1 \frac{\Delta t}{2} \frac{\partial}{\partial x_1} \left(\frac{1}{\rho} \frac{\partial p}{\partial x_1} \right)^n + u_2 \frac{\Delta t}{2} \frac{\partial}{\partial x_2} \left(\frac{1}{\rho} \frac{\partial p}{\partial x_1} \right)^n$$

$$\frac{u_2^{n+1} - \tilde{u}_2}{\Delta t} = -\frac{1}{\rho} \frac{\partial p}{\partial x_2}^n + u_1 \frac{\Delta t}{2} \frac{\partial}{\partial x_1} \left(\frac{1}{\rho} \frac{\partial p}{\partial x_1} \right)^n + u_2 \frac{\Delta t}{2} \frac{\partial}{\partial x_2} \left(\frac{1}{\rho} \frac{\partial p}{\partial x_2} \right)^n \tag{7.142}$$

Step 4: Temperature calculation

$$\frac{T^{n+1} - T^n}{\Delta t} = -u_1 \frac{\partial T}{\partial x_1}^n - u_2 \frac{\partial T}{\partial x_2}^n$$

$$+ \alpha \left(\frac{\partial^2 T}{\partial x_1^2} + \frac{\partial^2 T}{\partial x_2^2} \right)^n$$

$$+ u_1 \frac{\Delta t}{2} \frac{\partial}{\partial x_1} \left[u_1 \frac{\partial T}{\partial x_1} + u_2 \frac{\partial T}{\partial x_2} \right]^n$$

$$+ u_2 \frac{\Delta t}{2} \frac{\partial}{\partial x_2} \left[u_1 \frac{\partial T}{\partial x_1} + u_2 \frac{\partial T}{\partial x_2} \right]^n \tag{7.143}$$

The temporal discretization of the CBS scheme has now been completed, and the following subsection gives the spatial discretization procedure.

7.6.1 Spatial discretization

The Galerkin approximation and spatial discretization of the four steps discussed previously follow the same procedure as given for the convection–diffusion equation in Section 7.4.2. On assuming linear interpolation functions for all the variables, the spatial variation for a linear triangular element may be written as (refer to Figure 7.12)

$$u_1 = N_i u_{1i} + N_j u_{1j} + N_k u_{1k} = [\mathbf{N}]\{\mathbf{u_1}\}$$

$$u_2 = N_i u_{2i} + N_j u_{2j} + N_k u_{2k} = [\mathbf{N}]\{\mathbf{u_2}\}$$

$$p = N_i p_i + N_j p_j + N_k p_k = [\mathbf{N}]\{\mathbf{p}\}$$

$$T = N_i T_i + N_j T_j + N_k T_k = [\mathbf{N}]\{\mathbf{T}\} \tag{7.144}$$

The elemental convection, diffusion and other matrices are very similar to the one discussed for the convection–diffusion equation. However, the difference here is that the convection velocities are not constant. Also, a non-linearity is introduced in the convection terms of the momentum equation. The following element matrices arise from the CBS scheme after spatial discretization:

Elemental mass matrix

$$[\mathbf{M_e}] = \frac{A}{12} \begin{bmatrix} 2 & 1 & 1 \\ 1 & 2 & 1 \\ 1 & 1 & 2 \end{bmatrix} \tag{7.145}$$

Elemental convection matrix

$$[\mathbf{C_e}] = \frac{1}{24} \begin{bmatrix} (usu + u_{1i})b_i & (usu + u_{1i})b_j & (usu + u_{1i})b_k \\ (usu + u_{1j})b_i & (usu + u_{1j})b_j & (usu + u_{1j})b_k \\ (usu + u_{1k})b_i & (usu + u_{1k})b_j & (usu + u_{1k})b_k \end{bmatrix}$$

$$+ \frac{1}{24} \begin{bmatrix} (vsu + u_{2i})c_i & (vsu + u_{2i})c_j & (vsu + u_{2i})c_k \\ (vsu + u_{2j})c_i & (vsu + u_{2j})c_j & (vsu + u_{2j})c_k \\ (vsu + u_{2k})c_i & (vsu + u_{2k})c_j & (vsu + u_{2k})c_k \end{bmatrix} \tag{7.146}$$

where

$$usu = u_{1i} + u_{1j} + u_{1k}$$

$$vsu = u_{2i} + u_{2j} + u_{2k} \tag{7.147}$$

The differences in the above convection matrix from that of the convection matrix discussed in Section 7.4.2 are due to the variable velocity field. The diffusion matrix is the same as the convection–diffusion equation, but k is replaced with the kinematic viscosity v for the momentum equation. Two diffusion matrices are required for convection heat transfer problems, one for the momentum equation and another for the temperature equation. These are

$$[\mathbf{K_{me}}] = \frac{v}{4A} \begin{bmatrix} b_i^2 & b_i b_j & b_i b_k \\ b_j b_i & b_j^2 & b_j b_k \\ b_k b_i & b_k b_j & b_k^2 \end{bmatrix} + \frac{v}{4A} \begin{bmatrix} c_i^2 & c_i c_j & c_i c_k \\ c_j c_i & c_j^2 & c_j c_k \\ c_k c_i & c_k c_j & c_k^2 \end{bmatrix} \tag{7.148}$$

for the momentum diffusion and

$$[\mathbf{K_{te}}] = \frac{k}{4A} \begin{bmatrix} b_i^2 & b_i b_j & b_i b_k \\ b_j b_i & b_j^2 & b_j b_k \\ b_k b_i & b_k b_j & b_k^2 \end{bmatrix} + \frac{k}{4A} \begin{bmatrix} c_i^2 & c_i c_j & c_i c_k \\ c_j c_i & c_j^2 & c_j c_k \\ c_k c_i & c_k c_j & c_k^2 \end{bmatrix} \tag{7.149}$$

for the heat diffusion.

The stabilization matrix is

$$
\begin{aligned}
[\mathbf{K_{se}}] = {} & \frac{u_{1av}}{12A} usu
\begin{bmatrix}
b_i^2 & b_i b_j & b_i b_k \\
b_j b_i & b_j^2 & b_j b_k \\
b_k b_i & b_k b_j & b_k^2
\end{bmatrix} \\
& + \frac{u_{1av}}{12A} vsu
\begin{bmatrix}
b_i c_i & b_i c_j & b_i c_k \\
b_j c_i & b_j c_j & b_j c_k \\
b_k c_i & b_k c_j & b_k c_k
\end{bmatrix} \\
& + \frac{u_{2av}}{12A} usu
\begin{bmatrix}
c_i b_i & c_i b_j & c_i b_k \\
c_j b_i & c_j b_j & c_j b_k \\
c_k b_i & c_k b_j & c_k b_k
\end{bmatrix} \\
& + \frac{u_{2av}}{12A} vsu
\begin{bmatrix}
c_i^2 & c_i c_j & c_i c_k \\
c_j c_i & c_j^2 & c_j c_k \\
c_k c_i & c_k c_j & c_k^2
\end{bmatrix}
\end{aligned}
\tag{7.150}
$$

where u_{1av} and u_{2av} are average values of u_1 and u_2 over an element. The discretization of the CBS steps requires three more matrices and four forcing vectors to complete the process. The matrix from the discretized second-order terms for Step 2 is

$$
[\mathbf{K}] = \frac{1}{4A\rho}
\begin{bmatrix}
b_i^2 & b_i b_j & b_i b_k \\
b_j b_i & b_j^2 & b_j b_k \\
b_k b_i & b_k b_j & b_k^2
\end{bmatrix}
+ \frac{1}{4A\rho}
\begin{bmatrix}
c_i^2 & c_i c_j & c_i c_k \\
c_j c_i & c_j^2 & c_j c_k \\
c_k c_i & c_k c_j & c_k^2
\end{bmatrix}
\tag{7.151}
$$

The first gradient matrix in the x_1 direction is

$$
[\mathbf{G_1}] = \frac{1}{6}
\begin{bmatrix}
b_i & b_j & b_k \\
b_i & b_j & b_k \\
b_i & b_j & b_k
\end{bmatrix}
\tag{7.152}
$$

and the second gradient matrix in the x_2 direction is

$$
[\mathbf{G_2}] = \frac{1}{6}
\begin{bmatrix}
c_i & c_j & c_k \\
c_i & c_j & c_k \\
c_i & c_j & c_k
\end{bmatrix}
\tag{7.153}
$$

The forcing terms are the result of the application of Green's lemma to the second-order derivatives of the differential equations. This issue has been previously discussed in the context of the discretization of the convection–diffusion equations. However, one important change is that it will be assumed that the boundary integral values of the stabilization terms are equal to zero on the boundaries and will be ignored. This is an appropriate assumption as these terms will be equal to zero because the residual of the discrete equations are zero on the boundaries (Zienkiewicz and Taylor 2000). However, the forcing terms resulting from the discretization of the other second-order terms are important and need to be taken into account. The forcing vector of the x_1 component of the momentum equation is

$$\{\mathbf{f_1}\} = \frac{\Gamma}{4A} \nu \begin{bmatrix} b_i u_{1i} + b_j u_{1j} + b_k u_{1k} \\ b_i u_{1i} + b_j u_{1j} + b_k u_{1k} \\ 0 \end{bmatrix}^n n_1$$

$$+ \frac{\Gamma}{4A} \nu \begin{bmatrix} c_i u_{1i} + c_j u_{1j} + c_k u_{1k} \\ c_i u_{1i} + c_j u_{1j} + c_k u_{1k} \\ 0 \end{bmatrix}^n n_2 \qquad (7.154)$$

Note that ij is assumed as being the boundary edge of an element. The forcing vector of the x_1 component of the momentum equation is

$$[\mathbf{f_2}] = \frac{\Gamma}{4A} \nu \begin{bmatrix} b_i u_{2i} + b_j u_{2j} + b_k u_{2k} \\ b_i u_{2i} + b_j u_{2j} + b_k u_{2k} \\ 0 \end{bmatrix}^n n_1$$

$$+ \frac{\Gamma}{4A} \nu \begin{bmatrix} c_i u_{2i} + c_j u_{2j} + c_k u_{2k} \\ c_i u_{2i} + c_j u_{2j} + c_k u_{2k} \\ 0 \end{bmatrix}^n n_2 \qquad (7.155)$$

The forcing vector from the discretization of the second-order pressure terms in Step 2 is

$$[\mathbf{f_3}] = \frac{\Gamma}{4A\rho} \begin{bmatrix} b_i p_i + b_j p_j + b_k p_k \\ b_i p_i + b_j p_j + b_k p_k \\ 0 \end{bmatrix}^n n_1$$

$$+ \frac{\Gamma}{4A\rho} \begin{bmatrix} c_i p_i + c_j p_j + c_k p_k \\ c_i p_i + c_j p_j + c_k p_k \\ 0 \end{bmatrix}^n n_2 \qquad (7.156)$$

The above forcing vector has often been ignored in the past, which is not an unreasonable assumption. Finally, the forcing term due to the discretization of the second-order terms in the energy equation is

$$\{\mathbf{f_4}\} = \frac{\Gamma}{4A} k \begin{bmatrix} b_i T_i + b_j T_j + b_k T_k \\ b_i T_i + b_j T_j + b_k T_k \\ 0 \end{bmatrix}^n n_1$$

$$+ \frac{\Gamma}{4A} k \begin{bmatrix} c_i T_i + c_j T_j + c_k T_k \\ c_i T_i + c_j T_j + c_k T_k \\ 0 \end{bmatrix}^n n_2 \qquad (7.157)$$

The four steps of the CBS scheme may now be written in matrix form. The above elemental equations need to be assembled before they can be used in the steps. It will be assumed that the matrices without the subscript e are already assembled and therefore the steps in terms of the assembly (discrete form) can now be written as

Step 1: Intermediate velocity calculation x_1 component

$$[\mathbf{M}]\frac{\Delta\{\tilde{\mathbf{u}}_1\}}{\Delta t} = -[\mathbf{C}]\{\mathbf{u}_1\}^n - [\mathbf{K}_m]\{\mathbf{u}_1\}^n - [\mathbf{K}_s]\{\mathbf{u}_1\}^n + \{\mathbf{f}_1\} \tag{7.158}$$

and for the x_2 component

$$[\mathbf{M}]\frac{\Delta\{\tilde{\mathbf{u}}_2\}}{\Delta t} = -[\mathbf{C}]\{\mathbf{u}_2\}^n - [\mathbf{K}_m]\{\mathbf{u}_2\}^n - [\mathbf{K}_s]\{\mathbf{u}_2\}^n + \{\mathbf{f}_2\} \tag{7.159}$$

Step 2: Pressure calculation

$$[\mathbf{K}]\{\mathbf{p}\}^n = -\frac{1}{\Delta t}\left[[\mathbf{G}_1]\{\tilde{\mathbf{u}}_1\} + [\mathbf{G}_2]\{\tilde{\mathbf{u}}_2\}\right] + \{\mathbf{f}_3\} \tag{7.160}$$

Step 3: Velocity correction

$$[\mathbf{M}]\{\mathbf{u}_1\}^{n+1} = [\mathbf{M}]\{\tilde{\mathbf{u}}_1\} - \Delta t[\mathbf{G}_1]\{\mathbf{p}\}^n$$

$$[\mathbf{M}]\{\mathbf{u}_2\}^{n+1} = [\mathbf{M}]\{\tilde{\mathbf{u}}_2\} - \Delta t[\mathbf{G}_2]\{\mathbf{p}\}^n \tag{7.161}$$

Step 4: Temperature calculation

$$[\mathbf{M}]\frac{\Delta\{\mathbf{T}\}}{\Delta t} = -[\mathbf{C}]\{\mathbf{T}\}^n - [\mathbf{K}_t]\{\mathbf{T}\}^n - [\mathbf{K}_s]\{\mathbf{T}\}^n + \{\mathbf{f}_4\} \tag{7.162}$$

The above four steps are the cornerstone of the CBS scheme for the solution of the heat convection equations. An extension of the above steps for solving the conservation form and three-dimensional equations is straightforward. Interested readers should consult some of the appropriate publications (Nithiarasu 2003; Zienkiewicz *et al.* 1999).

The mass matrix [**M**] used in the above steps may be 'lumped' to simplify the solution procedure. This is an approximation, but a worthwhile and time-saving approximation. Mass lumping will eliminate the need for the matrix solution procedure necessary for consistent mass matrices. The lumped mass matrix for a linear triangular element is constructed by summing the rows and placing on the diagonals. The elemental lumped mass matrix of a linear triangular element is

$$[\mathbf{M}_{\mathbf{Le}}] = \frac{A}{12}\begin{bmatrix} 4 & 0 & 0 \\ 0 & 4 & 0 \\ 0 & 0 & 4 \end{bmatrix} = \frac{A}{3}\begin{bmatrix} 1 & 0 & 0 \\ 0 & 1 & 0 \\ 0 & 0 & 1 \end{bmatrix} \tag{7.163}$$

If the above mass lumping procedure is introduced into the CBS steps, some small errors will occur in the transient solution. For steady state solutions, however, no errors are introduced. However, for transient problems an accurate solution can still be obtained by appropriate mesh refinement.

7.6.2 Time-step calculation

The time-step restrictions are very similar to the convection–diffusion equation (Equation 7.119). The local time step at each and every node can be computed as follows:

$$\Delta t = \min(\Delta t_c, \Delta t_d) \tag{7.164}$$

The convection time step Δt_c is identical to that of Equation 7.120. The diffusion time steps contain two parts. One due to the kinematic viscosity and another to the thermal diffusivity of the fluid. The diffusion time step may be expressed as

$$\Delta t_d = \min \left(\frac{h^2}{2\nu}, \frac{h^2}{2\alpha} \right) \tag{7.165}$$

where ν is the kinematic viscosity and α is the thermal diffusivity. The local element size may be calculated using the same procedure as that discussed in Section 7.5. However, a more advanced method of the calculation of element size, for example, an element size in the streamline direction, is possible and readers are referred to the appropriate publication (Tezduyar *et al.* 2000).

7.6.3   Boundary and initial conditions

The two main boundary conditions prevalent in heat convection problems are the prescribed temperature, pressure and velocity (Dirichlet conditions) and flux boundary conditions (Neumann conditions). Other possibilities may be derived from these conditions.

Prescribed values If a value of the velocity components, temperature or pressure is given at a boundary node, the value will be 'forced' at these nodes. The implementation is easy and straightforward.

Flux conditions In a heat transfer calculation, it is possible to have prescribed heat flux conditions, which are normally given as

$$-k\frac{\partial T}{\partial n} = \overline{q} \tag{7.166}$$

where n is the normal direction to the surface on which the prescribed flux boundary is imposed. The heat flux condition is imposed by rearranging $\{\mathbf{f_4}\}$ (Equation 7.157) as follows:

$$\{\mathbf{f_4}\} = \frac{\Gamma}{2}\overline{q} \begin{bmatrix} 1 \\ 1 \\ 0 \end{bmatrix} \tag{7.167}$$

Often, symmetric (or zero flux) boundary conditions are employed in convection heat transfer calculations. In such cases, the forcing vector terms disappear. Other relevant boundary conditions will be discussed along with appropriate examples later in this chapter.

In many industrial heat transfer applications, convection heat transfer boundary conditions are common. If a boundary, as shown in Figure 7.14, is convecting to the atmosphere, then the boundary condition on this wall can be expressed as

$$-k\frac{\partial T}{\partial n} = h_c(T - T_a) \tag{7.168}$$

where the wall temperature T is unknown. The implementation is carried out by replacing $\overline{q}$ (Equation 7.167) by the right-hand side of the above equation. However, T must be treated as an unknown and should be evaluated at each time step.

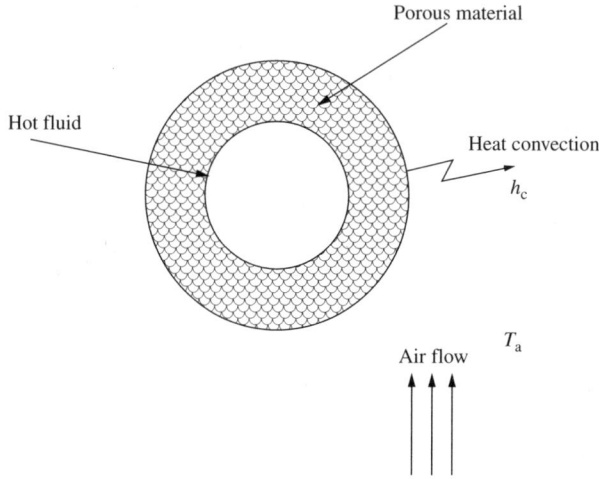

Figure 7.14   Example of convection boundary condition

The initial conditions, which describe the initial state of the fluid (temperature, pressure, velocity and properties), are employed at the onset of the heat convection calculations. These conditions are problem-dependent and are discussed for various applications in the latter sections of this chapter.

7.6.4   Steady and transient solution methods

A steady state solution for a problem can be obtained, using the CBS scheme, by time-stepping to achieve a steady state. This can be done by fixing a tolerance criterion as follows:

$$\sum_{i=1}^{n\ nodes} \frac{\phi_i^{n+1} - \phi_i^n}{\Delta t} \le \epsilon \tag{7.169}$$

where ϕ_i is any heat convection variable at a node, $n\ nodes$ is the total number of nodes and ϵ is a prescribed tolerance, which will tend to zero as the solution approaches steady state.

A transient solution can be of two types. The first type is the 'real' time variation of the solution for problems in which a steady state solution exists. The second category is one that has no real steady state, for instance, vortex shedding behind a cylinder or Bernard convection. In the first type, the calculations commence with prescribed initial conditions and progress with a suitable time-stepping algorithm until a steady state is reached. The time history of the variables need to be stored and monitored as the transient solution progresses in order to study the behaviour of the solution. In the second type of problems, that is, Bernard convection and vortex shedding, the steady state tolerance of Equation 7.169 is not applicable and steady state is never reached. The time history of these types of problems needs to be followed as long as the user is interested in the solution.

7.7 Artificial Compressibility Scheme

As mentioned before, convection heat transfer calculations can be carried out using a fully explicit Artificial Compressibility (AC) scheme. In AC schemes, an artificial compressibility is introduced at Step 2 of the CBS scheme, that is,

$$\frac{1}{\beta^2}\frac{\partial p}{\partial t} - \Delta t \left(\frac{\partial^2 p}{\partial x_1^2} + \frac{\partial^2 p}{\partial x_2^2}\right) + \frac{\partial \tilde{u}_1}{\partial x_1} + \frac{\partial \tilde{u}_1}{\partial x_2} = 0 \qquad (7.170)$$

where β is an artificial compressibility parameter. The above equation can be derived by assuming a density variation in the continuity equation by substituting

$$\frac{\partial \rho}{\partial t} \approx \frac{1}{c^2}\frac{\partial p}{\partial t} \qquad (7.171)$$

where c is the speed of sound, which, for incompressible flows, approaches infinity. However, c can be replaced by an artificial compressibility parameter β, as given in Equation 7.170, for the purpose of introducing an explicit scheme. In the artificial-compressibility-based CBS scheme, Step 2 will be replaced with

$$\frac{1}{\beta^2}[\mathbf{M}]\frac{\{\Delta\mathbf{p}\}}{\Delta\mathbf{t}} + [\mathbf{K}]\{\mathbf{p}\}^{\mathbf{n}} = -\frac{1}{\Delta t}\left[[\mathbf{G_1}]\{\tilde{\mathbf{u}}_1\} + [\mathbf{G_2}]\{\tilde{\mathbf{u}}_2\}\right] + \{\mathbf{f_3}\} \qquad (7.172)$$

where $\Delta\{\mathbf{p}\} = \{\mathbf{p}^{\mathbf{n+1}} - \mathbf{p}^{\mathbf{n}}\}$. The artificial compressibility parameter can be chosen as

$$\beta = \max(c_0, u_{conv}, u_{diff}, u_{therm}) \qquad (7.173)$$

where c_0 is a small constant (between 0.1 to 0.5) and u_{conv}, u_{diff} and u_{therm} are respectively the convection, diffusion and thermal velocities, which may be defined as

$$u_{conv} = \sqrt{u_1^2 + u_2^2}$$

$$u_{diff} = \frac{2v}{h}$$

$$u_{therm} = \frac{2\alpha}{h} \qquad (7.174)$$

All other steps of the CBS scheme remain the same. However, for the solution of transient problems, a dual time-stepping procedure has to be introduced. In this dual time-stepping procedure, a transient problem is split into several instantaneous steady states and integrated via a real global time-step. Further details on the dual time-stepping procedure can be found in references (Malan *et al.* 2002; Nithiarasu 2003).

7.8 Nusselt Number, Drag and Stream Function

The two important quantities of interest in many heat transfer applications are the rate of heat transfer (Nusselt number) and the flow resistance offered by a surface (drag). A stream function is often used to draw streamlines in order to better understand the flow pattern around a body. In this section, a brief summary is given on how to calculate these quantities.

7.8.1   Nusselt number

The Nusselt number is derived as follows. Let us assume that a hot surface is cooled by a cold fluid stream. The heat from the hot surface, which is maintained at a constant temperature, is diffused through a boundary layer and convected away by the cold stream. This phenomenon is normally defined by Newton's law of cooling per unit surface area as

$$h_c(T_w - T_f) = -k\frac{\partial T}{\partial n} \tag{7.175}$$

where h_c is the heat transfer coefficient, k is an average thermal conductivity of the fluid, T_f is the free stream temperature of the fluid and n is the normal direction to the heat transfer surface. The above equation can be rewritten as

$$\frac{h_c L}{k} = -\frac{1}{T_w - T_f}\frac{\partial T}{\partial n}L \tag{7.176}$$

where L is any characteristic dimension. The quantity on the left-hand side of the above equation is the Nusselt number. If we apply non-dimensional scales, as discussed in Section 3, we can rewrite the above equation as

$$N_u = -\frac{\partial T^*}{\partial n^*} \tag{7.177}$$

where N_u is the local Nusselt number. It should be observed that the local Nusselt number is equal to the local, non-dimensional, normal temperature gradient. The above definition of the Nusselt number is valid for any heat transfer problem as long as the surface temperature is constant, or a reference wall temperature is known. However, for prescribed heat flux conditions, a different approach is required to derive the Nusselt number. Let us assume a surface subjected to a uniform heat flux $\overline{q}$. We can write locally

$$\overline{q} = -k\frac{\partial T}{\partial n} = h_c(T_w - T_f) \tag{7.178}$$

where T_w is not a constant. The Nusselt number relation can be obtained by multiplying the RHS of the previous equations by L/k, that is,

$$\frac{h_c L}{k}(T_w - T_f) = \frac{qL}{k} \tag{7.179}$$

Rearranging, we obtain

$$N_u = \frac{\frac{qL}{k}}{(T_w - T_f)} \tag{7.180}$$

When a wall is subjected to heat flux boundary conditions, the temperature scale is qL/k, which non-dimensionalizes the temperature. Therefore, the above equation can be rewritten as

$$N_u = \frac{1}{T_w^* - T_f^*} \tag{7.181}$$

This equation is simpler than that derived for a constant wall temperature and is limited to the calculation of local non-dimensional wall temperatures (assuming T_f is constant). Therefore, the calculation of the Nusselt number on a wall subjected to a constant heat flux is straightforward in any numerical method. However, in the Nusselt number calculation for a surface subjected to a constant temperature, it is necessary to calculate the normal temperature gradient. This calculation is simple if using a finite element discretization, in which the normal gradient is equal to the boundary terms due to the discretization of the second-order temperature terms, that is,

$$\frac{\partial T}{\partial n} = \frac{\partial T}{\partial x_1} n_1 + \frac{\partial T}{\partial x_2} n_2 + \frac{\partial T}{\partial x_3} n_3 \tag{7.182}$$

where n_1, n_2 and n_3 are the direction cosines of the surface normal. All the above discussed quantities are local (on the surface nodes or elements). However, it is often necessary to have an average Nusselt number for a heat transfer problem. The average Nusselt number can be easily calculated by integrating the local Nusselt number over a length (in two dimensions) or over a surface (in three dimensions). For example, in two dimensions,

$$Nu_{av} = \frac{1}{l} \int_l Nu\,dl = \frac{1}{l} \sum_{i=1}^{nelem} Nu_i dl_i \tag{7.183}$$

where l is the total length of the wall, i indicates a single incremental length of a one-dimensional element on the wall on which the Nusselt number is calculated and $n\ elem$ indicates the total number of one-dimensional elements on the wall. If the length l in the above equation is replaced by an area, then it can be directly applied to three-dimensional problems. In order to use the above formula, the local Nusselt number over an incremental length (dl_i) is assumed to be constant.

7.8.2 Drag calculation

The drag force is the resistance offered by a body that is equal to the force exerted by the flow on the body at equilibrium conditions. The drag force arises from two different sources. One is from the pressure p acting in the flow direction on the surface of the body (form drag) and the second is due to the force caused by viscosity effects in the flow direction. In general, the drag force is characterized by a drag coefficient, defined as

$$C_d = \frac{D}{A_f \frac{1}{2} \rho_a u_a^2} \tag{7.184}$$

where D is the drag force, A_f is the frontal area in the flow direction and the subscript a indicates the free stream value. The drag force D contains the contributions from both the influence of pressure and friction, that is,

$$D = D_p + D_f \tag{7.185}$$

where D_p is the pressure drag force and D_f is the friction drag force in the flow direction. The pressure drag, or form drag, is calculated from the nodal pressure values. For a two-dimensional problem, the solid wall may be a curve or a line and the boundary elements on the solid wall are one-dimensional with two nodes if linear elements are used. The pressure may be averaged over each one-dimensional element to calculate the average pressure over the boundary element. If this average pressure is multiplied by the length of the element, the normal pressure acting on the boundary element is obtained. If the pressure force is multiplied by the direction cosine in the flow direction, we obtain the local pressure drag force in the flow direction. Integration of these forces over the solid boundary gives the drag force due to the pressure D_p.

The viscous drag force D_f is calculated by integrating the viscous traction in the flow direction, over the surface area. The relation for the total drag force in the x_1 direction may be written for a two-dimensional case as

$$D_{x_1} = \int_{A_s} [(-p + \tau_{11})n_1 + \tau_{12}n_2] \mathrm{d}A_s \qquad (7.186)$$

where n_1 and n_2 are components of the surface normal $\mathbf{n}$ as shown in Figure 7.15.

7.8.3 Stream function

In most fluid dynamics and convection heat transfer problems, it is often easier to understand the flow results if the streamlines are plotted. In order to plot these streamlines, or flow pattern, it is first necessary to calculate the stream function values at the nodes. The lines with constant stream function values, are referred to as *streamlines*. The stream function is defined by the following relationships:

$$u_1 = \frac{\partial \psi}{\partial x_2}$$

$$u_2 = -\frac{\partial \psi}{\partial x_1} \qquad (7.187)$$

where ψ is the stream function. If we differentiate the first relation with respect to x_2 and the second with respect to x_1 and then sum, we get the differential equation for the stream

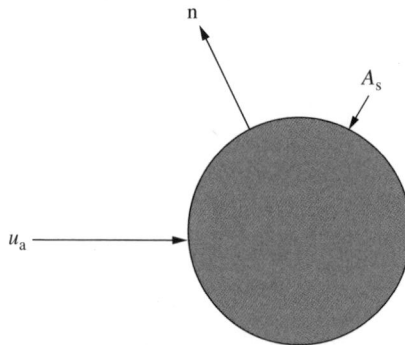

Figure 7.15   Normal gradient of velocity close to the wall

function as

$$\frac{\partial^2 \psi}{\partial x_2^2} + \frac{\partial^2 \psi}{\partial x_1^2} = \frac{\partial u_1}{\partial x_1} - \frac{\partial u_2}{\partial x_2} \qquad (7.188)$$

A solution to the above Laplacian equation is straightforward for any numerical procedure. This equation is similar to Step 2 of the CBS scheme and an implicit procedure immediately gives the solution. Unlike the pressure equation of Step 2, the stream function of a solution needs to be calculated only once.

7.9   Mesh Convergence

All numerical schemes are by their nature an approximation and the CBS scheme is no exception. However, if a scheme is to be convergent, the approximate solution should approach the exact answer as the mesh is refined. A converged solution is one that is nearly independent of meshing errors. An extremely coarse mesh would give a very approximate solution, which is far from reality. As the mesh is refined by reducing the size of the elements, the solution slowly approaches an exact solution. It should be noted that, in theory, the solution will not be exact until the mesh size is zero, which is obviously impossible. However, it is possible to fix a tolerance to the solution error and this can be achieved by solving the problem on several meshes.

In order to ensure that the solution obtained is as close as possible to reality, solutions should be obtained from several meshes starting with a very coarse mesh and finishing with a very fine mesh. Once these solutions are available, many key quantities can be compared and plotted against mesh densities (or number of points) as shown in Figure 7.16. If the difference between two consecutive meshes (or number of nodes) is less than a fixed tolerance, the coarser mesh is normally accepted as a suitable mesh for the analysis.

For two-dimensional problems, it is not difficult to carry out a detailed mesh convergence study for different parameters or cases. However, in large three-dimensional problems, it is often difficult to carry out a complete mesh convergence study. In such

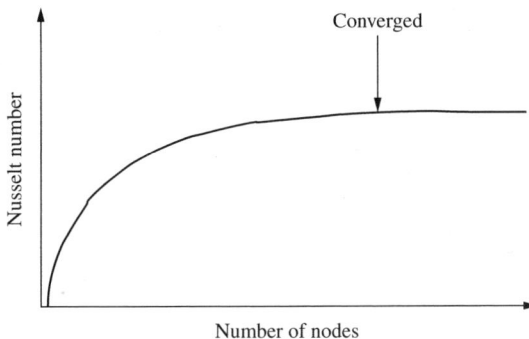

Figure 7.16   Typical convergence study

situations, it is customary to compare the results with analytical, or experimental, data if available. The past experience of the user also helps in obtaining an accurate solution for complicated problems.

7.10   Laminar Isothermal Flow

In this section, an example of a steady state isothermal flow problem is discussed. The isothermal solution procedure is obtained by neglecting the temperature, or energy, equation from the governing set of equations. In other words, Step 4 of the scheme is neglected thereby assuming isothermal flow. The problem selected is a simple two-dimensional developing flow in a rectangular channel as shown in Figure 7.17.

7.10.1   Geometry, boundary and initial conditions

The 'CBS flow' code is used to solve this problem. The steps employed are as discussed in Section 7.5. However, the 'CBS flow' code is written using a non-dimensional form of the governing equations. Therefore, the steps of the scheme have to undergo appropriate changes. The non-dimensional scaling discussed in Section 7.3.1 should be reflected in the geometry. The non-dimensional geometry used is shown in Figure 7.17. The defined inlet Reynolds number is based on the inlet height and is therefore equal to unity in the non-dimensional form. The length of the channel was assumed to be 15 times the height.

On the basis of the characteristic analysis discussed in many books, (Hirsch 1989), a subsonic, incompressible two-dimensional isothermal flow problem requires two boundary conditions at the inlet and one boundary condition at the exit. It is normal practice to impose the velocity components at the inlet and pressure at the exit. In order that pressure may be imposed at the exit, it is necessary that the flow does not undergo any appreciable variation close to the exit. In other words, the channel length should be much greater than the height.

The boundary conditions may be summarized as follows:

Inlet: Uniform velocity component u_1 of a non-dimensional value of unity and the velocity component u_2 equal to zero.

Exit: A constant non-dimensional pressure value is assumed. Here, the value is prescribed as being zero.

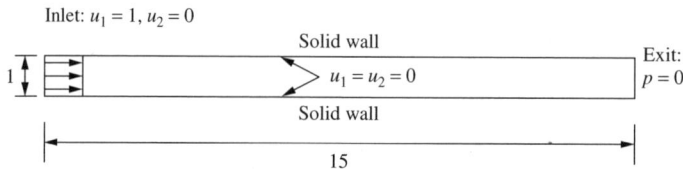

Figure 7.17   Flow through a two-dimensional rectangular channel. Geometry and boundary conditions

Walls: Both velocity components forced to zero (no-slip condition)

Initial conditions: Zero velocities and pressure at all points within the domain.

7.10.2   Solution

Figure 7.18 shows the unstructured mesh used for the calculations. It is a uniform mesh with 3242 linear triangular elements and 1782 nodes.

The inlet Reynolds number of the flow is assumed to be 100, which is well within the laminar range. Figure 7.19 shows the velocity profiles along the length of the channel.

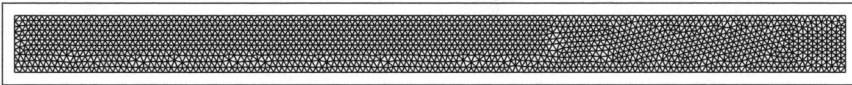

Figure 7.18   Flow through a two-dimensional rectangular channel. Finite element mesh

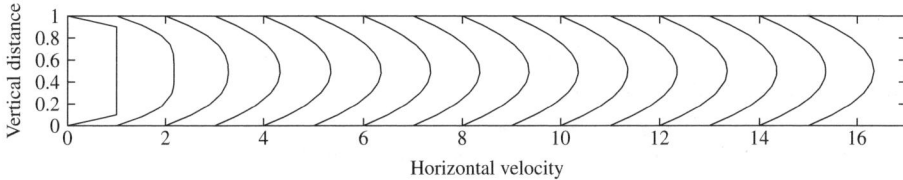

Figure 7.19   Flow through a two-dimensional rectangular channel. Velocity profiles at different sections

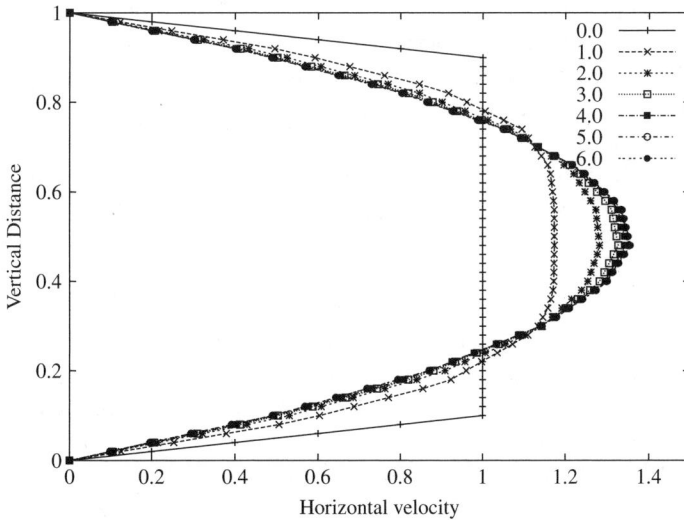

Figure 7.20   Flow through a two-dimensional rectangular channel. Comparison of velocity profiles at various distances

This solution is a steady state solution generated by an artificial compressibility form of the CBS scheme. The momentum boundary layer develops as the flow travels downstream. Figure 7.20 shows a comparison of the velocity profiles for non-dimensional distances between 0 and 6. It may be seen that the parabolic profile is developed close to a distance of 4.0. The analytical solution obtained from boundary layer theory (Schlichting 1968) gives an approximate relation for the non-dimensional developing length as

$$l_e = 0.04Re \tag{7.189}$$

which gives a $l_e = 4.0$ for a Reynolds number of 100. It should be noted that the velocity profile is continuously changing in the downstream direction. A completely unchanged u_1 velocity profile can be obtained only by extending the length of the channel further (Schlichting 1968). Also, more accurate velocity profiles can be obtained by either employing a structured mesh or using a finer unstructured mesh. The interested reader is advised to carry out a mesh convergence study on this type of problem.

7.11 Laminar Non-isothermal Flow

In this section, some examples of non-isothermal problems are discussed. In the previous section, the temperature effects are ignored, but they are included in this section in order to study some heat convection problems. The categories of forced convection, buoyancy-driven convection and mixed convection are discussed in the following subsections:

7.11.1 Forced convection heat transfer

Forced convection heat transfer is induced by forcing a liquid, or gas, over a hot body or surface. Two forced convection problems will be studied in this section. The first problem is the extension of flow through a two-dimensional channel as discussed in the previous section and the second one is of forced convection over a sphere. The difference between the first problem and the one in the previous section is that the top and bottom walls are at a higher temperature than that of the air flowing into the channel. The non-dimensional temperature scale employed is

$$T^* = \frac{T - T_a}{T_w - T_a} \tag{7.190}$$

Since the CBS flow code is based on non-dimensional governing equations, a non-dimensional scaling factor needs to be employed. This scale will give a temperature value of unity on the walls ($T = T_w$) and zero at the inlet ($T = T_a$). Dirichlet boundary conditions for temperature are not necessary at the exit. However, the boundary integrals resulting from the discretization of the second-order terms need to be evaluated and added to the equations. For a steady state solution, all four steps of the CBS scheme can be solved simultaneously, or firstly a steady flow solution is obtained and then using this result a temperature distribution can be established independently. The Reynolds number is again assumed to be equal to 100, and the velocity distribution is the same as shown in Figure 7.19. The temperature

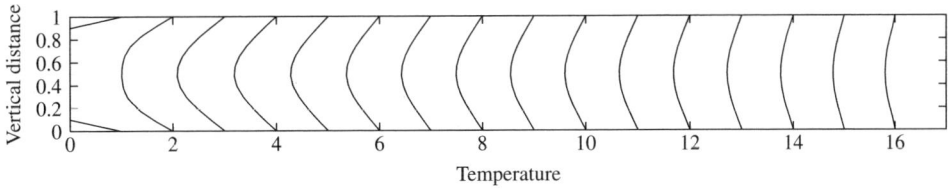

Figure 7.21   Forced convection flow through a two-dimensional rectangular channel. Temperature profiles at various distances

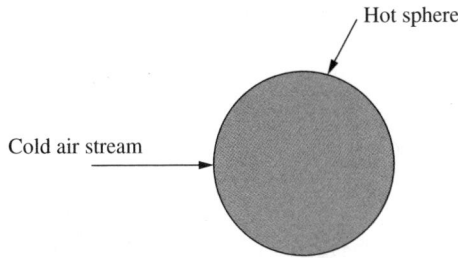

Figure 7.22   Forced convection flow past a sphere

profile distribution is as shown in Figure 7.21. As may be seen, a parabolic temperature profile is achieved at around the same distance from the entrance as that for the parabolic velocity profile. It should also be noted that as the length of the channel increases, the average temperature of the fluid also increases and approaches that of the wall temperature.

The second problem considered is a three-dimensional flow over a hot sphere. The heat transfer aspects of the hot sphere are studied as it is exposed to a cold air stream. The problem definition is different from that of the channel flow, which is an internal flow, for in this case the flow past a sphere is an external flow problem as shown in Figure 7.22.

As shown, the sphere is in an unbounded space, and an outer boundary needs defining in order to carry out the computation. The boundary conditions on the boundary walls should be fixed in such a way that they do not affect the heat transfer and flow properties close to the sphere. The best way to minimize the influence of these outer boundary conditions on the heat transfer and flow around the sphere is to place the boundaries far from the sphere.

In the problem discussed here, an outer boundary is fixed in such a way that the inlet is at a distance of five diameters from the centre of the sphere, and the exit is at 20 diameters downstream of the centre of the sphere (Nithiarasu *et al.* 2004). The side boundaries are also at a distance of five diameters away from the centre of the sphere. It is possible to imagine the sphere being placed inside a three-dimensional channel, which is 25 diameters long having 10 diameter sides. However, the difference from the previous channel problem is that there is no solid outer wall in this case.

The boundary conditions are simple as in the previous problem. The inlet has a non-dimensional velocity of unity and a non-dimensional temperature of zero. The surface of the sphere is subjected to a no-slip velocity boundary condition and a non-dimensional temperature of unity. All the side walls are subjected to a zero heat flux and a zero normal velocity value. At the exit, only the boundary integrals are evaluated and prescribed.

It is obvious that a three-dimensional mesh is required, and for the problem under consideration, linear tetrahedral elements were used. Three-dimensional meshes were generated using an efficient mesh generator as reported by Morgan *et al.* (1999). The total number of elements used in the computation was approximately a million. The sphere and a cross-sectional side view along the axis are shown in Figure 7.23.

The temperature contours near the vicinity of the sphere are shown in Figure 7.24 for inlet Reynolds numbers of 100 and 200 respectively. As mentioned previously, the temperature on the surface of the sphere is unity. This diagram shows a cut view along the

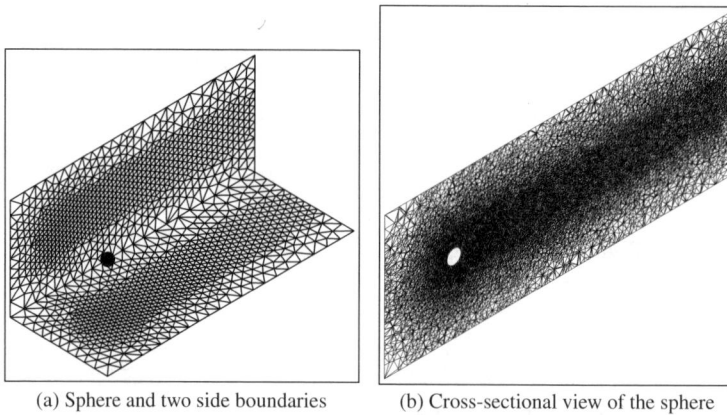

(a) Sphere and two side boundaries   (b) Cross-sectional view of the sphere

Figure 7.23   Forced convection heat transfer from a sphere. Three-dimensional mesh

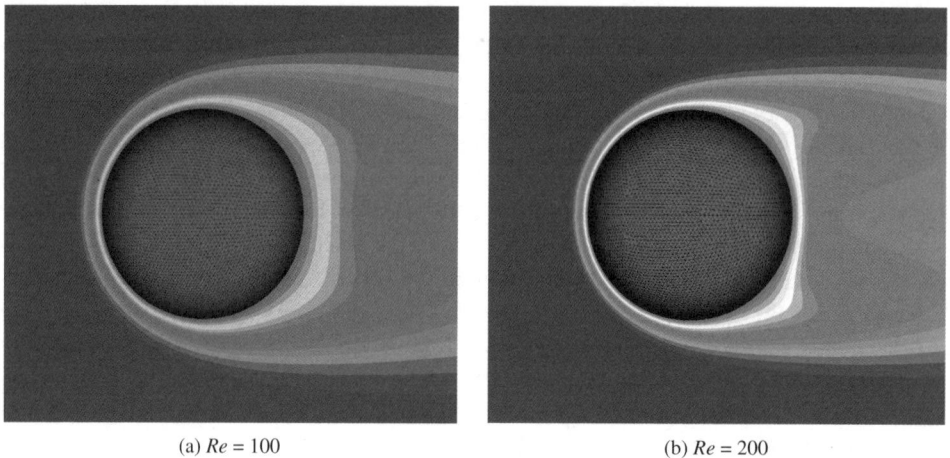

(a) *Re* = 100   (b) *Re* = 200

Figure 7.24   Forced convection heat transfer from a sphere. Temperature distribution in the vicinity of the sphere

axis in the direction of the flow. Therefore, the temperature values close to the surface of the sphere are near to unity, which reduce in value away from the sphere and finally reach zero value in the free air stream. In the downstream direction, however, the temperatures are greater than that of the free stream temperature all the way to the exit (see Figure 7.25). This indicates that the cold air stream removes heat from the sphere, which is then transported to the exit.

The values of drag coefficient and average Nusselt numbers are given in Tables 7.1 and 7.2 respectively. In Table 7.1, the quantity inside the brackets is the pressure drag coefficient.

7.11.2   Buoyancy-driven convection heat transfer

Buoyancy-driven convection is created by the occurrence of local temperature differences in a fluid. This type of convection can also be created by local concentration differences

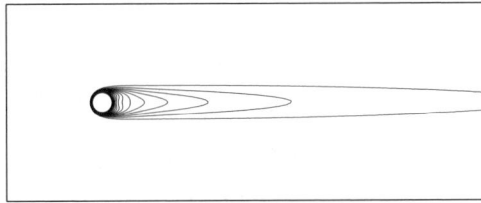

Figure 7.25   Forced convection flow past a sphere. Temperature contours, $Re = 100$

Table 7.1   Comparison of coefficient of drag with existing literature

Author Re	100	200
Clift *et al.* (Clift *et al.* 1978)	1.087	—
S. Lee (Lee 2000)	1.096 (0.512)	—
Gülçat and Aslan (Gülçat änd Aslan 1997)	1.07	0.78
Rimon and Cheng (Rimon and Cheng 1969)	1.014	0.727
Le Clair *et al.* (La Clair *et al.* 1970)	1.096 (0.590)	0.772 (0.372)
Magnaudet *et al.* (Magnaudet *et al.* 1995)	1.092 (0.584)	0.765 (0.368)
CBS	1.105 (0.564)	0.7708 (0.347)

Table 7.2   Comparison of average Nusselt number

Re	(Yuge 1960)	(Whitaker 1983)	(Feng *et al.* 2000)	CBS
50	5.4860	5.1764	5.4194	5.2176
100	6.9300	6.6151	6.9848	6.6589
200	8.9721	8.7219	9.1901	8.7599

within a fluid, but will not be considered within this text. Buoyancy-driven convection is present in most flow situations; however, its significance can vary according to the situation. For instance, in a situation in which a hot surface and a cold fluid interact, without any other external force, a buoyancy-driven convection pattern will develop. Examples include radiators inside a cold room, most solar appliances, some cooling applications of electronic devices and finally phase change applications (Lewis *et al.* 1995a; Ravindran and Lewis 1998; Usmani *et al.* 1992b,a).

The principles of buoyancy-driven convection are simple. A local temperature difference creates a local density difference within the fluid and results in fluid motion because of the local density variation. Although the principles are simple, the development of an accurate numerical solution for such buoyancy-driven flows is far from simple. This is mainly due to the very slow flow rates involved, which are often marked with turbulence, which again complicates the numerical prediction.

In order to demonstrate buoyancy-driven convection, we shall consider the standard benchmark problem of natural convection within a two-dimensional square enclosure, as shown in Figure 7.26. The geometry is a two-dimensional square of non-dimensional unit size. The walls are solid and subjected to no-slip velocity boundary conditions (zero-velocity components). One of the vertical walls is subjected to a higher temperature ($T = 1$) than the other vertical wall ($T = 0$). Both the top and bottom walls are assumed to be insulated (zero heat flux). The steady state solution to this problem is sought herein.

In order to obtain a steady state solution, the CBS flow code is used in its semi-implicit form with zero initial velocity and temperature values and a small constant value of pressure (0.1). A simple pressure boundary condition is essential in order to solve the pressure equations implicitly. One of the corner points has a fixed pressure value of zero at all times. The parameter varied in this problem is the Rayleigh number. The mesh employed in the calculations is a structured mesh and is shown in Figure 7.27. Unstructured meshes are equally valid but require a greater number of elements in order to obtain the same accuracy as structured meshes. The mesh shown in Figure 7.27 contains 5000 elements and 2601 nodes.

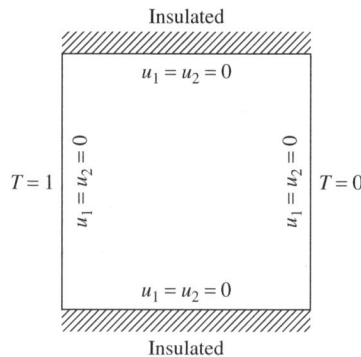

Figure 7.26 Buoyancy-driven flow in a square enclosure. Geometry and boundary conditions

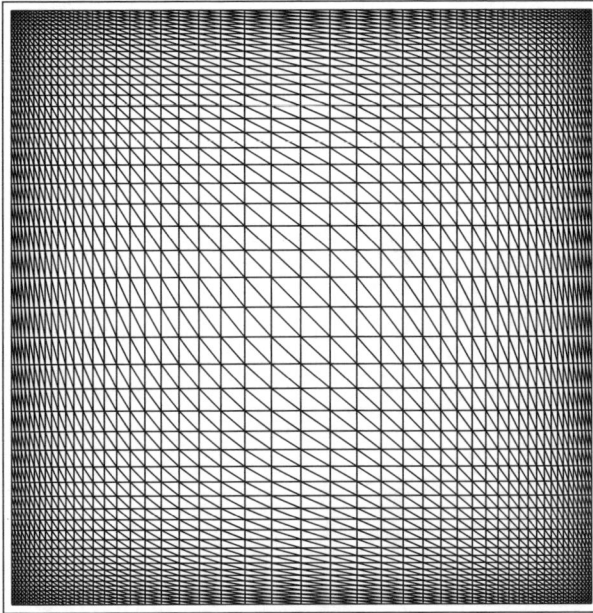

Figure 7.27 Buoyancy-driven flow in a square enclosure. Finite element mesh. Nodes: 2601, elements: 5000

Figures 7.28 shows the temperature contours and streamlines for different Rayleigh numbers. The flow raises alongside the hot left side wall, taking the heat with it and eventually losing it alongside the right side wall. As the Rayleigh number increases the flow becomes stronger and is marked with a thinner flow regime and thermal boundary layers close to the vertical walls.

Table 7.3 reports various quantities, which have been calculated for the natural convection in a square cavity (Massarotti *et al.* 1998). In Table 7.3, ψ is the stream function, Nu_{av} is the average Nusselt number and u_{2max} is the maximum vertical velocity component. These values compare very well with the benchmark data available in the literature.

Table 7.3 Quantitative results for natural convection in a square cavity

Ra	Nu_{av}	ψ_{max}	u_{2max}
10^3	1.116	1.175	3.692
10^4	2.243	5.075	19.63
10^5	4.521	9.153	68.85
10^6	8.806	16.49	221.6
10^7	16.40	30.33	702.3

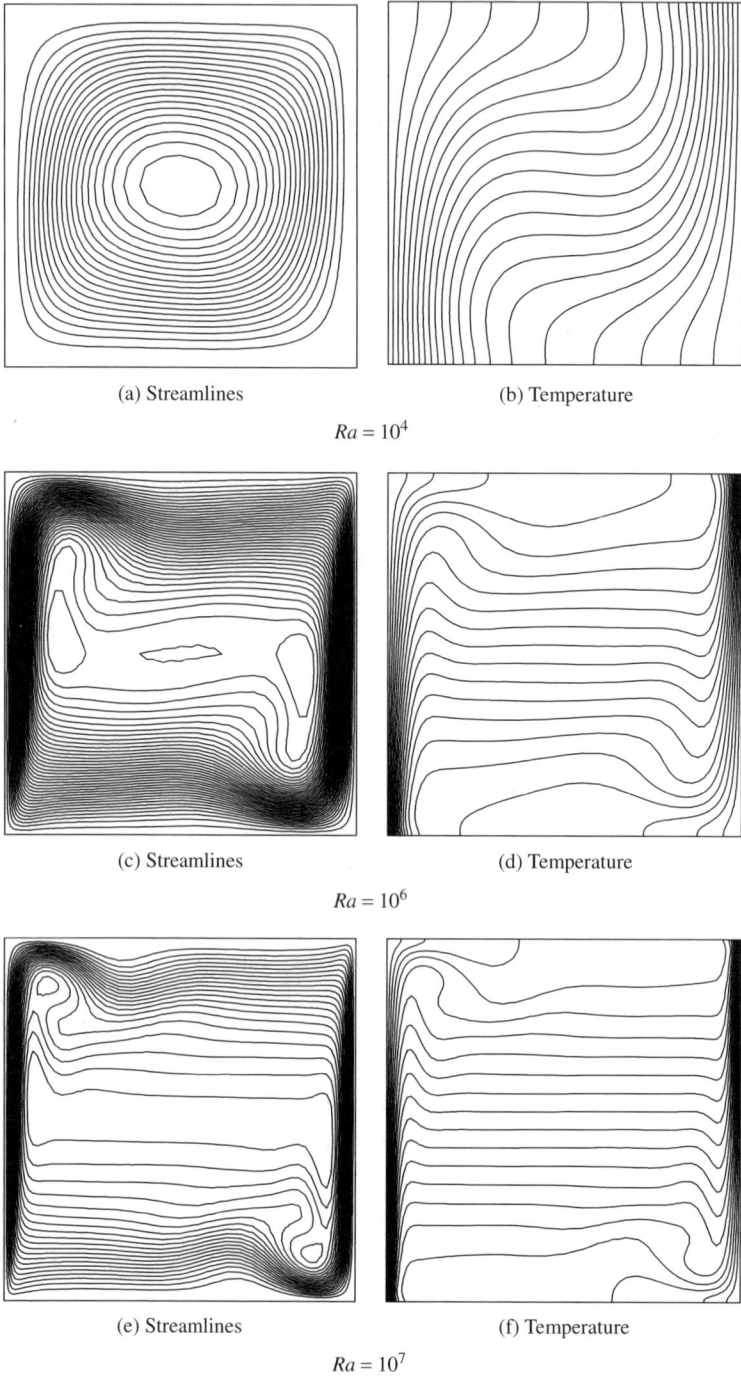

(a) Streamlines   (b) Temperature

$Ra = 10^4$

(c) Streamlines   (d) Temperature

$Ra = 10^6$

(e) Streamlines   (f) Temperature

$Ra = 10^7$

Figure 7.28   Natural convection in a square enclosure. Streamlines and temperature contours for different Rayleigh numbers, $Pr = 0.71$

7.11.3 Mixed convection heat transfer

A mixed convection heat transfer mode has features of both forced and natural convection. The mixed convection solution to a heat transfer problem is necessary if the Reynolds number is small and the importance of the buoyancy contribution is significant. The equations solved are those of forced convection with the addition of a source term (Equation 7.70) in the gravitational direction. If the direction of gravity is not aligned with either of the coordinate directions (x_1 and x_2), then appropriate components of the source term need to be added to the momentum equations. The effect of mixed convection can be measured by calculating the source term of Equation 7.70. If this term is close to zero, then the buoyancy effects can be ignored and a forced convection solution is sufficient. However, if the value of the source term is far from being zero (either in the negative or positive sense), then a mixed convection solution is essential.

Here we consider a simple mixed convection problem in a rectangular vertical channel as shown in Figure 7.29. In order to compare the results with the analytical solution for

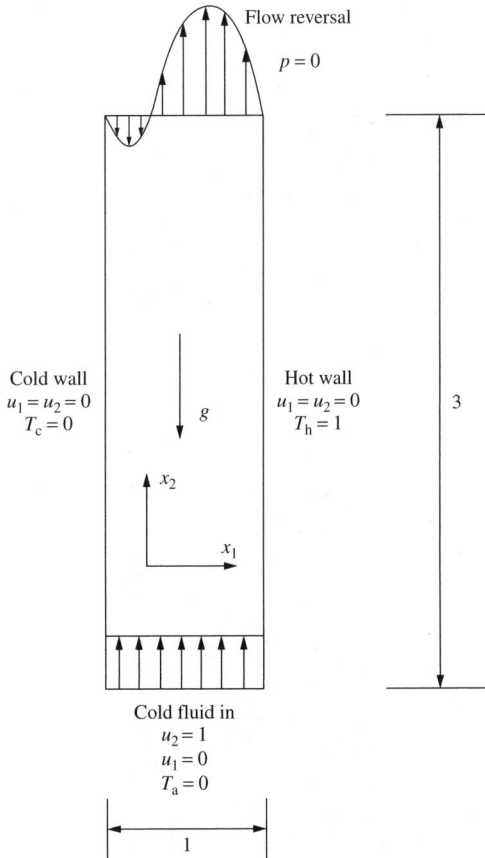

Figure 7.29 Mixed convection in a vertical channel. Geometry and boundary conditions

fully developed flow in a channel, as given in reference (Aung and Worku 1986a), the non-dimensional scales require changing. The scales used by Aung and Worku are

$$x_2^* = \frac{x_2}{ReL}; \quad u_1^* = \frac{u_1 L}{\nu} \tag{7.191}$$

All other scales are the same as the forced convection scale discussed in Section 7.3. The above scales lead to some changes in the non-dimensional form of the mixed convection equation. The source term GrT^*/Re^2 in the mixed convection equation will be GrT/Re and the Reynolds number at all other locations will disappear. The great advantage of applying this scale is that the non-dimensional length of the channel can be considerably reduced. The analytical solution for a fully developed mixed convection profile is given by Aung and Worku as

$$u_1 = \frac{Gr}{Re}(1 - r_T)\left(-\frac{x_1^3}{6} + \frac{x_1^2}{4} - \frac{x_1}{12}\right) - 6x_1^2 + 6x_1 \tag{7.192}$$

where

$$r_T = \frac{T_c - T_a}{T_h - T_a} \tag{7.193}$$

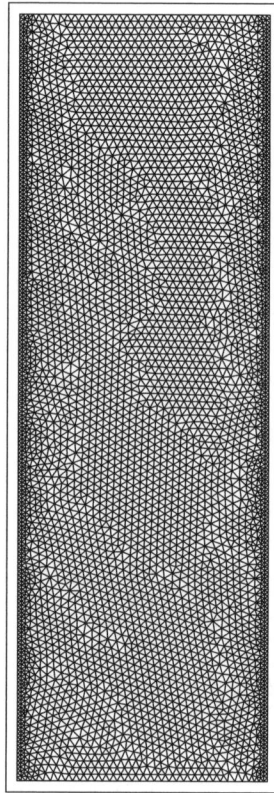

Figure 7.30   Mixed convection in a vertical channel. Unstructured finite element mesh

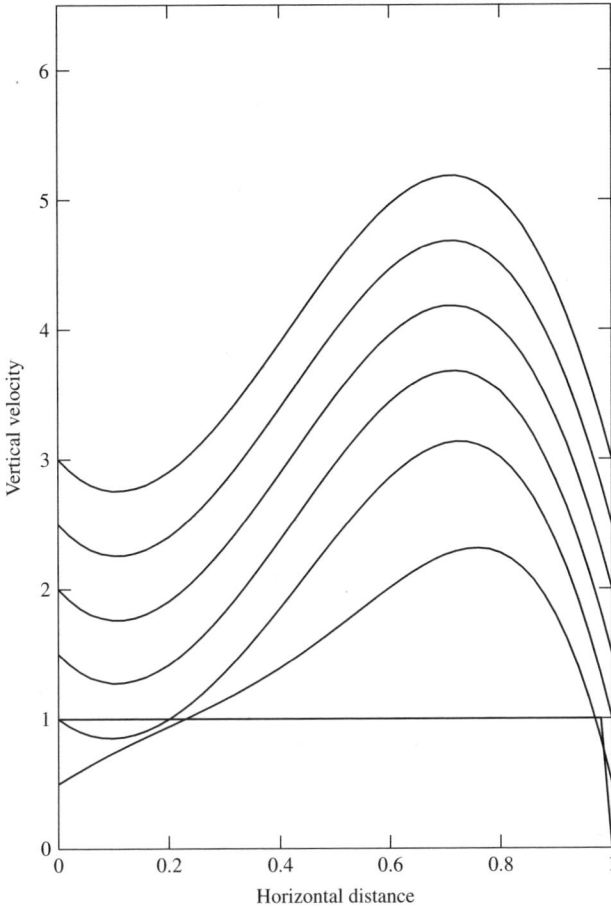

Figure 7.31 Mixed convection in a vertical channel. Developing velocity profiles at various vertical sections

Two vertical plates serve as the channel walls, one of them being at a higher temperature ($T_h = 1$) than that of the other wall. The temperature T_c of the cold wall is 0.5 and the cold fluid entering the channel from the bottom is zero ($T_a = 0$). A uniform, non-dimensional, vertical velocity of unity is imposed at the entrance ($u_2 = 1$). The direction of gravity is assumed to act in the negative x_2 direction. The inlet Reynolds number is 100 and the Grashof number is assumed to be 25,000, which results in a Gr/Re value of 250. At the exit, zero pressure values are imposed, and the total length of the channel is three times the width of the channel. The Reynolds number is defined with respect to the width of the channel.

This in an example of buoyancy-aided convective heat transfer, as the buoyancy is helping the flow to move quicker by creating a density-driven upward flow close to the hot wall. However, at very high Richardson numbers, the flow reversal is possible in this type of problem, as shown in Figure 7.29. It is quite possible in certain practical applications

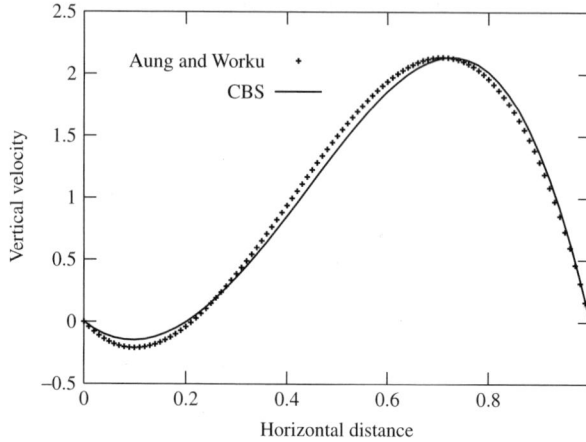

Figure 7.32   Mixed convection in a vertical channel. Comparison of velocity profile at exit with fully developed analytical solution (Aung and Worku 1986b)

that the flow will be forced from the top of the channel (in the negative x_2 direction). Such a flow will be called *opposing* flow in which the buoyancy-driven flow is in the opposite direction of the forced flow.

The mesh used in the computations was fully unstructured and is shown in Figure 7.30. The mesh is fine close to the solid walls and a total number of 8956 elements and 4710 nodes were employed. Figure 7.31 shows the velocity profile distributions at various heights. As seen, the air flows upwards close to the inlet and flow reversal occurs somewhere between the vertical distances of 0.5 and 1.0 from the inlet. The flow is nearly fully developed at a vertical distance of 2 from the inlet. As mentioned previously, the ratio (GR/Re) is 250 and a further increase in this ratio will lead to a stronger flow reversal. Further details regarding this type of problem may be found in references (Aung and Worku 1986a) and (Aung and Worku 1986b). A comparison of the fully developed velocity profile with the analytical solution is given in Figure 7.32 (Aung and Worku 1986a) and, as may be seen, the agreement is excellent.

7.12   Introduction to Turbulent Flow

In all convection heat transfer applications, turbulence becomes important for Reynolds or Rayleigh numbers beyond a certain critical value. However, turbulent convection is a complex phenomenon, but there are several ways of dealing with such problems. The three major methods of dealing with turbulent flow problems are the Reynolds Averaged Navier–Stokes (RANS) model (Launder and Spalding 1972; Mohammadi and Pironneau 1994; Wilcox 1993), the Large Eddy Simulation (LES) model (Sagaut 1998) and Direct Numerical Simulation (DNS) (Moin and Makesh 1998) technique. Of these three methods, the DNS technique gives a detailed and accurate description of turbulent flow, which is obtained by solving the

Navier–Stokes equations on a mesh with element sizes very close to zero. The disadvantage of DNS is that computing hardware is not yet available to tackle any reasonably sized practical problem. The LES technique is computationally less intensive than DNS and results in a time-dependent turbulent pattern, which is averaged in space. Currently available computing resources can only just model small-scale 3D problems. The RANS method is the most widely used turbulence modelling approach in the engineering industry due to the relatively small number of nodes required to compute turbulence as compared to the DNS and LES techniques. However, the results are averaged over a time scale and therefore only time-averaged quantities are obtained from these models. The accuracy of the results are highly dependent on the model and mesh employed. A detailed discussion on these methods is outside the scope of this book, but interested readers should consult available text books and research papers on the topic (Launder and Spalding 1972; Mohammadi and Pironneau 1994; Srinivas *et al.* 1994; Wilcox 1993; Wolfstein 1970; Zienkiewicz *et al.* 1996). However, a brief discussion on the RANS approach is given below.

In the RANS approach, all variables in the Navier–Stokes equations are replaced by the summation of an averaged value and the instantaneous variation, that is,

$$\phi_i = \overline{\phi}_i + \phi_i' \tag{7.194}$$

where ϕ_i' is the instantaneous variation of ϕ and $\overline{\phi}_i$ is a time-averaged value of ϕ given as

$$\overline{\phi}_i = \frac{1}{t} \int_0^t \phi_i \, dt \tag{7.195}$$

where t is a time scale greater than that of the turbulence scale. Figure 7.33 shows the time variation of the velocity. Following on from Equation 7.194, we can write the variation of the different variables as follows:

$$u_i = \overline{u}_i + u_i'; \quad p = \overline{p} + p'; \quad T = \overline{T} + T' \tag{7.196}$$

The substitution of the above quantities into the continuity and momentum equations will lead to the following RANS equations:

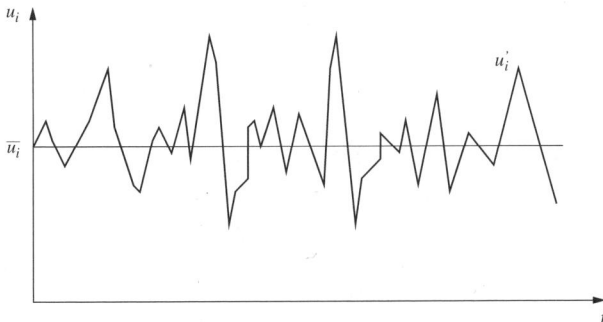

Figure 7.33 Turbulence velocity variation with time

Conservation of mass

$$\frac{\partial \overline{u_1}}{\partial x_1} + \frac{\partial \overline{u_2}}{\partial x_2} = 0 \tag{7.197}$$

Conservation of momentum, x_1 component

$$\frac{\partial \overline{u_1}}{\partial t} + \overline{u}_1 \frac{\partial \overline{u_1}}{\partial x_1} + \overline{u}_2 \frac{\partial \overline{u_1}}{\partial x_2} = -\frac{1}{\rho}\frac{\partial \overline{p}}{\partial x_1} + \frac{1}{\rho}\frac{\partial \overline{\tau_{11}}}{\partial x_1} + \frac{1}{\rho}\frac{\partial \overline{\tau_{12}}}{\partial x_2} - \frac{\partial}{\partial x_1}(\overline{u_1' u_1'}) - \frac{\partial}{\partial x_2}(\overline{u_1' u_2'})$$

$$\tag{7.198}$$

Conservation of momentum, x_2 component

$$\frac{\partial \overline{u_2}}{\partial t} + \overline{u}_1 \frac{\partial \overline{u_2}}{\partial x_1} + \overline{u}_2 \frac{\partial \overline{u_2}}{\partial x_2} = -\frac{1}{\rho}\frac{\partial \overline{p}}{\partial x_2} + \frac{1}{\rho}\frac{\partial \overline{\tau_{21}}}{\partial x_1} + \frac{1}{\rho}\frac{\partial \overline{\tau_{22}}}{\partial x_2} - \frac{\partial}{\partial x_1}(\overline{u_2' u_1'}) - \frac{\partial}{\partial x_2}(\overline{u_2' u_2'})$$

$$\tag{7.199}$$

All the terms of the above equations are very similar to the ones derived in the beginning of this chapter, with averaged quantities appearing as the main variable. The major difference, however, is due to the extra terms appearing in the equations, which are concerned with the turbulent eddy process. These extra terms are normally modelled using turbulence modelling techniques, in order to obtain time-averaged quantities. Therefore, to model the turbulence, it is necessary to consider the widely used Boussinesq hypothesis, namely,

$$\overline{u_i' u_j'} = \tau_{ij}^R = v_t \left(\frac{\partial \overline{u}_i}{\partial x_j} + \frac{\partial \overline{u}_j}{\partial x_i} - \frac{2}{3}\frac{\partial \overline{u}_k}{\partial x_k}\delta_{ij} \right) - \frac{2}{3}\kappa \delta_{ij} \tag{7.200}$$

where τ_{ij}^R is the so-called Reynolds stress, v_t is the turbulent eddy viscosity and κ is the turbulent kinetic energy.

On substituting Equation 7.200 into the time-averaged momentum Equations 7.198 and 7.199, we obtain the final form of the averaged momentum equations as

Conservation of momentum, x_1 component

$$\frac{\partial \overline{u_1}}{\partial t} + \overline{u}_1 \frac{\partial \overline{u_1}}{\partial x_1} + \overline{u}_2 \frac{\partial \overline{u_1}}{\partial x_2} = -\frac{1}{\rho}\frac{\partial \overline{p}}{\partial x_1} + \frac{1}{\rho}\frac{\partial \overline{\tau_{11}}}{\partial x_1} + \frac{1}{\rho}\frac{\partial \overline{\tau_{12}}}{\partial x_2} + \frac{\partial \overline{\tau_{11}}^R}{\partial x_1} + \frac{\partial \overline{\tau_{12}}^R}{\partial x_2} \tag{7.201}$$

Conservation of momentum, x_2 component

$$\frac{\partial \overline{u_2}}{\partial t} + \overline{u}_1 \frac{\partial \overline{u_2}}{\partial x_1} + \overline{u}_2 \frac{\partial \overline{u_2}}{\partial x_2} = -\frac{1}{\rho}\frac{\partial \overline{p}}{\partial x_2} + \frac{1}{\rho}\frac{\partial \overline{\tau_{21}}}{\partial x_1} + \frac{1}{\rho}\frac{\partial \overline{\tau_{22}}}{\partial x_2} + \frac{\partial \overline{\tau_{21}}^R}{\partial x_1} + \frac{\partial \overline{\tau_{22}}^R}{\partial x_2} \tag{7.202}$$

A closer examination of the time-averaged continuity Equation 7.197 and the momentum Equations 7.201 and 7.202, shows that the extra parameters which remain and require determination, are the turbulent eddy viscosity v_t and the turbulent kinetic energy κ.

The turbulent eddy viscosity may be calculated from several turbulence models. The accuracy of such turbulence models can vary, but in this case a one-equation turbulence model will be considered, which employs one transport equation in the calculation of the turbulent eddy viscosity. The turbulent eddy viscosity relation is given as

$$v_t = C_\mu^{1/4} \kappa^{1/2} l_{\mathrm{m}} \tag{7.203}$$

where C_μ is a constant equal to 0.09 and l_m is the Prandtl mixing length, which is assumed to be $l_m = 0.4y$, where y is the shortest distance from a node to the solid wall. The turbulent kinetic energy may be obtained by solving the following transport equation:

$$\frac{\partial \kappa}{\partial t} + \frac{\partial \overline{u}_i \kappa}{\partial x_j} = \frac{\partial}{\partial x_i}\left(\nu + \frac{\nu_t}{Prt}\right)\frac{\partial \kappa}{\partial x_i} + \tau_{ij}^R \frac{\partial \overline{u}_i}{\partial x_j} - \varepsilon \tag{7.204}$$

where Prt is the turbulent Prandtl number that is normally taken to be equal to unity. For the one equation model, the isotropic turbulence energy dissipation rate ε is

$$\varepsilon = C_D \frac{\kappa^{3/2}}{L} \tag{7.205}$$

where the length scale of the turbulence $L = l_m(C_D/C_\mu{}^3)^{1/4}$ and C_D is equal to 1.

7.12.1   Solution procedure and result

The solution procedure follows the steps of the CBS scheme as discussed previously in Section 7.6. If isothermal flow is of interest, then the temperature equation is ignored, and a solution to the turbulent kinetic energy equation becomes the fourth step. For non-isothermal problems, the temperature equation is solved at Step 4, and the turbulent kinetic energy equation is solved at Step 5. At each and every time step, the turbulent eddy viscosity is calculated and substituted into the averaged momentum equations. The example solved is for the case of isothermal flow through a two-dimensional, horizontal rectangular channel. The problem definition is the same as for the example given in Section 7.10. The difference being that the extra boundary condition for the turbulent kinetic energy needs to be imposed. The turbulent kinetic energy value is fixed at the inlet ($\kappa = 0.1$) and zero on the walls. The

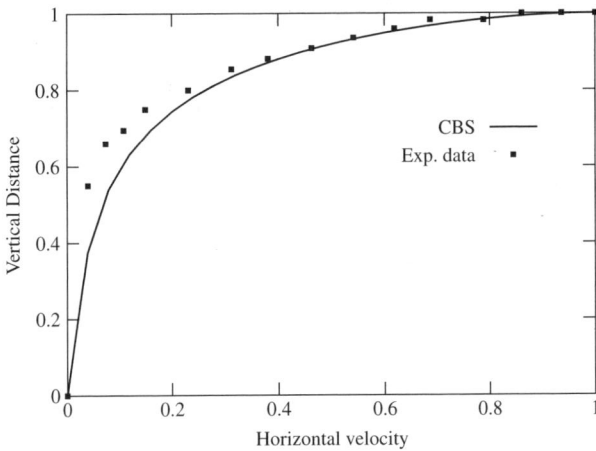

Figure 7.34   Flow through a two-dimensional rectangular channel. Comparison of the exit velocity profile with experimental data (Laufer 1951) at $Re = 24,600$

channel employed in this case is longer than that used for the laminar computation, that is, 40 times the height of the channel.

A structured mesh, with 12,000 elements and 6161 nodes, has been employed in the turbulent flow calculations. The horizontal velocity distribution at the exit of the channel is compared with available experimental data and is shown in Figure 7.34. The inlet Reynolds number is 24,600. The agreement between the experiments and the numerical results is excellent away from the wall. More advanced turbulence models will result in better accuracy of the results.

7.13   Extension to Axisymmetric Problems

The axisymmetric formulation of the heat conduction equations has been discussed in many of the earlier chapters. Here, an extension of the plane formulation to axisymmetric convection heat transfer problems will be discussed. The governing equations, in cylindrical coordinates, are given with respect to Figure 7.35 as follows:

Conservation of Mass

$$\frac{1}{r}\frac{\partial(ru_r)}{\partial r} + \frac{\partial u_z}{\partial z} = 0 \tag{7.206}$$

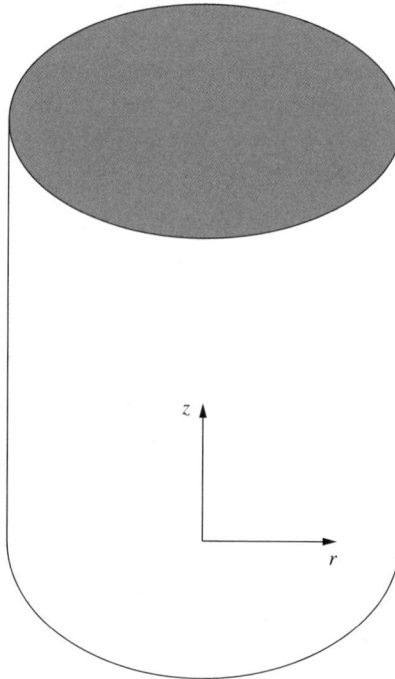

Figure 7.35   Coordinate system for axisymmetric geometries

r momentum component

$$\frac{\partial u_r}{\partial t} + u_r \frac{\partial u_r}{\partial r} + u_z \frac{\partial u_z}{\partial z} = -\frac{1}{\rho} \frac{\partial p}{\partial r} + \nu \left(\frac{1}{r} \frac{\partial}{\partial r} \left(r \frac{\partial u_r}{\partial r} \right) + \frac{\partial^2 u_r}{\partial z^2} - \frac{u_r}{r^2} \right) \qquad (7.207)$$

z momentum component

$$\frac{\partial u_z}{\partial t} + u_r \frac{\partial u_z}{\partial r} + u_z \frac{\partial u_r}{\partial z} = -\frac{1}{\rho} \frac{\partial p}{\partial z} + \nu \left(\frac{1}{r} \frac{\partial}{\partial r} \left(r \frac{\partial u_z}{\partial r} \right) + \frac{\partial^2 u_z}{\partial z^2} \right) \qquad (7.208)$$

Energy equation

$$\rho c_p \left(\frac{\partial T}{\partial t} + u_r \frac{\partial T}{\partial r} + u_z \frac{\partial T}{\partial z} \right) = k \left[\frac{1}{r} \frac{\partial}{\partial r} \left(r \frac{\partial T}{\partial x_r} \right) + \frac{\partial^2 T}{\partial x_z^2} \right] \qquad (7.209)$$

The CBS procedure follows the same steps as for the plane problem. However, the integration of the matrices will be different as the area of the element will no longer be two-dimensional. For example, let us consider the diffusion matrix of the momentum equation. The momentum diffusion matrix for the plane problem is given by Equation 7.148. We can rewrite this as

$$[\mathbf{K_{me_z}}] = \nu \int_\Omega \left(\frac{\partial \mathbf{N}^T}{\partial r} \frac{\partial \mathbf{N}}{\partial r} + \frac{\partial \mathbf{N}^T}{\partial z} \frac{\partial \mathbf{N}}{\partial z} \right) d\Omega$$

$$= \nu \int_\Omega \left(\frac{\partial \mathbf{N}^T}{\partial r} \frac{\partial \mathbf{N}}{\partial r} + \frac{\partial \mathbf{N}^T}{\partial z} \frac{\partial \mathbf{N}}{\partial z} \right) 2\pi r \, dA \qquad (7.210)$$

where the radial coordinate r is expressed as

$$r = N_i r_i + N_j r_j + N_k r_k \qquad (7.211)$$

The formula used in the integration is the same as for any linear triangular element (Equation 7.110). On applying Equation 7.110, Equation 7.210 becomes

$$\mathbf{K_{me_z}} = \nu \frac{2\pi A}{3} (r_i + r_j + r_k) \begin{bmatrix} b_i^2 & b_i b_j & b_i b_k \\ b_j b_i & b_j^2 & b_j b_k \\ b_k b_i & b_k b_j & b_k^2 \end{bmatrix}$$

$$+ \nu \frac{2\pi A}{3} (r_i + r_j + r_k) \begin{bmatrix} c_i^2 & c_i c_j & c_i c_k \\ c_j c_i & c_j^2 & c_j c_k \\ c_k c_i & c_k c_j & c_k^2 \end{bmatrix} \qquad (7.212)$$

All the other terms of the axisymmetric equations may be discretized in a similar fashion. In discretizing the r momentum diffusion terms, the term u_r/r^2 can be approximated by averaging r over an element.

7.14 Summary

In this chapter, we have given a brief overview of convection heat transfer. However, the subject is vast in extent and it is difficult to cover all aspects within a single chapter.

Several details have been neglected in order to keep the discussion brief. For instance, higher-order elements have not been discussed, and few solution procedures have been touched upon. Special topics such as adaptive meshing for heat transfer applications is not mentioned (Lewis *et al.* 1991; Nithiarasu 2002; Nithiarasu and Zienkiewicz 2000). However, the CBS scheme for convection heat transfer has been discussed in detail for linear triangular elements. A complete knowledge of such a single scheme will provide the reader with a strong starting point for understanding other relevant fluid dynamics and convection heat transfer solution procedures.

7.15 Exercise

Example 7.15.1 *Derive a convection–diffusion equation using a differential control volume approach.*

Example 7.15.2 *Derive the CG method for a convection–diffusion equation with the source term Q.*

Example 7.15.3 *Derive Navier–Stokes equations in cylindrical and spherical coordinates.*

Example 7.15.4 *Reduce the incompressible Navier–Stokes equations to solve a one-dimensional convection heat transfer problem.*

Example 7.15.5 *For natural convection problems, if α is replaced by ν in the non-dimensional scaling, derive the new non-dimensional form.*

Example 7.15.6 *Calculate laminar flow and heat transfer from a hot cylinder at Re = 40 using the CBS flow code. Assume the buoyancy effect is negligible.*

Example 7.15.7 *Compute the transient vortex shedding phenomenon behind a circular cylinder at Re = 100 using CBS flow. Assume that the flow is isothermal.*

Example 7.15.8 *Write a program in any standard scientific language to calculate stream functions from a computed velocity field.*

Bibliography

Aung W and Worku G 1986a Developing flow and flow reversal in a vertical channel with asymmetric wall temperatures, *ASME Journal of Heat Transfer*, **108**, 299–304.

Aung W and Worku G 1986b Theory of fully developed, combined convection including flow reversal, *ASME J. Heat Transfer*, **108**, 485–488.

Brooks AN and Hughes TJR 1982 Streamline upwind/Petrov-Galerkin formulation for convection dominated flows with particular emphasis on incompressible Navier–Stokes equation, *Computer Methods in Applied Mechanics and Engineering*, **32**, 199–259.

Cheung TJ 2002 *Computational Fluid Dynamics*, Cambridge University Press, Cambridge, UK.

Clift R, Grace JR and Weber ME 1978 *Bubbles Drops and Particles*, Academic Press, New York.

de Vahl Davis G 1983 Natural convection in a square cavity: a benchmark numerical solution, *International Journal for Numerical Methods in Fluids*, textbf3, 249–264.

Donea J 1984 A Taylor–Galerkin method for convective transport problems, *International Journal for Numerical Methods in Fluids*, **20**, 101–119.

Donea A and Huerta A 2003 *Finite Element Method for Flow Problems*, John Wiley & Sons, Chichester.

Feng ZG and Michaelides EE 2000 A numerical study on the heat transfer from a sphere at high Reynolds and Peclet numbers, *International Journal of Heat Mass Transfer*, **43**, 4445–4454.

Fletcher CAJ 1988 *Computational Techniques for Fluid Dynamics, Vol.1, Fundamentals and General Techniques*, Springer-Verlag.

Gowda YTK, Narayana PAA and Seetharamu KN 1998 Finite element analysis of mixed convection over in-line tube bundles, *International Journal of Heat and Mass Transfer*, **41**, 1613–1619.

Gresho PM and Sani RL 2000 *Incompressible Flow and the Finite Element Method, Vol. 2, Isothermal Laminar Flow*, John Wiley & Sons, Chichester.

Gülçat Ü and Aslan AR 1997 Accurate 3D viscous incompressible flow calculations with FEM, *International Journal for Numerical Methods in Fluids*, **25**, 985–1001.

Hirsch C 1989 *Numerical Computation of Internal and External Flows*, Vol. 1, John Wiley.

Jaluria Y 1986 *Natural Convection Heat and Mass Transfer*, Pergamon Press.

Jaluria Y and Torrance KE 1986 *Computational Heat Transfer*, Hemisphere Publishing Corporation.

Le Clair BP, Hamielec AE and Pruppacher HR 1970 A numerical study of the drag on a sphere at low and intermediate Reynolds numbers, *Journal of Atmospheric Sciences*, **27**, 308–315.

Laufer J 1951 *Investigation of Turbulent Flow in a Two Dimensional Channel*, Report 1053, NACA.

Launder BE and Spalding DB 1972 *Mathematical Models of Turbulence*, Academic Press, New York.

Lee S 2000 A numerical study of the unsteady wake behind a sphere in a uniform flow at moderate Reynolds numbers, *Computers and Fluids*,**29**, 639–667.

Lewis RW, Huang HC, Usmani AS and Cross J 1991 Finite element analysis of heat transfer and flow problems using adaptive remeshing, *International Journal for Numerical Methods in Engineering*, **32**, 767–782.

Lewis RW, Huang HC, Usmani AS and Cross J 1995 Efficient mould filling simulation in castings by an explicit finite element method, *International Journal for Numerical Methods in Fluids*,**20**, 493–506.

Lewis RW, Morgan K, Thomas HR and Seetharamu KN 1996 *The Finite Element Method for Heat Transfer Analysis*, John Wiley & Sons.

Lewis RW, Ravindran K and Usmani AS 1995 Finite element solution of incompressible flows using an explicit segregated approach, *Archives of Computational Methods in Engineering*, **2**, 69–93.

Löhner R 2001 *Applied CFD Techniques*, John Wiley & Sons, New York.

Löhner R, Morgan K and Zienkiewicz OC 1984 The solution of non-linear hyperbolic equation systems by the finite element method, *International Journal of Numerical Methods in Fluids*, **4**, 1043–1063.

Magnaudet J, Rivero M and Fabre J 1995 Accelerated flows past a rigid sphere or a spherical bubble. Part I: Steady straining flow, *Journal of Fluid Mechanics*, **284**, 97–135.

Malan AG, Lewis RW and Nithiarasu P 2002 An improved unsteady, unstructured, artificial compressibility, finite volume scheme for viscous incompressible flows: Part I. Theory and implementation, *International Journal for Numerical Methods in Engineering*, **54**, 695–714.

Massarotti N, Nithiarasu P and Zienkiewicz OC 1998 Characteristic - based - split (CBS) algorithm for incompressible flow problems with heat transfer, *International Journal of Numerical Methods for Heat and Fluid Flow*, **8**, 969–990.

Minkowycz WJ, Sparrow EM, Schneider GE and Pletcher RH 1988 *Handbook of Numerical Heat Transfer*, John Wiley & Sons.

Mohammadi B and Pironneau O 1994 *Analysis of k-ε Turbulence Model*, John Wiley & Sons.

Moin P and Makesh K 1998 Direct numerical simulation: a tool in turbulence research, *Annual Review of Fluid Mechanics*, **30**, 539–578.

Morgan K, Weatherhill NP, Hassan O, Brookes PJ, Said R and Jones J 1999 A parallel framework for multi-disciplinary aerospace engineering simulations using unstructured meshes, *International Journal for Numerical Methods in Fluids*, **31**, 159–173.

Nithiarasu P 2002 An adaptive remeshing scheme for laminar natural convection problems, *Heat and Mass Transfer*, **38**, 243–250.

Nithiarasu P 2003 An efficient artificial compressibility (AC) scheme based on the characteristic based split (CBS) method for incompressible flows, *International Journal for Numerical Methods in Engineering*, **56**, 1815–1845.

Nithiarasu P, Massarotti N and Mathur JS 2004 Three-dimensional convection heat transfer calculations using the characteristic based split (CBS) scheme, *ASME/ISHMT Conference*, Chennai, India, January.

Nithiarasu P, Seetharamu KN and Sundararajan T 1998 Finite element analysis of transient natural convection in an odd-shaped enclosure, *International Journal of Numerical Methods for Heat and Fluid Flow*, **8**, 199–216.

Nithiarasu P and Zienkiewicz OC 2000 Adaptive mesh generation for fluid mechanics problems, *International Journal for Numerical Methods in Engineering*, **47**, 629–662.

Patnaik BSV, Gowda YTK, Ravisankar MS, Narayana PAA and Seetharamu KN 2001 Finite element simulation of internal flows with heat transfer using a velocity correction approach, *Sadhana –Academy Proceedings in Engineering Sciences*, **26**, 251–283.

Pironneau O 1989 *Finite Element Method for Fluids*, John Wiley & Sons, Chichester.

Ravindran K and Lewis RW 1998 Finite element modelling of solidification effects in mould filling, *Finite Element Analysis and Design*, **31**, 99–116.

Rimon Y and Cheng SI 1969 Numerical solution of a uniform flow over a sphere at intermediate Reynolds numbers, *Phys. Fluids*, **12**, 949–959.

Sai BVKS, Seetharamu KN and Narayana PAA 1994 Solution of laminar natural convection in a square cavity by an explicit finite element scheme, *Numerical Heat Transfer Part A: Applications*, **25**, 593–609.

Sagaut P 1998 *Large Eddy Simulation for Incompressible Flows*, Springer, Berlin.

Shames IH 1982 Mechanics of Fluids, McGraw-Hill.

Schlichting H 1968 Boundary Layer Theory, Sixth Edition, McGraw-Hill book company.

Spalding DB 1972 A novel finite difference formulation for differential equations involving both first and second derivatives, *International Journal for Numerical Methods in Engineering*, **4**, 551–559.

Srinivas M, Ravisankar MS, Seetharamu KN and Aswathanarayana PA 1994 Finite element analysis of internal flows with heat transfer, *Sadhana –Academy Proceedings in Engineering*, **19**, 785–816.

Tezduyar TE, Osawa Y, Stein K, Benney R, Kumar V and McCunne J 2000 Computational methods for parachute aerodynamics, *Proceedings of Computational Fluid Dynamics for the 21st Century*, Kyoto, Japan.

Usmani AS, Cross JT and Lewis RW A 1992 finite element model for the simulation of mould filling in metal casting and the associated heat transfer, *International Journal for Numerical Methods in Engineering*, **35**, 787–806.

Usmani AS, Lewis RW and Seetharamu KN 1992 Finite element modelling of natural convection controlled change of phase, *International Journal for Numerical Methods in Fluids*, **14**, 1019–1036.

Whitaker S 1983 *Fundamental Principles of Heat Transfer*, Krieger Publishing Company, Malabar.

Wilcox DC 1993 *Turbulence Modelling for CFD*, DCW Industries, Inc.

Wolfstein M 1970 Some solutions of plane turbulent impinging jets, *ASME Journal of Basic Engineering*, **92**, 915–922.

Yuge T 1960 Experiments on heat transfer from spheres including combined natural and forced convection, *ASME J. Heat Transfer*, **82**, 214–220.

Zienkiewicz OC and Codina R 1995 A general algorithm for compressible and incompressible flow, Part I, The split characteristic based scheme, *International Journal for Numerical Methods in Fluids*, **20**, 869–885.

Zienkiewicz OC, Nithiarasu P, Codina R, Vazquez M and Ortiz P 1999 An efficient and accurate algorithm for fluid mechanics problems. The characteristic based split (CBS) algorithm, *International Journal for Numerical Methods in Fluids*, **31**, 359–392.

Zienkiewicz OC and Taylor RL 2000 *The Finite Element Method, Vol.3, Fluid Dynamics*, Butterworth and Heinemann, Oxford.

Zienkiewicz OC, Sai BVKS, Morgan K and Codina R 1996 Split characteristic based semi-implicit algorithm for laminar/turbulent incompressible flows, *International Journal of Numerical Methods in Fluids*, **23**, 1–23.

8

Convection in Porous Media

8.1 Introduction

The phenomenon of fluid flow and heat transfer in porous media has been recognized as a separate engineering topic for the last three decades. Several books have been published on this topic (Kaviany 1991; Lewis and Schrefler 1998; Nield and Bejan 1992; Zienkiewicz *et al.* 1999). Convective heat transfer in porous media occurs in many engineering applications including packed beds, thermal insulation, metal solidification and geothermal problems. Advanced applications such as petroleum reservoirs, multi-phase flows and drying have also been studied using finite elements (Lewis and Ferguson 1990; Lewis *et al.* 1984, 1983, 1989; Lewis and Sukirman 1993; Murugesan *et al.* 2001; Pao *et al.* 2001). A wide variety of solution methodologies, both analytical and numerical, are available for solving porous media flow and heat transfer. Analytical methods are limited by many factors and the solution of realistic field problems is normally intractable by such techniques. With the advent of computing power in the last three decades, solutions to many practical porous medium problems are feasible using numerical methods (Lewis and Schrefler 1998; Zienkiewicz *et al.* 1999). Such numerical solution procedures have their own limitations, for example, accuracy, implementation difficulties and so forth. However, with a proper combination of algorithms and discretization techniques, it is possible to obtain reasonably accurate solutions for complex problems, in which analytical approaches would not be feasible. In this chapter, the finite element modelling of incompressible flow and heat transfer through porous media will be outlined in detail.

The flow of fluid in a saturated porous media was quantified by a simple, phenomenological, linear relation by *Darcy* in the nineteenth century (Darcy 1856). Darcy's law relates the pressure drop (head) to the flow rate across a porous column. The following relation can be written from such observations:

$$u_i = -\frac{\kappa}{\mu} \frac{\partial p}{\partial x_i} \tag{8.1}$$

Fundamentals of the Finite Element Method for Heat and Fluid Flow   R. W. Lewis, P. Nithiarasu and K. N. Seetharamu
© 2004 John Wiley & Sons, Ltd   ISBNs: 0-470-84788-3 (HB); 0-470-84789-1 (PB)

Where u_i are the seepage velocity components, κ (m^2) is the permeability of the medium, μ is the dynamic viscosity of the fluid, p is the pressure and x_i are the coordinate axes. For two-dimensional flow, we can rewrite the velocity components as

$$u_1 = -\frac{\kappa}{\mu}\frac{\partial p}{\partial x_1}$$

$$u_2 = -\frac{\kappa}{\mu}\frac{\partial p}{\partial x_2} \tag{8.2}$$

It is interesting to note that the above equation is very similar to Ohm's law for the flow of electricity, Fourier's law of heat conduction and Fick's law for mass diffusion. However, simple relations such as Darcy's law are not always applicable, and further modifications or extensions are necessary in order to accurately predict the flow field in porous media.

Several years after the introduction of Darcy's law, two major additions to the model have extended its use in many engineering disciplines including chemical, mechanical and civil engineering. The first extension was due to *Forchheimer* (Forchheimer 1901), and this modification accounted for moderate and high Reynolds number effects with the addition of a nonlinear term in the Darcy equation. A relationship for the drag force was introduced by Forchheimer, Figure 8.1, as

$$D_p = au_i + bu_i^2 \tag{8.3}$$

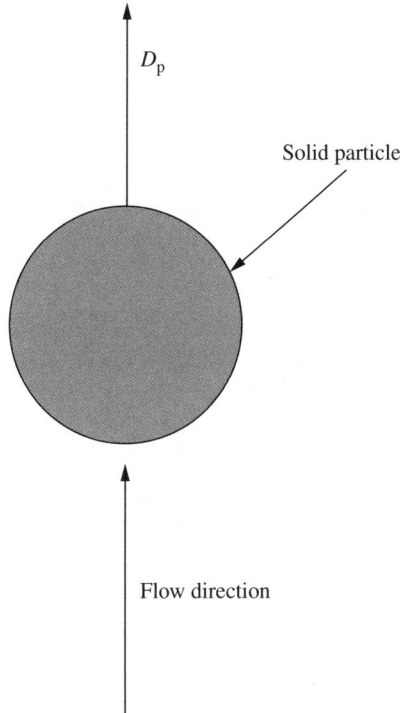

Figure 8.1   Drag force on a porous medium grain

which is balanced by the pressure force as follows:

$$au_i + bu_i^2 = -\frac{\partial p}{\partial x_i} \tag{8.4}$$

In the above equation, the first term on the left-hand side is, in essence, similar to the linear drag term introduced by Darcy, and the second term is the nonlinear drag term. The parameters a and b are determined by empirical relations and one such correlation was given by Ergun (Ergun 1952), that is,

$$a = 150\frac{(1 - \epsilon^2)}{\epsilon^3}\frac{\mu_f}{d_p^2} \tag{8.5}$$

and

$$b = 1.75\frac{(1 - \epsilon)}{\epsilon^3}\frac{\rho_f}{d_p} \tag{8.6}$$

It should be noted, however, that other suitable correlations may also be employed for different ranges of the bed porosity, ϵ, to obtain the non-Darcian flow behaviour inside a porous medium. In the above equations, d_p is the solid particle size in a porous medium, and ρ_f is the fluid density. The above solid matrix drag relation can also be expressed in terms of the medium permeability κ by defining

$$\kappa = \frac{\epsilon^3 d_p^2}{150(1 - \epsilon)^2} \tag{8.7}$$

The flow relationship, given by Equation 8.4, can be rewritten in terms of permeability as

$$\frac{\mu_f u_i}{\kappa} + \frac{1.75}{\sqrt{150}}\frac{\rho_f}{\sqrt{\kappa}}\frac{|\mathbf{V}|}{\epsilon^{3/2}}u_i = -\frac{\partial p}{\partial x_i} \tag{8.8}$$

Although the above equation gives an accurate solution at higher Reynolds numbers, it is not accurate enough to solve flow in highly porous and confined media. In order to deal with the viscous and higher porosity effects, *Brinkman* introduced an extension to the Darcy model in 1947, which included a second-order viscous term with an equivalent viscosity for the porous medium (Brinkman 1947). The viscous extension, as given by Brinkman, can be written as (Figure 8.2)

$$au_i = -\frac{\partial p}{\partial x_i} + \mu_e\frac{\partial^2 u_i}{\partial x_i^2} \tag{8.9}$$

where μ_e is the equivalent viscosity of the porous medium. This modification takes into account the no-slip conditions that exist on the confining walls (Tong and Subramanian 1985).

The Darcy model and the extensions discussed above have been widely used in the past. However, a generalized model, incorporating the flow regimes covered by both Darcy's model and its extension, will have several advantages (Hsu and Cheng 1990; Nithiarasu et al. 1997, 2002; Vafai and Tien 1981; Whitaker 1961). One of these is that the generalized flow model approaches the standard incompressible Navier–Stokes equations when

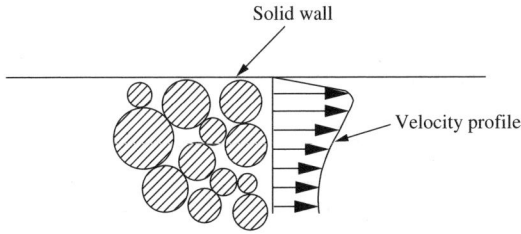

Figure 8.2 Viscous forces on a bounding wall of a porous medium

porosity approaches a value of unity. The discussion on convection in porous media in this chapter will be brief and based on the generalized porous medium approach. Readers should be aware of the CBS scheme and the notations used in the previous chapter before reading this section.

8.2 Generalized Porous Medium Flow Approach

In this section, a generalized model for solving porous medium flows will be presented. Let us consider the balance of mass, momentum, energy and species for two-dimensional flow in a fluid-saturated porous medium of variable porosity. The derivations are very similar to the one discussed in Chapter 7. We shall assume the medium to be isotropic with constant physical properties, except for the medium porosity. Let a_f be the fraction of area available for flow per unit of cross-sectional area (Figure 8.3), at a location in a given direction. In fact, a_f is an averaged quantity, the average being taken over the length scale of the voids (or the length scale of the particles, if the porous bed is made up of particles), in the flow direction. For an isotropic porous bed, a_f will be identical in all directions and can also be equal to the local bed porosity, ϵ. In spite of averaging over the void length scale, the

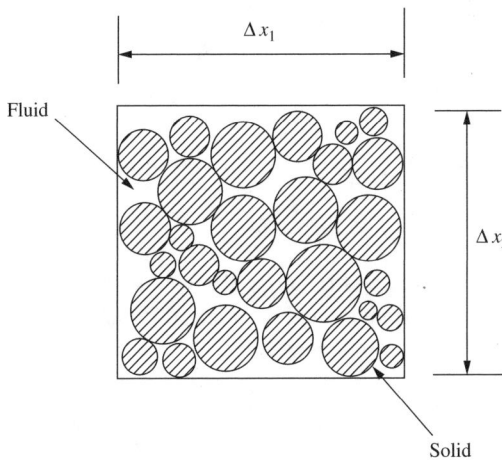

Figure 8.3 Fluid-saturated porous medium. Infinitesimal control volume

fractional area a_f may vary from location to location on the macro-length scale 'L' of the physical problem owing to the variation of the bed porosity.

The porosity, ϵ, of the medium is defined as

$$\epsilon = \frac{\text{void volume}}{\text{total volume}} = \frac{a_f \Delta x_1 \Delta x_2}{\Delta x_1 \Delta x_2} = a_f \tag{8.10}$$

Now, the mass balance of an arbitrary control volume, as shown in Figure 8.3, gives (refer to Chapter 7)

$$\frac{\partial \rho_f}{\partial t} + \frac{\partial (\rho_f u_{1f})}{\partial x_1} + \frac{\partial (\rho_f u_{2f})}{\partial x_2} = 0 \tag{8.11}$$

where the subscript 'f' stands for fluid, ρ is the density and u_1 and u_2 are the velocity components in the x_1 and x_2 directions respectively. The volume averaged velocity components may be defined as (Nield and Bejan 1992),

$$u_1 = \epsilon u_{1f} \qquad u_2 = \epsilon u_{2f} \tag{8.12}$$

Equation 8.11 can be simplified for an incompressible flow (constant density) as follows:

$$\frac{\partial u_1}{\partial x_1} + \frac{\partial u_2}{\partial x_2} = 0 \tag{8.13}$$

Similarly, the equation for momentum balance can be derived. For instance, in the x_2 direction, the momentum balance gives

$$\frac{\rho_f}{\epsilon} \left[\frac{\partial u_2}{\partial t} + \frac{\partial}{\partial x_1} \left(\frac{u_1 u_2}{\epsilon} \right) + \frac{\partial}{\partial x_2} \left(\frac{u_2^2}{\epsilon} \right) \right] =$$
$$-\frac{1}{\epsilon} \frac{\partial}{\partial x_2} (p_f \epsilon) + \frac{\mu_e}{\epsilon} \left(\frac{\partial^2 u_2}{\partial x_1^2} + \frac{\partial^2 u_2}{\partial x_2^2} \right) + (\rho_{\text{ref}} - \rho_f) g - D_{x_2} \tag{8.14}$$

where μ_e is the equivalent viscosity, p_f the fluid pressure, g the acceleration due to gravity and D_{x_2} is the matrix drag per unit volume of the porous medium. The particle drag can be expressed in the following form, as discussed in Section 8.1:

$$D_p = aV + bV^2 \tag{8.15}$$

for a one-dimensional flow with velocity V. For two-dimensional flow, the drag in the x_2 direction is given as

$$D_{x_2} = au_2 + b(u_1^2 + u_2^2)^{1/2} u_2 \tag{8.16}$$

by resolving the vertical drag expression along the x_2 direction. In the present formulation, Ergun's correlation for the constants a and b, given in Equations 8.5 and 8.6, will be used.

Now, the solid matrix drag component D_{x_2} can be written as

$$D_{x_2} = \frac{\mu_f u_2}{\kappa} + \frac{1.75}{\sqrt{150}} \frac{\rho_f}{\sqrt{\kappa}} \frac{|\mathbf{V}|}{\epsilon^{3/2}} u_2 \tag{8.17}$$

where $\mathbf{V}$ is the velocity vector in the field. By substituting Equation 8.17 into Equation 8.14, we obtain

$$\frac{\rho_f}{\epsilon}\left[\frac{\partial u_2}{\partial t} + \frac{\partial}{\partial x_1}\left(\frac{u_1 u_2}{\epsilon}\right) + \frac{\partial}{\partial x_2}\left(\frac{u_2^2}{\epsilon}\right)\right] = -\frac{1}{\epsilon}\frac{\partial}{\partial x_2}(p_f\epsilon) + \frac{\mu_e}{\epsilon}\left(\frac{\partial^2 u_2}{\partial x_1^2} + \frac{\partial^2 u_2}{\partial x_2^2}\right)$$

$$+(\rho_{ref} - \rho_f)g - \frac{\mu_f u_2}{\kappa} - \frac{1.75}{\sqrt{150}}\frac{\rho_f}{\sqrt{\kappa}}\frac{|\mathbf{V}|}{\epsilon^{3/2}}u_2 \tag{8.18}$$

Similarly, other momentum components can also be derived, and the final form of the governing equations for incompressible flow through a porous medium in dimensional form can be given, using indicial notation, as

Continuity

$$\frac{\partial u_i}{\partial x_i} = 0 \tag{8.19}$$

Momentum

$$\frac{\rho_f}{\epsilon}\left[\frac{\partial u_i}{\partial t} + \frac{\partial}{\partial x_j}\left(\frac{u_i u_j}{\epsilon}\right)\right] = -\frac{1}{\epsilon}\frac{\partial}{\partial x_i}(p_f\epsilon) + \frac{\mu_e}{\epsilon}\frac{\partial^2 u_i}{\partial x_i^2}$$

$$+(\rho_{ref} - \rho_f)g\gamma_i - \frac{\mu_f u_i}{\kappa} - \frac{1.75}{\sqrt{150}}\frac{\rho_f}{\sqrt{\kappa}}\frac{|\mathbf{V}|}{\epsilon^{3/2}}u_i \tag{8.20}$$

The previous equation can be simplified by substituting Equation 8.19 into Equation 8.20. The energy conservation equation is also derived in a similar manner. The final form of the energy equation is
Energy

$$\left[\epsilon(\rho c_p)_f + (1 - \epsilon)(\rho c_p)_s\right]\frac{\partial T}{\partial t} + (\rho c_p)_f u_i \frac{\partial T}{\partial x_i} = k\left(\frac{\partial^2 T}{\partial x_i^2}\right) \tag{8.21}$$

In the above equation, t is the time, c_p is the specific heat, γ_i is a unit vector in the gravity direction, T is the temperature and k is the equivalent thermal conductivity. The subscripts f and s stand for the fluid and solid phases respectively.

It should be noted that the permeability and thermal conductivity values can be directional, in which case they are tensors.

8.2.1 Non-dimensional scales

The non-dimensional form of the equations simplifies most of the calculations. The following final form of the non-dimensional equations may be obtained by suitable scaling.

Continuity equation

$$\frac{\partial u_i^*}{\partial x_i^*} = 0 \tag{8.22}$$

Momentum equations

$$\frac{1}{\epsilon}\frac{\partial u_i^*}{\partial t^*} + \frac{1}{\epsilon}u_j^*\frac{\partial}{\partial x_j^*}\left(\frac{u_i^*}{\epsilon}\right) = -\frac{1}{\epsilon}\frac{\partial}{\partial x_i^*}(\epsilon p_f^*) - \frac{u_i^*}{ReDa}$$

$$-\frac{1.75}{\sqrt{150}}\frac{|\mathbf{V}^*|}{\sqrt{Da}}\frac{u_i^*}{\epsilon^{3/2}} + \frac{J}{Re\epsilon}\left(\frac{\partial^2 u_i^*}{\partial x_i^{*2}}\right) + \gamma_i\frac{Gr}{Re^2}T^* \tag{8.23}$$

Energy equation

$$\sigma\frac{\partial T^*}{\partial t^*} + u_i^*\frac{\partial T^*}{\partial x_i^*} = \frac{k^*}{RePr}\left(\frac{\partial^2 T^*}{\partial x_i^{*2}}\right) \tag{8.24}$$

In the previous equations, the parameters governing the flow and heat transfer are the Darcy number (Da), Reynolds number (Re), Prandtl number (Pr), Grashof number (Gr), the ratio of heat capacities (σ); porosity of the medium (ϵ), conductivity ratio (k^*), viscosity ratio (J), and the anisotropic property ratios, for the case of an anisotropic medium. The definitions for the scales and non-dimensional parameters are

$$x_i^* = \frac{x_i}{L}; u_i^* = \frac{u_i}{u_a}; t^* = \frac{tu_a}{L}; p_f^* = \frac{p_f}{\rho_f u_a^2}; T^* = \frac{T - T_a}{T_w - T_a}; J = \frac{\mu_e}{\mu_f};$$

$$\sigma = \frac{\epsilon(\rho c_p)_f + (1 - \epsilon)(\rho c_p)_s}{(\rho c_p)_f}; k^* = \frac{k}{k_f}; Re = \frac{\rho_f u_a L}{\mu_f};$$

$$Pr = \frac{\nu_f}{\alpha_f}; Da = \frac{\kappa}{L^2}; Gr = \frac{g\beta\Delta TL^3}{\nu_f^2} \tag{8.25}$$

The above scales are suitable for most forced and mixed convection problems. However, for buoyancy-driven flows, it is convenient to handle the equations using the following definition of the Rayleigh number (Ra), that is,

$$Ra = \frac{g\beta\Delta TL^3}{\nu\alpha} \tag{8.26}$$

where the following different scales need to be employed in solving natural convection problems:

$$u_i^* = \frac{u_i L}{\alpha_f}; t^* = \frac{t\alpha_f}{L^2}; p^* = \frac{pL^2}{\rho_f\alpha_f^2} \tag{8.27}$$

The non-dimensional governing equations for natural convection are

Continuity equation

$$\frac{\partial u_i^*}{\partial x_i^*} = 0 \tag{8.28}$$

Momentum equations

$$\frac{1}{\epsilon}\frac{\partial u_i^*}{\partial t^*} + \frac{1}{\epsilon}u_j^*\frac{\partial}{\partial x_j^*}\left(\frac{u_i^*}{\epsilon}\right) = -\frac{1}{\epsilon}\frac{\partial}{\partial x_i^*}(\epsilon p_f^*) - \frac{Pr u_i^*}{Da}$$

$$-\frac{1.75}{\sqrt{150}}\frac{|\mathbf{V}^*|}{\sqrt{Da}}\frac{u_i^*}{\epsilon^{3/2}} + \frac{JPr}{\epsilon}\left(\frac{\partial^2 u_i^*}{\partial x_i^{*2}}\right) + \gamma_i Ra Pr T^* \tag{8.29}$$

Energy equation

$$\sigma \frac{\partial T^*}{\partial t^*} + u_i^* \frac{\partial T^*}{\partial x_i^*} = k^* \left(\frac{\partial^2 T^*}{\partial x_i^{*2}} \right) \tag{8.30}$$

Other alternative scales are possible and the appropriate references should be consulted to learn more about scaling. In the above formulation, the buoyancy effects are incorporated by invoking the Boussinesq approximation as discussed in Chapter 7. The kinematic viscosity v, used in the above scales, is defined as

$$v = \frac{\mu}{\rho} \tag{8.31}$$

and α is the thermal diffusivity, given as

$$\alpha_f = \frac{k_f}{(\rho c_p)_f} \tag{8.32}$$

It may be observed that the scales and non-dimensional parameters are defined by using the fluid properties. Often, a quantity called *the Darcy–Rayleigh number* is used in the literature as a governing non-dimensional parameter for Darcy flow. This is the product of the Darcy (Da) and fluid Rayleigh (Ra) numbers as defined previously.

8.2.2 Limiting cases

The equations discussed above represent a porous medium, which tends to a solid as the porosity, $\epsilon \rightarrow 0$. Thus, a conjugate problem, in which part of the domain is completely solid, can be dealt with by using the above equations.

Another limiting case of these equations is that they approach the incompressible Navier–Stokes equations as $\epsilon \rightarrow 1$. Again, a very general problem in which the porous medium and a single-phase fluid are part of the domain (porous-fluid interface (Massarotti *et al.* 2001)) can be solved by using the above equations. Thus, many applications such as alloy solidification (Sinha *et al.* 1992) and heat exchanger design can be analysed via these equations.

8.3 Discretization Procedure

The CBS scheme will be employed to solve the porous medium flow equations. In this context, the same four steps, with minor modifications, will be utilized as discussed in the previous chapter.

In the following subsections, the temporal and spatial discretization schemes are given, which will then be employed to solve the porous medium equations. Use will be made only of simple, linear triangular elements to study porous medium flow problems.

8.3.1 Temporal discretization

Before going into the details of the CBS split, let us first consider the temporal discretization of the governing equations. The momentum equation is subjected to the characteristic

Galerkin procedure, as discussed in the previous chapter, namely,

$$\frac{u_i^{n+1} - u_i^n}{\epsilon \Delta t} = -\frac{1}{\epsilon} \frac{\partial (p\epsilon)^{n+\theta}}{\partial x_i} - \left[\frac{u_j}{\epsilon} \frac{\partial}{\partial x_j} \left(\frac{u_i}{\epsilon} \right) \right]^{n+\theta_1}$$

$$+ \left[\frac{1}{\epsilon Re} \frac{\partial^2 u_i}{\partial x_i^2} \right]^{n+\theta_2} - \left[\frac{u_i}{Re\,Da} + C \frac{|\mathbf{V}|}{\sqrt{Da}} \frac{u_i}{\epsilon^{3/2}} \right]^{n+\theta_3} + \text{CG terms} \qquad (8.33)$$

The body force terms are neglected in the above equation in order to simplify the presentation. Additional dissipation, due to the characteristic Galerkin terms, may be neglected here as we are dealing with very slow speed flow problems, especially at lower Rayleigh or Reynolds numbers.

In Equation 8.33, the parameter 'C' is a constant equal to $1.75/\sqrt{150}$ (see Equation 8.21). The parameters θ, θ_1, θ_2 and θ_3 all vary between zero and unity and with appropriate values, different schemes of interest can be established. The superscript θ should be interpreted as

$$f^{n+\theta} = \theta f^{n+1} + (1 - \theta) f^n \qquad (8.34)$$

where the superscript n indicates the nth time iteration.

In the CBS scheme, the velocities are calculated by splitting Equation 8.33 into two parts as below. In order to simplify the presentation, θ_1, θ_2 and θ_3 are assumed to be equal to zero. It is important to note, however, that such an assumption severely restricts the time step, which can be employed in the calculations. The semi- and quasi- implicit schemes, as discussed in Section 8.3.3, are the schemes widely employed for porous media flow calculations.

In Step 1, the pressure term is completely removed from Equation 8.33 and the intermediate velocity components $\tilde{u}_i$ are calculated (similar to Step 1 of the CBS scheme discussed in Chapter 7) as

$$\frac{\Delta \tilde{u}_i}{\epsilon \Delta t} = \frac{\tilde{u}_i - u_i^n}{\epsilon \Delta t} = -\left[\frac{u_j}{\epsilon} \frac{\partial}{\partial x_j} \left(\frac{u_i}{\epsilon} \right) \right]^n + \left[\frac{1}{\epsilon Re} \frac{\partial^2 u_i}{\partial x_i^2} \right]^n$$

$$- \left[\frac{1}{Re\,Da} u_i + C \frac{|\mathbf{V}|}{\sqrt{Da}} \frac{u_i}{\epsilon^{3/2}} \right]^n \qquad (8.35)$$

The velocities can be corrected using the following equation, which has been derived by subtracting Equation 8.35 from Equation 8.33, that is,

$$\frac{\Delta u_i}{\epsilon \Delta t} = \frac{u_i^{n+1} - u_i^n}{\epsilon \Delta t} = \frac{\Delta \tilde{u}_i}{\Delta t} - \frac{1}{\epsilon} \frac{\partial (p\epsilon)^{n+\theta}}{\partial x_i} \qquad (8.36)$$

However, the value of the pressure in the above equation is not known. In order to establish the pressure field, a pressure Poisson equation can be derived from the above equation and may be written as (see Section 7.6)

$$\frac{1}{\epsilon} \frac{\partial^2}{\partial x_i^2} (p\epsilon)^{n+\theta} = \frac{1}{\Delta t} \frac{\partial u_i^*}{\partial x_i} \qquad (8.37)$$

The above simplified equation has been derived by substituting the equation of continuity. Thus, the conservation of mass is satisfied indirectly without explicitly solving for the mass conservation Equation 8.23.

We have a total of three steps to obtain a solution for the momentum and continuity equations. As discussed in Chapter 7, Equation 8.35 is solved at the first step, followed by Equation 8.37 in the second step and Equation 8.36 in the third step. Additional steps, such as temperature or concentration calculations, can be added as an addition to the above three steps.

In problems in which non-isothermal and mass transfer effects are involved, additional equations will be solved, after velocity correction. If no coupling exists between the velocities and the other variables, such as temperature and concentration and the steady state solution is only of interest, the steady velocity and pressure fields can be established first, and the rest of the variables can be calculated using the steady state velocity and pressure values.

8.3.2 Spatial discretization

Once a temporal discretization of the equations has been achieved, then a spatial discretization may be carried out. In this text, the finite element discretization will be carried out using linear triangular elements. Assuming a Galerkin approximation, the variables can be expressed as

$$u_i = [\mathbf{N}]\{\mathbf{u_i}\}; \; \Delta u_i = [\mathbf{N}]\{\Delta \mathbf{u_i}\}; \; \Delta \tilde{u}_i = [\mathbf{N}]\{\Delta \tilde{\mathbf{u}}_i\}; \; p = [\mathbf{N}]\{\mathbf{p}\}; \; \epsilon = [\mathbf{N}]\{\epsilon\} \tag{8.38}$$

where [$\mathbf{N}$] are the shape functions. We assume that the equations are solved in the order mentioned before, that is, first the intermediate velocity components, then the pressure field and, finally, the velocity correction. On considering the intermediate velocity calculation, we have the following weak form, in which porosity is assumed to be an averaged quantity over an element and body forces are neglected for the sake of simplicity:

$$\int_{\Omega} \frac{1}{\epsilon} [\mathbf{N}]^{\mathrm{T}} \Delta \tilde{u}_i d\Omega = \frac{\Delta t}{\epsilon} \left[-\int_{\Omega} [\mathbf{N}]^{\mathrm{T}} u_j \frac{\partial}{\partial x_j} \left(\frac{u_i}{\epsilon} \right) d\Omega \right]^n$$

$$- \left[\frac{1}{Re} \int_{\Omega} \frac{1}{\epsilon} \frac{\partial [\mathbf{N}]^{\mathrm{T}}}{\partial x_i} \frac{\partial u_i}{\partial x_i} d\Omega \right]^n$$

$$- \int_{\Omega} [\mathbf{N}]^{\mathrm{T}} \left[\frac{\Delta t}{Re Da} u_i + \frac{C}{\sqrt{Da}} \frac{|\mathbf{V}|}{\epsilon^{3/2}} u_i \right]^n d\Omega + b.t \tag{8.39}$$

where b.t. represents the boundary integral resulting from an integration by parts of the second-order terms (Green's lemma, Appendix 1). The weak form of the Step 2 calculation for the pressure field can be written (assuming $\theta = 1$) as

$$-\frac{1}{\epsilon} \int_{\Omega} \frac{\partial [\mathbf{N}]^{\mathrm{T}}}{\partial x_i} \frac{\partial (\epsilon p)^{n+1}}{\partial x_i} d\Omega = \frac{1}{\Delta t} \int_{\Omega} [\mathbf{N}]^{\mathrm{T}} \frac{\partial \tilde{u}_i}{\partial x_i} d\Omega \tag{8.40}$$

Finally, Step 3 can be written in a weak form as

$$\int_{\Omega} [\mathbf{N}]^{\mathrm{T}} \Delta u_i \, d\Omega = \int_{\Omega} [\mathbf{N}]^{\mathrm{T}} \Delta \tilde{u}_i \, d\Omega - \Delta t \int_{\Omega} [\mathbf{N}]^{\mathrm{T}} \frac{\partial p}{\partial x_i}^{n+1} \, d\Omega \tag{8.41}$$

Other field variables, such as temperature and concentration, can be established in a similar fashion via Step 1 and will be discussed later.

The final matrix form of the assembled equations is obtained by introducing Equation 8.38 into Equations 8.39 to 8.41 and are written in a matrix form, as follows:

Step 1: Intermediate velocity calculation

x_1 momentum component

$$[\mathbf{M_p}]\{\Delta \tilde{\mathbf{u}}_1\} = \Delta t \left[-[\mathbf{C_p}]\{\mathbf{u_1}\} - [\mathbf{K_p}]\{\mathbf{u_1}\} - [\mathbf{M_{p1}}]\{\mathbf{u_1}\} - [\mathbf{M_{p2}}]\{\mathbf{u_1}\} \right]^n + \{\mathbf{f_1}\} \tag{8.42}$$

x_2 momentum component

$$[\mathbf{M_p}]\{\Delta \tilde{\mathbf{u}}_2\} = \Delta t \left[-[\mathbf{C_p}]\{\mathbf{u_2}\} - [\mathbf{K_p}]\{\mathbf{u_2}\} - [\mathbf{M_{p1}}]\{\mathbf{u_2}\} - [\mathbf{M_{p2}}]\{\mathbf{u_2}\} \right]^n + \{\mathbf{f_2}\} \tag{8.43}$$

Step 2: Pressure field

$$[\mathbf{K_{p1}}]\{\mathbf{p}\}^{n+1} = -\frac{1}{\Delta t} \left[[\mathbf{G_{p1}}]\{\tilde{\mathbf{u}}_1\} + [\mathbf{G_{p2}}]\{\tilde{\mathbf{u}}_2\} \right]^n - \{\mathbf{f_3}\} \tag{8.44}$$

Step 3: Momentum correction

$$[\mathbf{M_p}]\{\Delta \mathbf{u_1}\} = [\mathbf{M_p}]\{\Delta \tilde{\mathbf{u}}_1\} - \Delta t [\mathbf{G_{p1}}]\{\mathbf{p}\}^{n+1}$$

$$[\mathbf{M_p}]\{\Delta \mathbf{u_2}\} = [\mathbf{M_p}]\{\Delta \tilde{\mathbf{u}}_2\} - \Delta t [\mathbf{G_{p2}}]\{\mathbf{p}\}^{n+1} \tag{8.45}$$

The matrices in the above equations are the assembled global matrices. The elemental matrices of the porous medium equations, for linear triangular elements, are (similar to the ones reported in Chapter 7)

Elemental mass matrix

$$[\mathbf{M_{pe}}] = \frac{A}{12\epsilon} \begin{bmatrix} 2 & 1 & 1 \\ 1 & 2 & 1 \\ 1 & 1 & 2 \end{bmatrix} \tag{8.46}$$

Elemental convection matrix

$$[\mathbf{C_{pe}}] = \frac{1}{24\epsilon^2} \begin{bmatrix} (usu + u_{1i})b_i & (usu + u_{1i})b_j & (usu + u_{1i})b_k \\ (usu + u_{1j})b_i & (usu + u_{1j})b_j & (usu + u_{1j})b_k \\ (usu + u_{1k})b_i & (usu + u_{1k})b_j & (usu + u_{1k})b_k \end{bmatrix}$$

$$+ \frac{1}{24\epsilon^2} \begin{bmatrix} (vsu + u_{2i})c_i & (vsu + u_{2i})c_j & (vsu + u_{2i})c_k \\ (vsu + u_{2j})c_i & (vsu + u_{2j})c_j & (vsu + u_{2j})c_k \\ (vsu + u_{2k})c_i & (vsu + u_{2k})c_j & (vsu + u_{2k})c_k \end{bmatrix} \tag{8.47}$$

where

$$usu = u_{1i} + u_{1j} + u_{1k}$$

$$vsu = u_{2i} + u_{2j} + u_{2k} \tag{8.48}$$

Here, i, j and k represent the three nodes of a linear triangular element. Refer to Chapter 7 for the definitions of b_i, b_j, b_k, c_i, c_j and c_k. The momentum diffusion matrix is

$$[\mathbf{K}_{\mathrm{me}}] = \frac{1}{4A\,Re\epsilon}\begin{bmatrix} b_i^2 & b_i b_j & b_i b_k \\ b_j b_i & b_j^2 & b_j b_k \\ b_k b_i & b_k b_j & b_k^2 \end{bmatrix} + \frac{1}{4A\,Re\epsilon}\begin{bmatrix} c_i^2 & c_i c_j & c_i c_k \\ c_j c_i & c_j^2 & c_j c_k \\ c_k c_i & c_k c_j & c_k^2 \end{bmatrix} \qquad (8.49)$$

The characteristic stabilization matrices have been ignored, but can be included for the purpose of oscillations at very high Reynolds and Rayleigh numbers (see Chapter 7). At lower Reynolds and Rayleigh numbers, however, these terms may be neglected in order to save computational time.

The matrix form of the discretized second-order term for Step 2 is

$$[\mathbf{K}_{\mathrm{p1e}}] = \frac{1}{4A}\begin{bmatrix} b_i^2 & b_i b_j & b_i b_k \\ b_j b_i & b_j^2 & b_j b_k \\ b_k b_i & b_k b_j & b_k^2 \end{bmatrix} + \frac{1}{4A}\begin{bmatrix} c_i^2 & c_i c_j & c_i c_k \\ c_j c_i & c_j^2 & c_j c_k \\ c_k c_i & c_k c_j & c_k^2 \end{bmatrix} \qquad (8.50)$$

The first-gradient matrix in the x_1 direction is

$$[\mathbf{G}_{\mathrm{p1e}}] = \frac{1}{6}\begin{bmatrix} b_i & b_j & b_k \\ b_i & b_j & b_k \\ b_i & b_j & b_k \end{bmatrix} \qquad (8.51)$$

and the second-gradient matrix in the x_2 direction is

$$[\mathbf{G}_{\mathrm{p2e}}] = \frac{1}{6}\begin{bmatrix} c_i & c_j & c_k \\ c_i & c_j & c_k \\ c_i & c_j & c_k \end{bmatrix} \qquad (8.52)$$

The matrices due to the fluid drag on the solid are

$$[\mathbf{M}_{\mathrm{p1e}}] = \frac{1}{Re\epsilon}[\mathbf{M}_{\mathrm{pe}}]$$

$$[\mathbf{M}_{\mathrm{p2e}}] = \frac{C}{\sqrt{Da}}\frac{|\mathbf{V}|}{\epsilon^{3/2}}[\mathbf{M}_{\mathrm{pe}}] \qquad (8.53)$$

The forcing vectors (boundary terms) are, for the x_1 momentum component,

$$\{\mathbf{f}_1\} = \frac{\Gamma}{4A}\frac{1}{Re\epsilon}\begin{bmatrix} b_i u_{1i} + b_j u_{1j} + b_k u_{1k} \\ b_i u_{1i} + b_j u_{1j} + b_k u_{1k} \\ 0 \end{bmatrix}^n n_1$$

$$+ \frac{\Gamma}{4A}\frac{1}{Re\epsilon}\begin{bmatrix} c_i u_{1i} + c_j u_{1j} + c_k u_{1k} \\ c_i u_{1i} + c_j u_{1j} + c_k u_{1k} \\ 0 \end{bmatrix}^n n_2 \qquad (8.54)$$

Note that ij is assumed to be the boundary edge of an element. The forcing vector of the x_2 component of the momentum equation is

$$\{\mathbf{f}_2\} = \frac{\Gamma}{4A}\frac{1}{Re\epsilon}\begin{bmatrix} b_i u_{2i} + b_j u_{2j} + b_k u_{2k} \\ b_i u_{2i} + b_j u_{2j} + b_k u_{2k} \\ 0 \end{bmatrix}^n n_1$$

$$+ \frac{\Gamma}{4A}\frac{1}{Re\epsilon}\begin{bmatrix} c_i u_{2i} + c_j u_{2j} + c_k u_{2k} \\ c_i u_{2i} + c_j u_{2j} + c_k u_{2k} \\ 0 \end{bmatrix}^n n_2 \tag{8.55}$$

The forcing vector, arising from the discretization of the second-order pressure terms in Step 2, is

$$\{\mathbf{f}_3\} = \frac{\Gamma}{4A}\begin{bmatrix} b_i p_i + b_j p_j + b_k p_k \\ b_i p_i + b_j p_j + b_k p_k \\ 0 \end{bmatrix}^n n_1$$

$$+ \frac{\Gamma}{4A}\begin{bmatrix} c_i p_i + c_j p_j + c_k p_k \\ c_i p_i + c_j p_j + c_k p_k \\ 0 \end{bmatrix}^n n_2 \tag{8.56}$$

The implementation of the flux and other boundary conditions is very similar to the method discussed in the previous chapter.

8.3.3   Semi- and quasi-implicit forms

Single-phase incompressible fluid flow problems can be solved in a fully explicit form, which is quite popular in fluid dynamics calculations (Malan *et al.* 2002; Nithiarasu 2003). However, a solution for the generalized porous medium equations using a fully explicit form has been less successful. This is mainly due to the large values of the solid matrix drag terms, especially at smaller Darcy numbers. In order to eliminate some of the time-step restrictions imposed by these terms, schemes other than the fully explicit forms are discussed below.

In the semi-implicit (SI) form (Nithiarasu and Ravindran 1998), the porous medium source terms and pressure equation are treated implicitly. In other words, $\theta = \theta_3 = 1$ and $\theta_1 = \theta_2 = 0$. Although this scheme has good convergence characteristics, further complications are introduced by the scheme. The split in the momentum equation (Equation 8.35) will be different, that is,

$$\frac{\tilde{u}_i - u_i^n}{\epsilon \Delta t} + \frac{1}{ReDa}\tilde{u}_i + C\frac{|\mathbf{V}|}{\sqrt{Da}}\frac{\tilde{u}_i}{\epsilon^{3/2}} = -\left[\frac{u_j}{\epsilon}\frac{\partial}{\partial x_j}\left(\frac{u_i}{\epsilon}\right)\right]^n + \left[\frac{1}{\epsilon Re}\frac{\partial^2 u_i}{\partial x_i^2}\right]^n \tag{8.57}$$

or

$$\tilde{u}_i\left(\frac{1}{\epsilon \Delta t} + \frac{1}{ReDa} + C\frac{|\mathbf{V}|}{\sqrt{Da}}\frac{1}{\epsilon^{3/2}}\right) = \frac{u_i^n}{\epsilon \Delta t} - \left[\frac{u_j}{\epsilon}\frac{\partial}{\partial x_j}\left(\frac{u_i}{\epsilon}\right)\right]^n + \left[\frac{1}{\epsilon Re}\frac{\partial^2 u_i}{\partial x_i^2}\right]^n \tag{8.58}$$

The Step 2 pressure calculation becomes

$$\frac{1}{\epsilon}\frac{\partial^2}{\partial x_i^2}(p\epsilon)^{n+\theta} = \left(\frac{1}{\Delta t\epsilon} + \frac{1}{ReDa} + \frac{C}{\sqrt{Da}}\frac{|\mathbf{V}|}{\epsilon^{3/2}}\right)\frac{\partial \tilde{u}_i}{\partial x_i} \tag{8.59}$$

Step 3 is also different and is given as

$$\left(\frac{1}{\Delta t\epsilon} + \frac{1}{ReDa} + \frac{C}{\sqrt{Da}}\frac{|\mathbf{V}|}{\epsilon^{3/2}}\right)u_i^{n+1} =$$
$$\left(\frac{1}{\Delta t\epsilon} + \frac{1}{ReDa} + \frac{C}{\sqrt{Da}}\frac{|\mathbf{V}|}{\epsilon^{3/2}}\right)\tilde{u}_i - \frac{1}{\epsilon}\frac{(\partial p\epsilon)^{n+\theta}}{\partial x_i} \tag{8.60}$$

Although extra complications were introduced in the semi-implicit form at Step 1 for steady state solutions, we can avoid simultaneous solution of the algebraic equations by taking the coefficient

$$CO = \left(\frac{1}{\Delta t\epsilon} + \frac{1}{ReDa} + \frac{C}{\sqrt{Da}}\frac{|\mathbf{V}|}{\epsilon^{3/2}}\right) \tag{8.61}$$

on to the RHS. Thus, the system can be enabled for the mass lumping procedure (Nithiarasu and Ravindran 1998) when discretized in space. The final matrix form of the three steps are

Step 1: Intermediate velocity calculation

x_1 momentum component

$$[\mathbf{M_p}]\{\tilde{\mathbf{u}}_1\} = [\mathbf{M_p}]\frac{\{\mathbf{u}_1\}}{\epsilon\Delta t} + CO^{-1}\left[-[\mathbf{C_p}]\{\mathbf{u}_1\} - [\mathbf{K_p}]\{\mathbf{u}_1\} + \{\mathbf{f}_1\}\right]^n \tag{8.62}$$

x_2 momentum component

$$[\mathbf{M_p}]\{\tilde{\mathbf{u}}_2\} = [\mathbf{M_p}]\frac{\{\mathbf{u}_2\}}{\epsilon\Delta t} + CO^{-1}\left[-[\mathbf{C_p}]\{\mathbf{u}_2\} - [\mathbf{K_p}]\{\mathbf{u}_2\} + \{\mathbf{f}_2\}\right]^n \tag{8.63}$$

Step 2: Pressure field

$$[\mathbf{K_{p1}}]\{\mathbf{p}\}^{n+1} = -\frac{CO}{\Delta t}\left[[\mathbf{G_{p1}}]\{\tilde{\mathbf{u}}_1\} + [\mathbf{G_{p2}}]\{\tilde{\mathbf{u}}_2\} - \{\mathbf{f}_3\}\right]^n \tag{8.64}$$

Step 3: Momentum correction

$$[\mathbf{M_p}]\{\mathbf{u}_1\}^{n+1} = [\mathbf{M_p}]\{\tilde{\mathbf{u}}_1\} - CO^{-1}[\mathbf{G_{p1}}]\{\mathbf{p}\}^{n+1}$$
$$[\mathbf{M_p}]\{\mathbf{u}_2\}^{n+1} = [\mathbf{M_p}]\{\tilde{\mathbf{u}}_2\} - CO^{-1}[\mathbf{G_{p2}}]\{\mathbf{p}\}^{n+1} \tag{8.65}$$

The quasi-implicit (QI) form is very similar to that of the above scheme but now the viscous, second-order terms are also treated implicitly ($\theta_2 = 1$) (Nithiarasu et al. 1997). The important difference, however, is that the quasi-implicit scheme does not benefit from mass lumping when solving for the intermediate velocity values. A simultaneous solution of the LHS matrices is essential here. It has been proven that both the QI and SI schemes generally perform well (Nithiarasu 2001).

8.4 Non-isothermal Flows

Several examples of porous medium flow problems are non-isothermal in nature. The main focus in this case will be to demonstrate non-isothermal flow through a porous medium. As mentioned previously, an energy equation needs to be solved, in addition to the momentum and pressure equations if the flow is non-isothermal. For steady state problems, if no coupling exists between the momentum and energy equation, the temperature field can be established after calculation of the velocity fields. The temporal discretization of the energy equation can be written in a similar form to the momentum equation and is given as

$$\sigma \frac{T^{n+1} - T^n}{\Delta t} = -\left[u_i \frac{\partial T}{\partial x_i}\right]^{n+\theta_1} + \frac{k^*}{RePr}\left[\frac{\partial^2 T}{\partial x_i^2}\right]^{n+\theta_2} \tag{8.66}$$

where θ_1 and θ_2 have the same meaning as previously discussed in Section 8.3. The variable involved in this case is temperature and can be spatially approximated as

$$T = [N]\{T\} \tag{8.67}$$

The weak form of the energy equation can be written (assuming θ_1 and θ_2 are both equal to zero) as

$$\int_\Omega \sigma [N]^T \Delta T d\Omega = -\Delta t \int_\Omega \left[[N]^T u_i \frac{\partial T}{\partial x_i}\right]^n d\Omega - \frac{k^* \Delta t}{RePr}\int_\Omega \left[\frac{\partial [N]^T}{\partial x_i}\frac{\partial T}{\partial x_i}\right]^n d\Omega + b.t. \tag{8.68}$$

where

$$\Delta T = T^{n+1} - T^n \tag{8.69}$$

The substitution of Equation 8.67 into Equation 8.68 yields the final global matrix form of the energy equation, that is,

$$\sigma[M_p]\{\Delta T\} = -\Delta t \left[[C_p]\{T\} + [K_T]\{T\} - \{f_4\}\right]^n \tag{8.70}$$

where the elemental matrices are

$$[K_{Te}] = \frac{k^*}{4ARePr}\begin{bmatrix} b_i^2 & b_ib_j & b_ib_k \\ b_jb_i & b_j^2 & b_jb_k \\ b_kb_i & b_kb_j & b_k^2 \end{bmatrix} + \frac{k^*}{4ARePr}\begin{bmatrix} c_i^2 & c_ic_j & c_ic_k \\ c_jc_i & c_j^2 & c_jc_k \\ c_kc_i & c_kc_j & c_k^2 \end{bmatrix} \tag{8.71}$$

and the forcing vector is

$$\{f_4\} = \frac{\Gamma}{4A}\frac{1}{RePr}\begin{bmatrix} b_iT_i + b_jT_j + b_kT_k \\ b_iT_i + b_jT_j + b_kT_k \\ 0 \end{bmatrix}^n n_1$$

$$+ \frac{\Gamma}{4A}\frac{1}{RePr}\begin{bmatrix} c_iT_i + c_jT_j + c_kT_k \\ c_iT_i + c_jT_j + c_kT_k \\ 0 \end{bmatrix}^n n_2 \tag{8.72}$$

It should be noted that both the flux and convective heat transfer boundary conditions are treated by using the boundary integral, as discussed in the previous chapter. At higher Reynolds numbers convection stabilization of Equation 8.70 is essential. This can be achieved by introducing characteristic Galerkin method (Chapter 7).

8.5 Forced Convection

Flow through packed beds are important in many chemical engineering applications. Generally, the grain size in the packed beds will vary depending on the application. As the particle size increases, the packing close to the walls will become non-uniform, thereby creating a channelling effect close to the solid walls. In such cases, the porosity value can be close to unity near the walls, but will decrease to a free stream value away from the walls.

In such situations, the ability to vary the porosity within the domain itself is essential in order to obtain a correct solution. Although the theoretical determination of the near wall porosity variation is difficult, there are some experimental correlations available to tackle this issue. One such widely employed correlation, given by Berenati and Brosilow (Berenati and Brosilow 1962), will be used, that is,

$$\epsilon = \epsilon_e \left[1 + \exp\left(-\frac{cx}{d_p} \right) \right] \tag{8.73}$$

where ϵ_e is the free stream bed porosity taken to be equal to 0.39, and c is an empirical constant ($c = 2$ for $d_p = 5$ mm). In general, the problem in this case is formulated on the basis of particle size d_p, that is, the Reynolds number is based on the particle size.

Figure 8.4 shows the problem definition of forced flow through a packed bed. The inlet channel width is 10 times the size of the grain. The length of the channel is 6 times that of

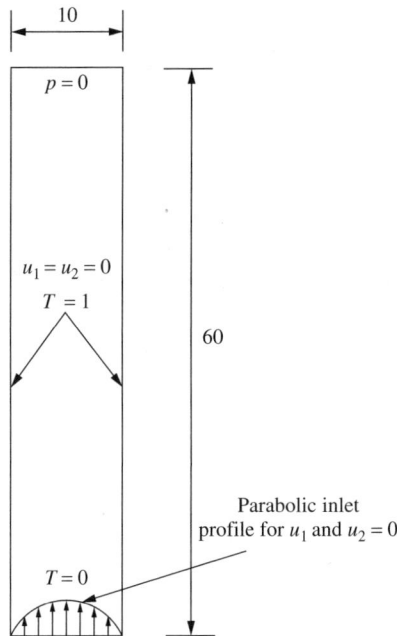

Figure 8.4 Forced convection in a channel filled with a variable porosity medium. Geometry and boundary conditions

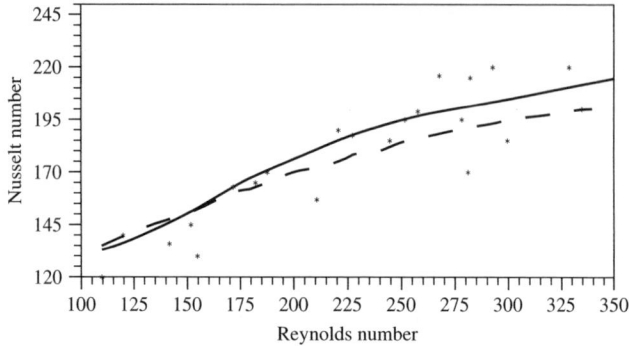

Figure 8.5   Forced convection in a channel. Comparison of the Nusselt number with experimental data for different particle Reynolds numbers. Points—experimental (Vafai *et al.*
1984); dashed line—numerical (Vafai *et al.* 1984); solid—CBS

the inlet width. Zero pressure conditions are assumed at the exit. The inlet velocity profile
is parabolic and no-slip boundary conditions apply on the solid side walls. Both the walls
are assumed to be at a higher, uniform temperature than that of the inlet fluid temperature.
The analysis is carried out for different particle Reynolds numbers ranging from 150 to 350.
The *quasi-implicit* (QI) scheme with $\theta = 1$, $\theta_1 = 0$ and $\theta_2 = \theta_3 = 1$ has been employed
to solve this problem. A non-uniform mesh with triangular elements was also used in the
analysis. The mesh is fine close to the walls, and coarse towards the centre. The total
number of nodes and elements used in the calculation are 3003 and 5776 respectively.

Figure 8.5 shows a comparison of the calculated steady state average Nusselt number
distribution on a hot wall with the available experimental and numerical data. The Nusselt
number is calculated as

$$Nu = \frac{hL}{k} = \int_0^L \frac{\partial T}{\partial x_1} \, \mathrm{d}x \tag{8.74}$$

Figure 8.6 shows the difference between the generalized model and the Brinkman and
Forchheimer extensions for the velocity profiles close to the wall in a variable porosity
medium at steady state. As may be seen, the Forchheimer and Brinkman extensions fail to
predict the channelling effect close to the wall. While the Brinkman extension is insensitive
to porosity values, the Forchheimer model does not predict the viscous effect close to the
channel walls.

8.6   Natural Convection

The fluid flow in a variable porosity medium within an enclosed cavity, under the influence
of buoyancy, is another interesting and difficult problem to analyse. In order to study such
a problem, an enclosure packed with a fluid-saturated porous medium is considered. The
aspect ratio of the enclosure is 10 (ratio between height and width). All the enclosure
walls are subjected to 'no-slip' boundary conditions. The left vertical wall is assumed to
be at a higher, uniform temperature than that of the right side wall. Both the horizontal

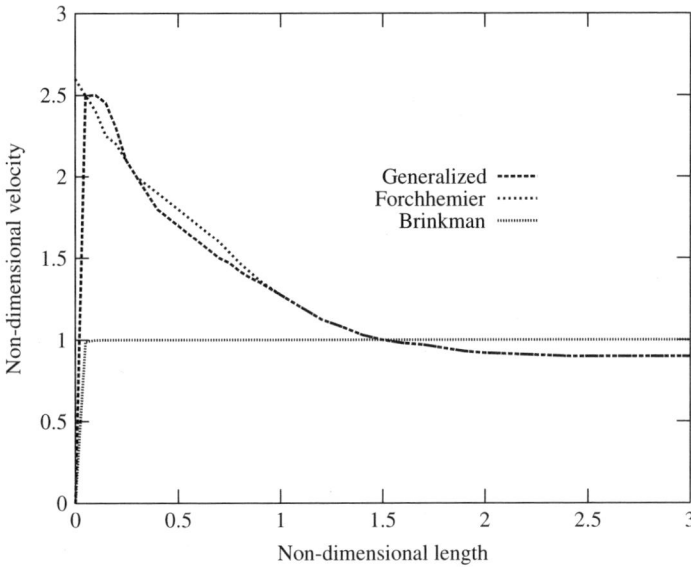

Figure 8.6 Forced convection in a channel. Comparison between the generalized model, Forchheimer and Brinkman extensions to Darcy's law

Table 8.1 Average hot wall Nusselt number distribution for natural convection in a variable porosity medium, aspect ratio $= 10$

Fluid	d_p	ϵ_e	Pr	k^*	Ra	Experimental	Numerical	CBS
Water	5.7	0.39	7.1	1.929	1.830×10^7	2.595	2.405	2.684
					3.519×10^7	3.707	3.496	3.892
Ethyl alcohol	5.7	0.39	2.335	15.4	2.270×10^8	12.56	13.08	12.17
					3.121×10^8	15.13	15.57	14.28

walls are assumed to be insulated (Figure 8.7). The properties of the saturating fluid are assumed to be constant, other than that of the density. The density variation is invoked by the Boussinesq approximation.

Table 8.1 shows the steady state quantitative results and a comparison with the available numerical and experimental data. These data were obtained on a non-uniform structured 61×61 mesh. The accuracy of the prediction can be improved by further refining the mesh. An extremely fine mesh is essential near the cavity walls in order to predict the channelling effect in this region. In Table 8.1, experimental data is obtained from reference (Inaba and Seki 1981), and the numerical data for comparison is obtained from reference (David *et al.* 1991). The following Nusselt number relation was used for this problem.

$$Nu = \frac{1}{L} \int_0^L \frac{\partial T}{\partial x} \, dx \tag{8.75}$$

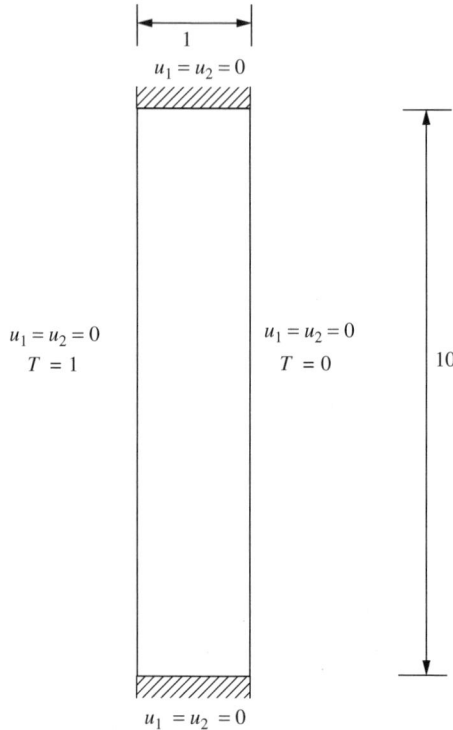

Figure 8.7 Natural convection in a fluid-saturated variable porosity medium. Problem boundary conditions

8.6.1 Constant porosity medium

Problems in which the variation in porosity is less significant normally occur in porous media, which have small, solid particle sizes. For instance, thermal insulation is one such example in which the variation in porosity near the solid walls is not important but the uniform free stream porosity value can be very high. In order to investigate such media, a benchmark problem involving buoyancy-driven convection in a square cavity has been solved.

The problem definition is similar to the one shown in Figure 8.7, the difference being that the aspect ratio is unity. The square enclosure is filled with a fluid-saturated porous medium, with constant and uniform properties except for the fluid density, which is again incorporated via the Boussinesq approximation. A 51×51 non-uniform mesh (Figure 8.8), is employed for this problem.

The Darcy and non-Darcy flow regime classifications and the Darcy number limits have been discussed by many researchers. One important suggestion was given in the paper by Tong and Subramanian (Tong and Subramanian 1985). In Figure 8.9, we show the velocity and temperature distribution at different Darcy and Rayleigh numbers. In this case, the product of the Darcy and Rayleigh numbers is kept at a constant value in order to amplify

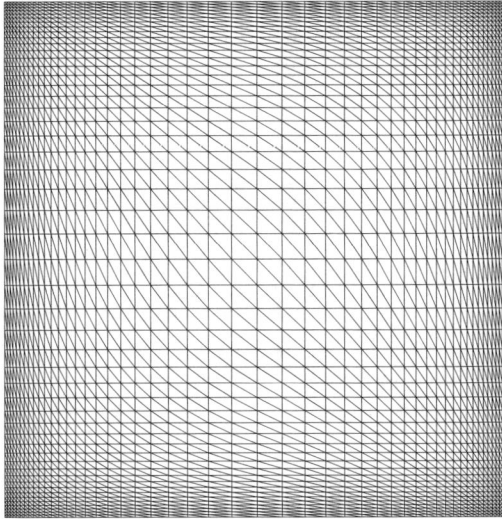

Figure 8.8 Buoyancy-driven flow in a fluid-saturated porous medium. Finite element mesh. Nodes: 2601, elements: 5000

the non-Darcy effects. It is clearly obvious that the maximum velocity in the Darcy flow regime, at a Darcy number of 10^{-6}, is located very close to the solid walls. The non-Darcy velocity profile, at a Darcy number of 10^{-2}, on the other hand, looks very similar to that of a single-phase fluid, and the maximum velocity is located away from the solid walls. At a Darcy number of 10^{-4}, the flow undergoes a transition from a Darcy flow regime to a non-Darcy flow regime. The temperature contours also undergo noticeable changes as the Darcy number increases from 10^{-6} to 10^{-2}.

Both the scheme and the model implementation have been designed in such a way that as the Darcy number increases, the flow approaches a single-phase fluid flow, which is evident from Figure 8.9

In Table 8.2, the quantitative results obtained from the above analysis (only for the Darcy flow regime, $Da < 10^{-5}$) are compared with other available analytical and numerical

Table 8.2 Average Nusselt number comparison with analytical and numerical results

$Ra^* = Ra\,Da$	Nu			
	Analytical	Numerical1	Numerical2	CBS
10	–	1.07	–	1.08
50	1.98	–	2.02	1.96
100	3.09	3.09	3.27	3.02
500	8.40	–	–	8.38
1000	12.49	13.41	18.38	12.52

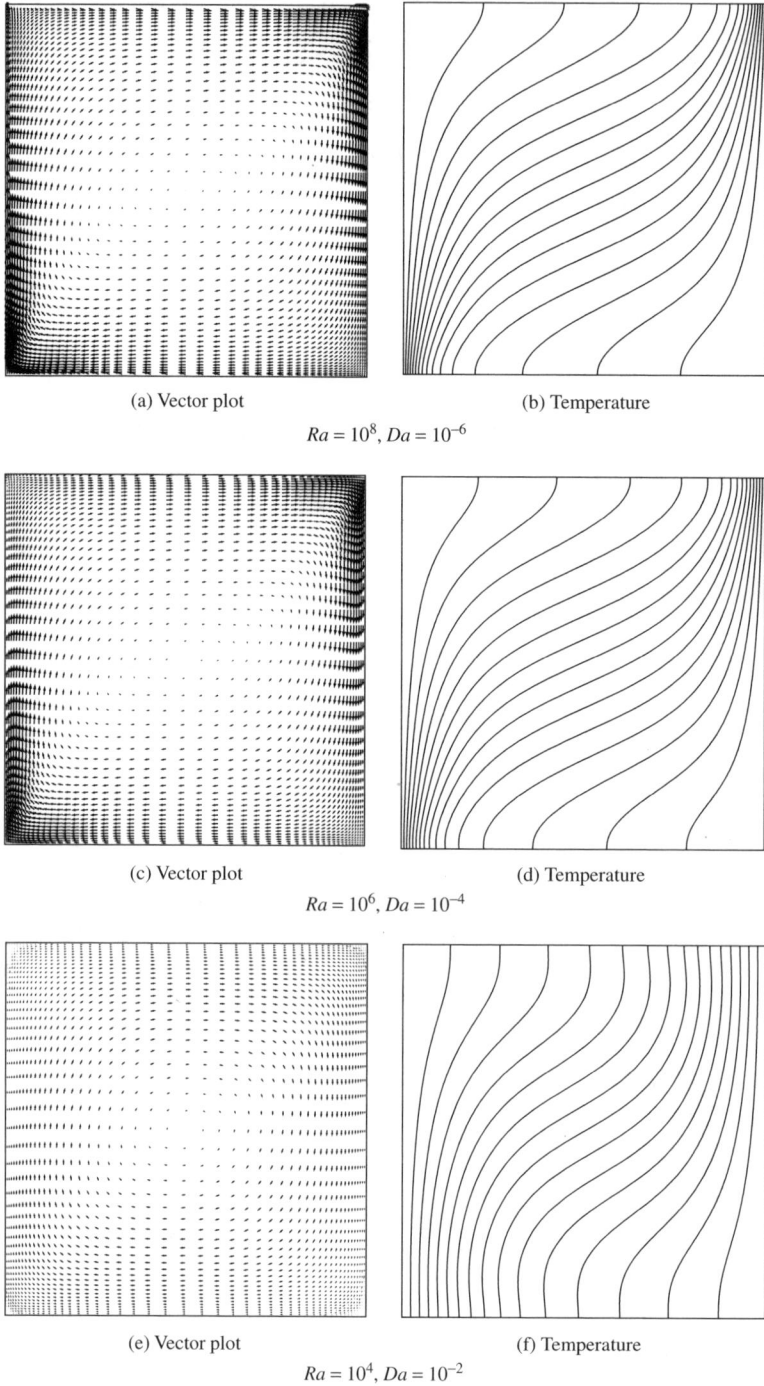

(a) Vector plot   (b) Temperature

$Ra = 10^8, Da = 10^{-6}$

(c) Vector plot   (d) Temperature

$Ra = 10^6, Da = 10^{-4}$

(e) Vector plot   (f) Temperature

$Ra = 10^4, Da = 10^{-2}$

Figure 8.9 Natural convection in a fluid-saturated porous, square enclosure. Vector plots and temperature contours for different Rayleigh and Darcy numbers; $Pr = 0.71$

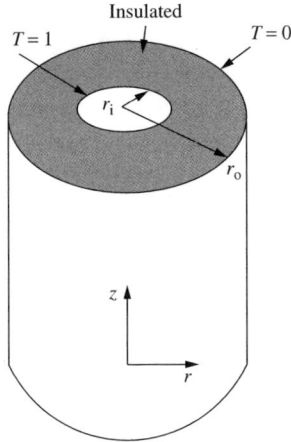

Figure 8.10 Natural convection in a fluid-saturated constant porosity medium. Problem definition

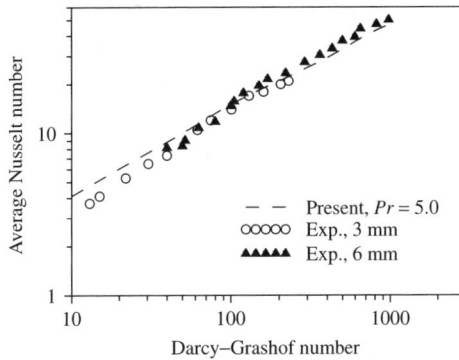

Figure 8.11 Natural convection in a fluid-saturated constant porosity medium within an annular enclosure. Comparison of hot wall steady state Nusselt number with the experimental and numerical data (Prasad *et al.* 1985)

results. As seen, the results are in excellent agreement with the reported results. In Table 8.2, the analytical solution has been obtained from reference (Walker and Homsy 1978), 'Numerical1' and 'Numerical2' have been obtained from references (Lauriat and Prasad 1989) and (Trevisan and Bejan 1985) respectively.

It should be noted that the results by Walker and Homsy (Walker and Homsy 1978) are analytical. The numerical results presented by Trevisan and Bejan (Trevisan and Bejan 1985) over-predict the results, which may be due to the coarse mesh employed.

In order to compare the present numerical results with experimental data, an axisymmetric model was developed and a buoyancy-driven flow problem was studied. The boundary and initial conditions are the same as for the previous problem, the main difference being in the definition of the geometry. In this case, the geometry is an annulus with a radius ratio (ratio between outer and inner radii) of 5.338 (see Figure 8.10). The fluid used to saturate the medium is water with a Prandtl number of 5. The results are generated for different Grashof numbers (Ra/Pr) and compared with the experimental Nusselt number predictions as shown in Figure 8.11. In general, the comparison is excellent for the range of Grashof numbers considered.

8.7 Summary

In this chapter, a brief summary of convection in porous media has been discussed. It is important to fully understand the concepts given in Chapter 7 before carrying out the porous medium flow calculations. Several details have deliberately not been included in this chapter in order to keep the discussion brief. It is important that readers, who may be interested in carrying out further research on the topic, read the books and papers listed in the bibliography to further enhance their knowledge.

8.8 Exercise

Exercise 8.8.1 *Write down the Darcy flow and heat convection equations for a fluid-saturated porous medium at steady state.*

Exercise 8.8.2 *Derive the governing equations for flow and convection in a fluid-saturated porous medium in cylindrical coordinates.*

Bibliography

Berenati RF and Brosilow CB 1962 Void fraction distribution in packed beds, *AIChE Journal*, **8**, 359–361.

Brinkman HC 1947 A calculation of viscous force exerted by a flowing fluid on a dense swarm of particles, *Applied Science Research*, **1**, 27–34.

Darcy H 1856 *Les Fontaines Publiques de la ville de Dijon*, Dalmont, Paris.

David E, Lauriat G and Cheng P 1991 A numerical solution of variable porosity effects on natural convection in a packed sphere cavity, *ASME Journal of Heat Transfer*, **113**, 391–399.

Ergun S 1952 Fluid flow through packed column, *Chemical Engineering Progress*, **48**, 89–94.

Forchheimer P 1901 Wasserbewegung durch bodem, *Z. Ver. Deutsch. Ing.*, **45**, 1782.

Hsu CT and Cheng P 1990 Thermal dispersion in a porous medium, *International Journal of Heat and Mass Transfer*, **33**, 1587–1597.

Inaba H and Seki N 1981 An experimental study of transient heat transfer characteristics in a porous layer enclosed between two opposing vertical surfaces with different temperatures, *International Journal of Heat and Mass Transfer*, **24**, 1854–1857.

Kaviany M 1991 *Principles of Heat Transfer in Porous Media*, Springer-Verlag, New York.

Lauriat G and Prasad V 1989 Non-Darcian effects on natural convection in a vertical porous enclosure, *International Journal of Heat Mass Transfer*, **32**, 2135–2148.

Lewis RW and Ferguson WJ 1990 The effect of temperature and total gas pressure on the moisture content in a capillary porous body, *International Journal for Numerical Methods in Engineering*, **29**, 357–369.

Lewis RW, Morgan K and Johnson KH 1984 A finite element study of 2-D multi-phase flow with a particular reference to the five-spot problem, *Computer Methods in Applied Mechanics and Engineering*, **44**, 17–47.

Lewis RW, Morgan K, Pietlicki R and Smith TJ 1983 The application of adaptive mesh methods to petroleum reservoir simulation, *Revue de Institut Francais de Petrol*, **36**, 751–761.

Lewis RW, Roberts PJ and Schrefler BA 1989 Finite element modelling of two phase heat and fluid flow in deforming porous media, *Transport in Porous Media*, **4**, 319–334.

Lewis RW and Schrefler BA 1998 *The Finite Element Method in the Deformation and Consolidation of Porous Media*, John Wiley & Sons, Chichester.

Lewis RW and Sukirman Y 1993 Finite element modelling of three-phase flow in deforming saturated oil reservoirs, *International Journal for Numerical and Analytical Methods in Geomechanics*, **17**, 577–598.

Malan AG, Lewis RW and Nithiarasu P 2002 An improved unsteady, unstructured, artificial compressibility, finite volume scheme for viscous incompressible flows: Part I. Theory and implementation, *International Journal for Numerical Methods in Engineering*, **54**, 695–714.

Massarotti N, Nithiarasu P and Zienkiewicz OC 2001 Porous medium—fluid interface problems. The finite element analysis by using the CBS procedure, *International Journal for Numerical Methods in Heat Fluid Flow*, **11**, 473–490.

Murugesan K, Suresh HN, Seetharamu KN, Narayana PAA and Sundararajan T 2001 A theoretical model of brick drying as a conjugate problem, *International Journal of Heat and Mass Transfer*, **44**, 4075–4086.

Nield DA and Bejan A 1992 *Convection in Porous Media*, Springer-Verlag, New York.

Nithiarasu P 2001 A comparative study on the performance of two time stepping schemes for convection in a fluid saturated porous medium, *International Journal of Numerical Methods for Heat and Fluid Flow*, **11**, 308–328.

Nithiarasu P 2003 An efficient artificial compressibility (AC) scheme based on the characteristic based split (CBS) method for incompressible flows, *International Journal for Numerical Methods in Engineering*, **56**, 1815–1845.

Nithiarasu P and Ravindran K 1998 A new semi-implicit time stepping procedure for buoyancy driven flow in a fluid saturated porous medium, *Computer Methods in Applied Mechanics and Engineering*, **165**, 147–154.

Nithiarasu P, Seetharamu KN and Sundararajan T 1997 Natural convective heat transfer in an enclosure filled with fluid saturated variable porosity medium, *International Journal of Heat and Mass Transfer*, **40**, 3955–3967.

Nithiarasu P, Seetharamu KN and Sundararajan T 2002 Finite element modelling of flow, heat and mass transfer in fluid saturated porous media, *Archives of Computational Methods in Engineering, State of the Art Reviews*, **9**, 3–42.

Pao WKS, Lewis RW and Masters I 2001 A fully coupled hydro-thermo-poro-mechanical model for black oil reservoir simulation, *International Journal of Numerical and Analytical Methods for Geomechanics*, **25**, 1229–1256.

Prasad V, Kulacki FA and Keyhani M 1985 Natural convection in porous media, *Journal of Fluid Mechanics*, **150**, 80.

Sinha SK, Sundararajan T and Garg VK 1992 A variable property analysis of alloy solidification using the anisotropic porous medium approach, *International Journal of Heat Mass Transfer* **35**, 2865–2877.

Tong TW and Subramanian E 1985 A boundary layer analysis for natural convection in vertical porous enclosures—use of Brinkman—extended Darcy model, *International Journal of Heat and Mass Transfer*, **28**, 563–571.

Trevisan OV and Bejan A 1985 Natural convection with combined heat and mass transfer buoyancy effects in porous medium, *International Journal of Heat and Mass Transfer*, **28**, 1597–1611.

Vafai K, Alkire RL and Tien CL 1984 An experimental investigation of heat transfer in variable porosity media, *ASME J Heat Transfer*, **107**, 642–647.

Vafai K and Tien CL 1981 Boundary and inertia effects on flow and heat transfer in porous media, *International Journal of Heat Mass Transfer*, **24**, 195–203.

Walker KL and Homsy GM 1978 Convection in a porous cavity, *Journal of Fluid Mechanics*, **87**, 449–474.

Whitaker S 1961 Diffusion and dispersion in porous media, *American Institute of Chemical Engineering Journal*, **13**, 420–427.

Zienkiewicz OC, Chan AHC, Pastor M, Schrefler BA and Shiomi T 1999 *Computational Geomechanics with Special Reference to Earthquake Engineering*, John Wiley & Sons, Chichester.

9

Some Examples of Fluid Flow and Heat Transfer Problems

9.1 Introduction

In this chapter, we discuss some solved examples of fluid flow and heat transfer problems. First, the readers are made aware of the benchmark problems available to test their codes. The second objective is to provide more experience to the readers in tackling problems of their own interest. In addition to discussing the benchmark problems, we also provide a few application problems in heat transfer. Only a brief discussion of the solution will be provided for most of the problems considered. Isothermal flow (no heat transfer), non-isothermal problems and a transient solution are included in this chapter.

9.2 Isothermal Flow Problems

Isothermal flow problems obviously do not involve heat transfer but are quite important in testing and validating the fluid dynamics part of an algorithm or a developed code. Both steady and unsteady isothermal flow problems are considered in the following subsections.

9.2.1 Steady state problems

Steady state problems are problems that are independent of time, and a solution to such problems can be obtained using either the steady Navier–Stokes equations, along with an appropriate implicit fluid dynamics solver (Taylor and Hughes 1981), or the unsteady state Navier–Stokes equations and the appropriate time marching procedure (Donea and Huerta 2003; Gresho and Sani 2000; Löhner 2001; Zienkiewicz and Taylor 2000). Solutions to all the fluid flow problems presented in this chapter are produced using the characteristic-based-split (CBS) scheme, which is a time marching algorithm. Details of the CBS scheme

Fundamentals of the Finite Element Method for Heat and Fluid Flow   R. W. Lewis, P. Nithiarasu and K. N. Seetharamu
© 2004 John Wiley & Sons, Ltd   ISBNs: 0-470-84788-3 (HB); 0-470-84789-1 (PB)

are available in Chapter 7. In this subsection, two important benchmark problems that are commonly employed in testing codes will be discussed. In addition, a very recently proposed benchmark test case will also be considered.

Flow in a lid-driven cavity

Flow in a lid-driven cavity is one of the most widely used benchmark problems to test steady state incompressible fluid dynamics codes. Our interest will be to present this problem as a benchmark for the steady state solution. The definition of the problem is given in Figure 9.1. The geometry is a simple square enclosure with solid walls on all four sides. All the walls, except for the top one, are fixed. The top wall is assumed to be moving with a given velocity; therefore, the fluid attached to this wall also moves with the same velocity in the direction shown in Figure 9.1. A pressure value of zero is forced at the node in the bottom left-hand corner of the cavity as shown.

In order to demonstrate the influence of mesh density on the solution procedure, six different meshes have been selected for this problem. We start with a very coarse mesh, as shown in Figure 9.2(a), and refine uniformly by increasing the number of elements as shown in the fourth mesh (Figure 9.2(d)). The fifth mesh is generated by refining the mesh along the cavity walls and coarsening the mesh at the centre as shown in Figure 9.2(e). The meshes shown in Figures 9.2(a) to (e) are all unstructured in nature. The sixth and final mesh is a structured mesh of 100×100 uniform divisions, as shown in Figure 9.2(f). At this point, the readers are reminded that a structured mesh gives better accuracy as compared to an unstructured mesh for the same number of nodes.

A Reynolds number of 5000 is selected to demonstrate the influence of mesh refinement. The initial values of the velocities at all inside nodes are taken as $u_1 = 1$ and $u_2 = 0$. The pressure is assumed to be equal to zero at the beginning of the computation. The semi-implicit form of the CBS scheme (see Chapter 7) was used to calculate the solution in time for all the six meshes. Non-dimensional time step values, ranging between 10^{-3} and 10^{-2}, were employed in the calculations. In order to achieve a steady state solution, the

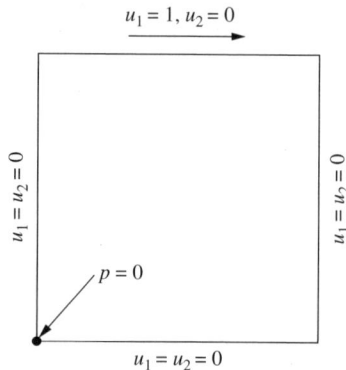

$$u_1 = 1, u_2 = 0$$

$$u_1 = u_2 = 0$$

$$u_1 = u_2 = 0$$

$$p = 0$$

$$u_1 = u_2 = 0$$

Figure 9.1   Incompressible isothermal flow in a lid-driven cavity. Geometry and boundary conditions

(a) Mesh1, nodes:127, elements:211

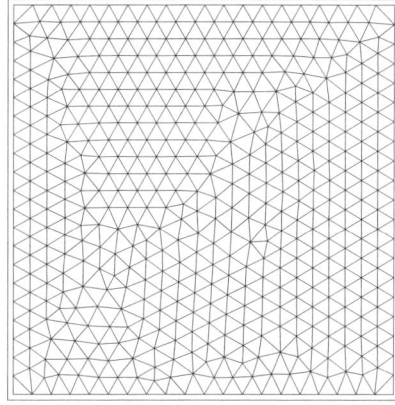

(b) Mesh2, nodes:485, elements:887

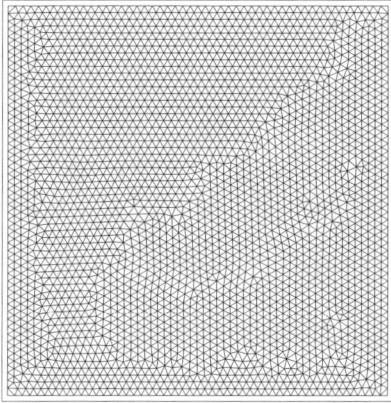

(c) Mesh3, nodes:2909, elements:5163

(d) Mesh4, nodes:5139, elements:10,008

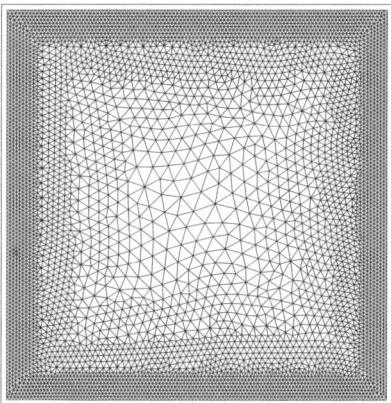

(e) Mesh5, nodes:5515, elements:10,596

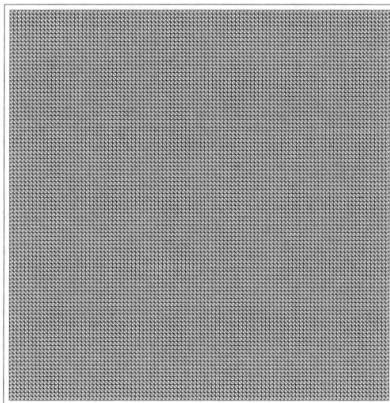

(f) Mesh6, nodes:10,201, elements:20,000

Figure 9.2 Linear triangular element meshes, (a–e) unstructured meshes, (f) 100×100 structured mesh

calculation was continued until the maximum difference of the variables u_1, u_2 and p between two consecutive time steps became less than 10^{-6}. Other criteria, as discussed in Chapter 7, could also have been employed to decide whether the steady state solution had been reached.

In Figure 9.3, the pressure contours generated from all the meshes are shown. As seen, the pressure contours are distinguished by large oscillations when the mesh was relatively

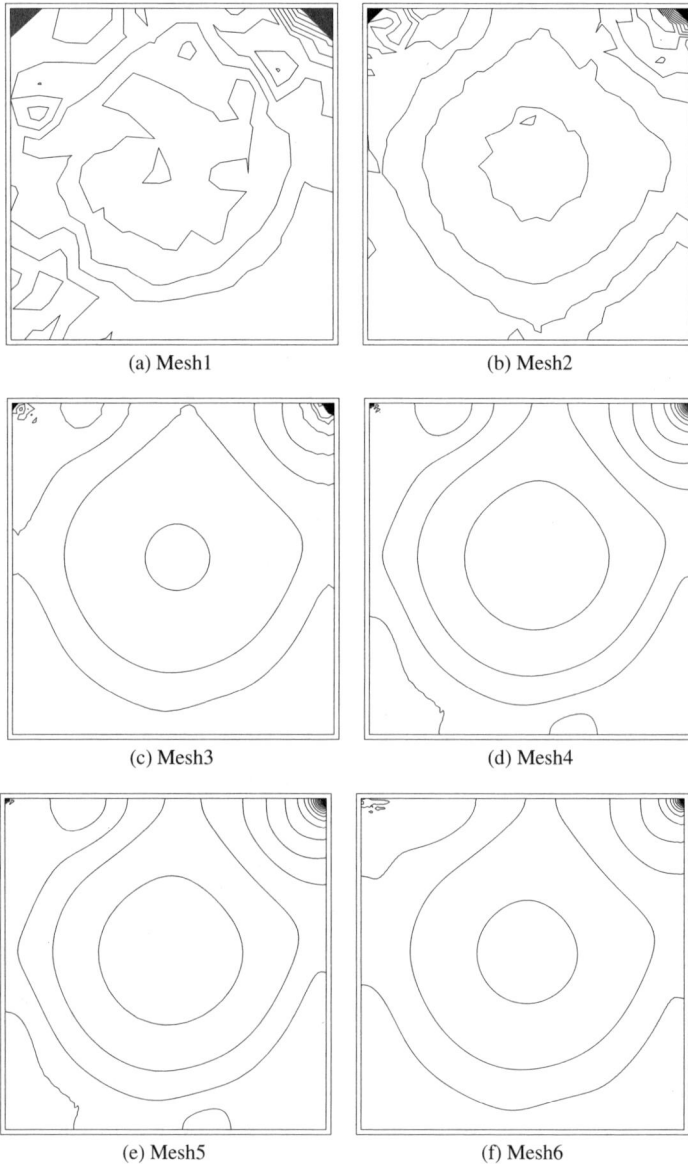

(a) Mesh1	(b) Mesh2
(c) Mesh3	(d) Mesh4
(e) Mesh5	(f) Mesh6

Figure 9.3   Isothermal flow in a lid-driven cavity. Pressure contours at $Re = 5000$

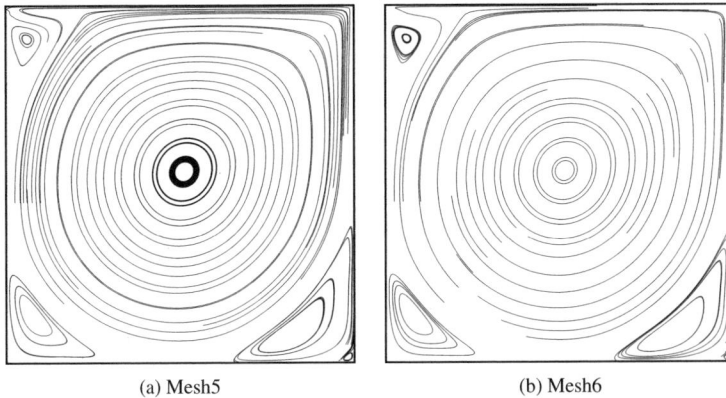

(a) Mesh5   (b) Mesh6

Figure 9.4   Isothermal flow in a lid-driven cavity. Stream traces at $Re = 5000$

coarse (Figures 9.3(a) and (b)). These oscillations disappear from most of the domain as the mesh is refined. The last two meshes (Figures 9.3(e) and (f)) result in much smoother contours than for the other meshes. However, even the fine meshes give oscillatory solutions close to the singular point at the top left corner of the cavity.

The stream traces of meshes five and six are shown in Figure 9.4. At a Reynolds number of 5000, a secondary vortex appeared close to the bottom right-hand corner. In general, it is difficult to predict this vortex, and very fine meshes are necessary if this is to be achieved. Owing to the small size of the secondary vortex, the first four meshes failed to produce its occurrence. However, the last two meshes (Figures 9.3(e) and (f)) were capable of predicting the secondary vortex as shown in Figure 9.4. In addition to this small secondary vortex, the figure also shows the recirculating vortices at both the bottom corners and close to the top left-hand corner.

The quantitative result selected for this study was the horizontal velocity component distribution at the mid-vertical plane of the cavity. The horizontal velocity components of all the meshes have been calculated and plotted as shown in Figure 9.5. It is obvious that the first and second meshes result in inaccurate solutions because of insufficient mesh resolution. However, from the third mesh onwards, sensible solutions were obtained. The comparison of the computed solution with the available benchmark data shows that the results obtained by the sixth mesh agreed excellently with the fine mesh solution of Ghia et al. (Ghia et al. 1982). The third, fourth and fifth meshes also give solutions that were close to that of Ghia et al. but were not identical.

The stream traces and pressure contours for Reynolds numbers of 400 and 1000 are shown in Figure 9.6. These results were generated using the sixth mesh. A comparison of the velocity profiles for the steady state solution is shown in Figure 9.7. The comparison between the present solution and the benchmark solution of Ghia et al. (Ghia et al. 1982) indicates excellent agreement. Further details may be obtained from references (Lewis et al. 1995b; Malan et al. 2002; Nithiarasu 2003) and the readers are encouraged to compute results for other Reynolds numbers. Several other papers on the lid-driven cavity are available in the open literature but are not listed here for the sake of brevity.

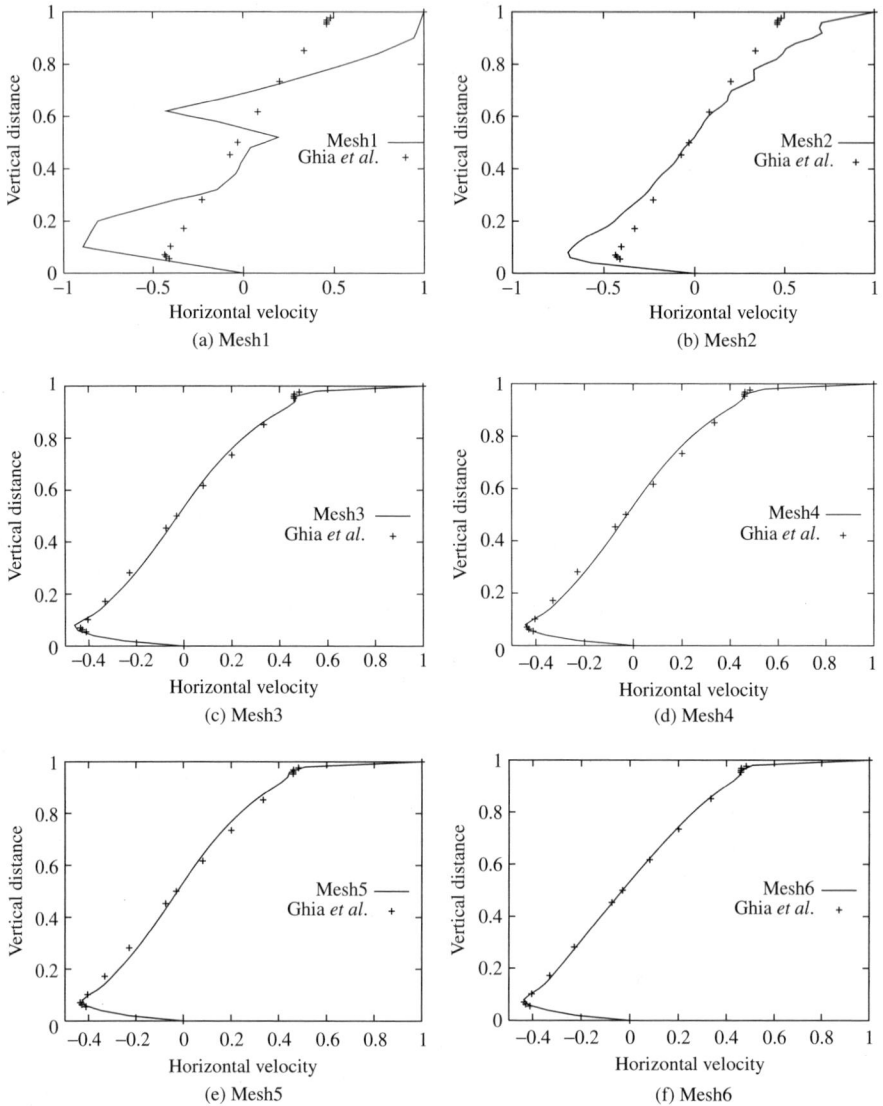

Figure 9.5   Incompressible isothermal flow in a lid-driven cavity. u_1 velocity profile along the mid-vertical line. Comparison with the benchmark steady state results of Ghia *et al.* (Ghia *et al.* 1982)

Flow past a backward-facing step

The lid-driven cavity problem considered in the previous subsection was a good example of flow inside an enclosed area. It is therefore appropriate to consider a problem in which the fluid is allowed to enter from an inlet section and exit from an outlet section. A typical case of such an example is the flow past a backward-facing step, which is widely employed

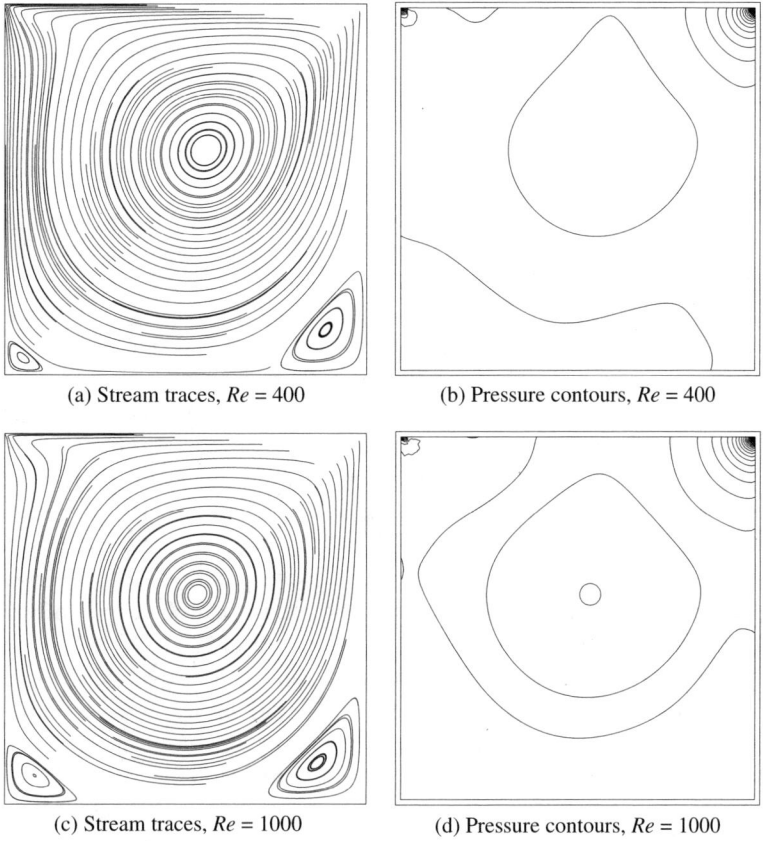

(a) Stream traces, $Re = 400$

(b) Pressure contours, $Re = 400$

(c) Stream traces, $Re = 1000$

(d) Pressure contours, $Re = 1000$

Figure 9.6   Isothermal flow in a lid-driven cavity. Stream traces and pressure contours for different Reynolds numbers

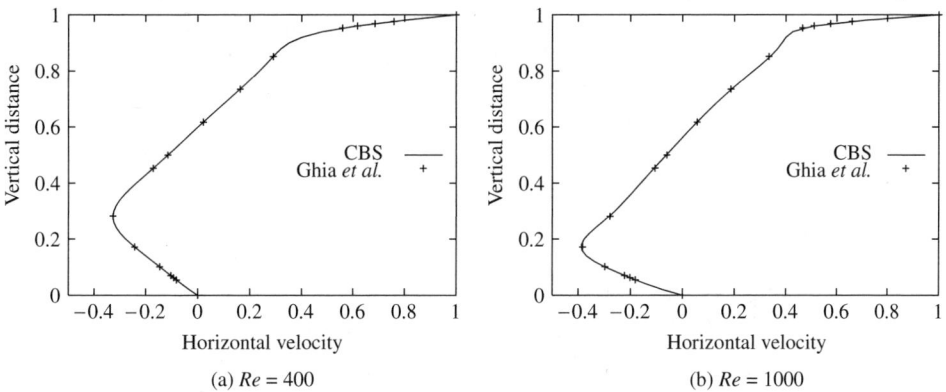

(a) $Re = 400$

(b) $Re = 1000$

Figure 9.7   Isothermal flow in a lid-driven cavity. Comparison of mid-vertical plane u_1 velocity profiles for different Reynolds numbers with Ghia *et al.* (Ghia *et al.* 1982)

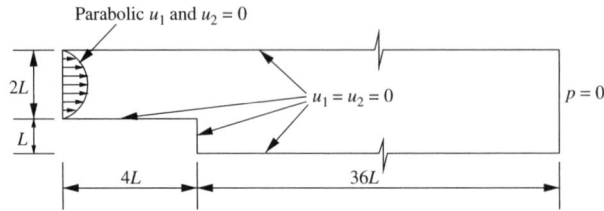

Figure 9.8   Incompressible isothermal flow past a backward-facing step. Problem definition and boundary conditions

by researchers in validating flow solvers. In addition to the available numerical solutions, experimental data is also available for flow past a backward-facing step.

The problem definition is shown in Figure 9.8. The inlet is situated at a distance of $4L$ upstream of the step, where L is the height of the step as shown in Figure 9.8. The inlet section is twice as high as the step. The total length of the channel is taken to be equal to 40 times the height of the step. Apart from the inlet and exit, all the other boundaries are assumed to be solid walls, in which no slip boundary conditions are assumed to prevail. At the inlet to the channel, a nearly parabolic velocity profile of u_1 was assumed. The reason a perfect parabolic velocity profile was not taken is that the experimental data was not available on a perfectly parabolic velocity profile. In order to compare the numerical results with the available experimental data, we imposed the experimental inlet velocity profile from the reference (Denham and Patrik 1974), which was not perfectly parabolic. The u_2 velocity at the inlet was assumed to be equal to zero at all times. The exit of the problem was situated at a distance of 36 times the step height in order to make sure that the disturbance created by the recirculation in the vicinity of the step was stabilized by the time the flow reached the exit. At the exit, the pressure was prescribed as being equal to zero.

The Reynolds number, based on the average inlet velocity and step height, was taken to be equal to 229 in order to compare the velocity profiles with the available experimental velocity profile. The flow was assumed to be laminar and the computation was started with an initial value of u_1 equal to unity and u_2 equal to zero. In addition to the velocity values, an initial pressure value of zero was assumed at all nodal points.

Two different unstructured meshes were employed in the calculations. The first mesh was generated by refining the regions close to the solid walls as shown in Figure 9.9(a).

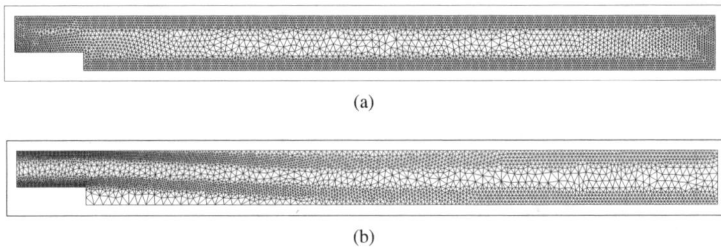

(a)

(b)

Figure 9.9   Incompressible isothermal flow past a backward-facing step. Finite element meshes. (a) Nodes:4656, elements:8662, (b) nodes:3818, elements:7155

The second mesh was generated by adapting the mesh for the solution generated on a coarse mesh (see reference (Nithiarasu and Zienkiewicz 2000) for details) as shown in Figure 9.9(b). It should be observed that the adapted mesh is not fine in the region close to the recirculation zone, and this may lead to inaccuracies in that region. However, the use of unstructured meshes was preferred so that the flexibility of the method could easily be proven.

In Figure 9.10, the results that were produced by the CBS scheme in its fully explicit form are shown. Here, the use of local time-stepping techniques accelerated the solution towards the steady state as compared to a fixed global time step (Malan *et al.* 2002; Nithiarasu 2003).

The u_1 velocity and pressure contours generated by the two meshes are given in Figures 9.10(a), (b), (c) and (d). In Figure 9.10 (e), the velocity profiles generated from

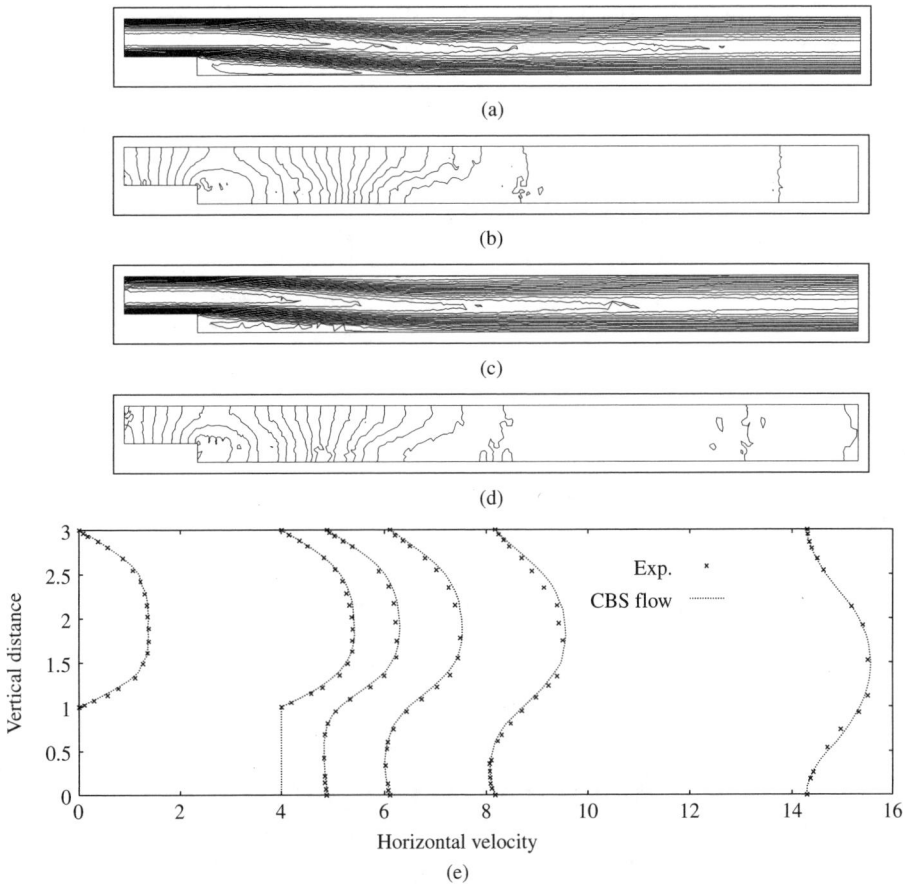

Figure 9.10   Incompressible isothermal flow past a backward-facing step. (a) u_1 velocity contours (mesh1), (b) pressure contours (mesh1), (c) u_1 velocity contours (mesh2), (d) pressure contours (mesh2) and (e) comparison of velocity profiles with experimental data (mesh1), $Re = 229$

the first mesh (Figure 9.9 (a)), at different sections of the geometry, are compared with the experimental data of Denham *et al.* (Denham and Patrik 1974).

The u_1 velocity contours (Figures 9.10(a) and (b)) are marked with the recirculation pattern downstream of the step. This was the expected pattern in a problem of this nature. The pressure contours are marked with minor oscillations, which was due to the unstructured mesh used. The use of some form of artificial dissipation would eliminate these oscillations but compromise the accuracy of the solution.

Double-driven cavity

As the name suggests, a double-driven cavity is different from the lid-driven cavity, discussed in the previous subsection, because of the way the double lids are used. In a double-driven cavity, the lids are moved on both the top and the bottom sides of the cavity. In order to study the effects of a double-driven action, the geometry shown in Figure 9.11(a)

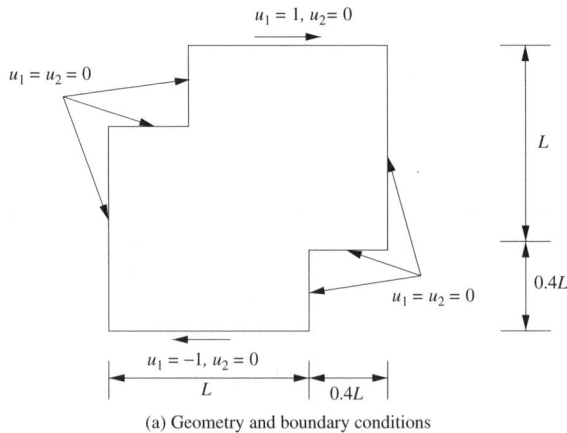

(a) Geometry and boundary conditions

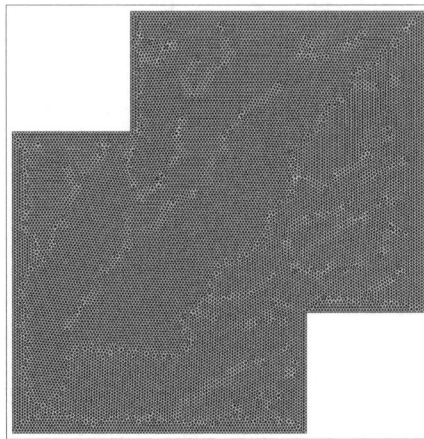

(b) Uniform unstructured mesh, Nodes:18,717, elements:36,834

Figure 9.11   Incompressible isothermal flow in a double-driven cavity. Geometry and mesh

was chosen. This problem was suggested as a benchmark by Zhou *et al.* (Zhou *et al.* 2003), and it is a diagonally symmetrical enclosure with a longer side of size L and a smaller side of size $0.4L$. The top lid is assumed to move at a prescribed positive horizontal velocity and the bottom lid moves with a negative velocity, with a magnitude equal to the velocity of the top lid. The Reynolds number is defined on the basis of the magnitude of the prescribed velocities at the top and bottom lids and the length L. If the semi-implicit form is used, a minimum of one pressure value needs to be prescribed at one solid wall node.

Several meshes have been used in the analysis to obtain a mesh-independent solution. The mesh shown in Figure 9.11(b) was found to be adequate to get an accurate solution. All the solutions presented here were generated from the fine uniform unstructured mesh of Figure 9.11(b).

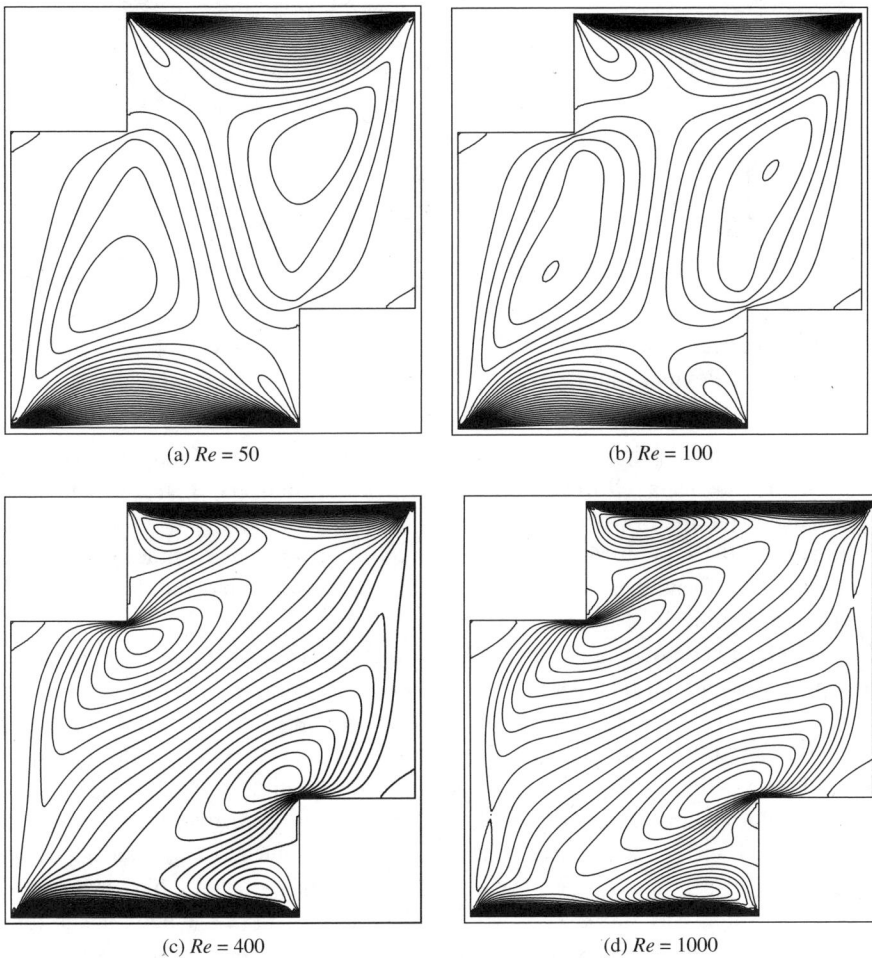

(a) $Re = 50$

(b) $Re = 100$

(c) $Re = 400$

(d) $Re = 1000$

Figure 9.12   Incompressible isothermal flow in a double-driven cavity. u_1 velocity contours for different Reynolds numbers

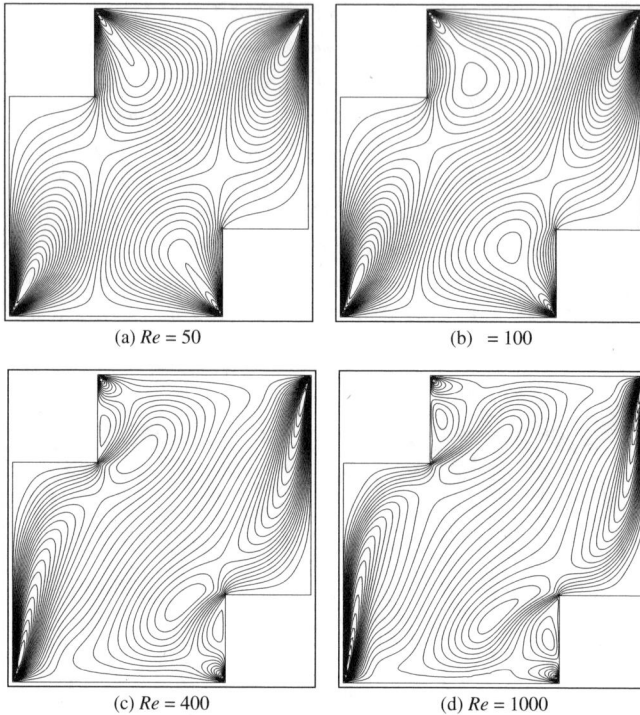

(a) $Re = 50$ (b) $= 100$

(c) $Re = 400$ (d) $Re = 1000$

Figure 9.13   Incompressible isothermal flow in a double-driven cavity. u_2 velocity contours for different Reynolds numbers

Theoretically, the steady state solution, if one exists, should be symmetric with respect to either of the diagonals. However, at higher Reynolds numbers, a steady state solution may not exist as reported by Zhou et al. (Zhou et al. 2003).

Figures 9.12, 9.13 and 9.14 show the contours of all the three variables for different Reynolds numbers. From these contours it is clear that the solution obtained was symmetric with respect to the diagonals.

The u_1 velocity contours in Figure 9.12 show the existence of strong u_1 gradients close to the top and the bottom lids. As the Reynolds number increases, this gradient increases in strength as indicated by the closely packed contours near the top and the bottom lids at $Re = 400$ and 1000. Also, at higher Reynolds numbers ($Re = 400, 1000$), stronger u_1 gradients develop close to the inward corners of the enclosure.

The u_2 velocity contours in Figure 9.13 show steeper gradients close to the corners along the vertical walls. The pressure contours shown in Figure 9.14 are marked with very high gradients close to the top and the bottom corners of the cavity. This was expected because of the singularity introduced by the sudden change in the velocity at the top and the bottom corners. A comparison of the unstructured mesh solution with the published structured fine mesh solution (Zhou et al. 2003) is shown in Figure 9.15. It is clear that both the finite element solution on unstructured meshes and the fine structured mesh solution are almost identical.

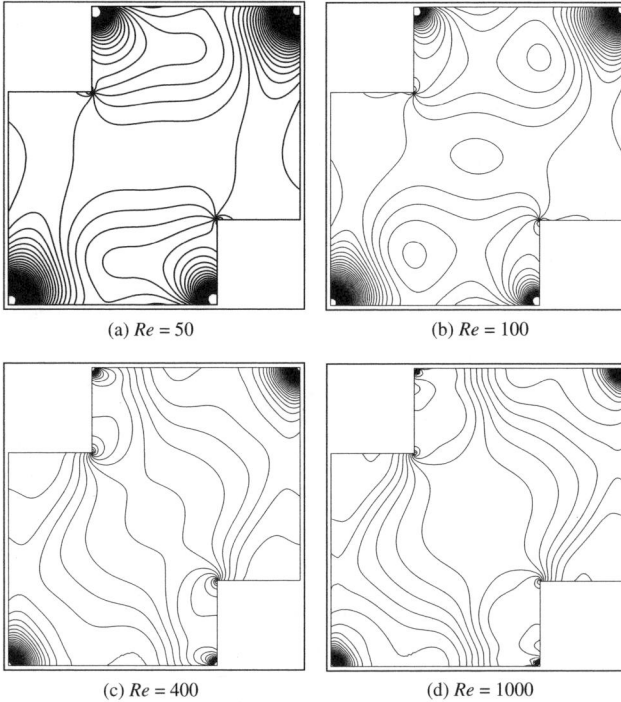

(a) $Re = 50$ (b) $Re = 100$

(c) $Re = 400$ (d) $Re = 1000$

Figure 9.14   Incompressible isothermal flow in a double-driven cavity. Pressure contours for different Reynolds numbers

9.2.2   Transient flow

In this section, a widely used transient benchmark problem of periodic vortex shedding behind a circular cylinder is briefly considered. The problem definition is simple and is shown in Figure 9.16. A circular cylinder of diameter D is placed in a fluid stream with a uniform approaching velocity. The computational domain inlet and exit are placed at lengths of $4D$ upstream from the centre of the cylinder and $12D$ downstream from the centre of the cylinder respectively. The top and bottom boundaries are situated at a distance of $4D$ from the centre of the cylinder.

The inlet velocity was assumed to be uniform with a prescribed non-zero value for u_1 and a zero value for u_2 velocity components. On both the bottom and the top sides, the normal velocity component u_2 was assumed to be equal to zero. On the cylinder surface, the no-slip condition of zero velocity components was applied. At the exit, the pressure value was assumed to be constant. In this study, a zero value for pressure was assumed at the exit. The inlet Reynolds number was defined on the basis of the free stream inlet velocity and the diameter D of the cylinder.

A three-dimensional mesh was used in the vortex-shedding calculations. For three-dimensional flow calculations, two additional boundary conditions are necessary on the two additional surfaces at the front and the back (see Figure 9.17). The two additional

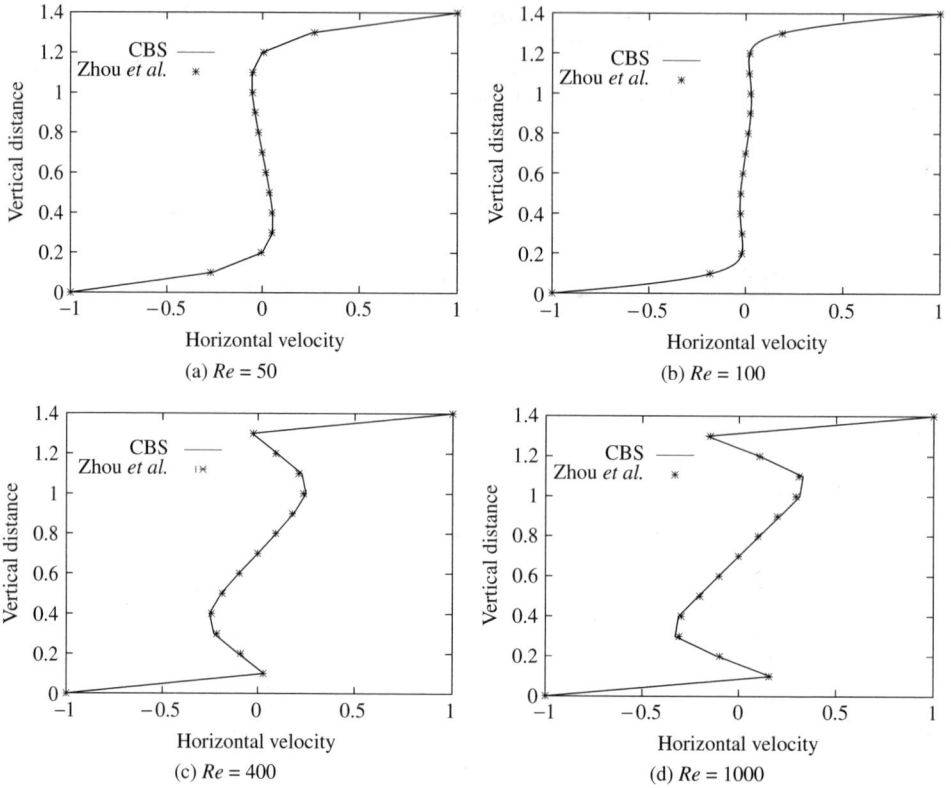

Figure 9.15   Incompressible isothermal flow in a double-driven cavity. Comparison of horizontal velocity profile at mid-vertical section with Zhou *et al.* (Zhou *et al.* 2003) for different Reynolds numbers

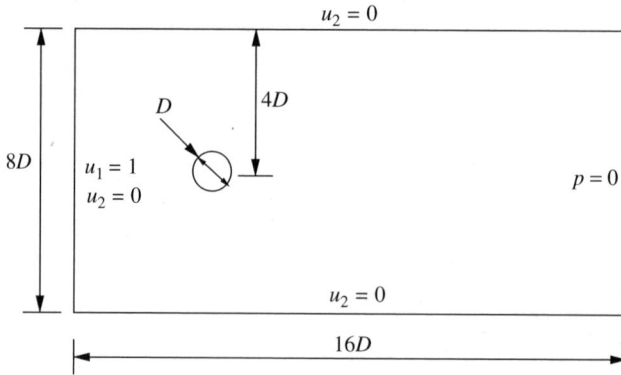

Figure 9.16   Isothermal flow past a circular cylinder. Geometry and boundary conditions

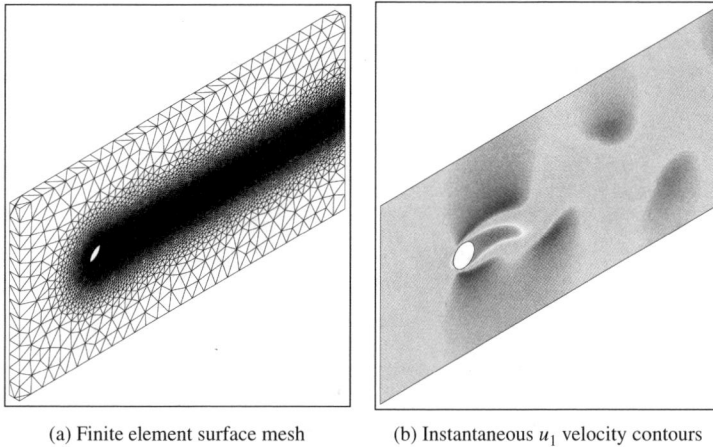

(a) Finite element surface mesh   (b) Instantaneous u_1 velocity contours

Figure 9.17   Isothermal flow past a circular cylinder. Three-dimensional finite element mesh and an instantaneous u_1 velocity contour, $Re = 100$

surfaces were assumed to have no flow in the direction normal to the surfaces. Since the two-dimensional problem was solved in three dimensions by introducing a third dimension, the width of the domain in the third dimension is arbitrary. The smaller the size of the domain in the third dimension, the smaller will be the number of elements in the mesh. For the three-dimensional computations carried out here, the length in the third dimension was assumed to be equal to $0.5D$.

The three-dimensional surface mesh is shown in Figure 9.17(a). The volume mesh used within the domain was generated using linear tetrahedral elements. A total number of approximately 600,000 elements were used in the calculations. As may be observed, the mesh is very fine behind the cylinder, along the expected von Karman vortex street. This is essential in order to accurately predict the flow. A mesh convergence study in three dimensions is time-consuming and difficult, and it is advisable to analyse many meshes in order to prove the convergence of the results. Alternatively, if the problem has existing results, then a comparison with these will give confidence about the results generated. Here, we chose the alternative approach and compared our results with the existing data.

The calculation was carried out using the fully explicit form of the CBS scheme (Nithiarasu 2003). The initial values of u_1 and u_2 were assumed to be equal to unity and zero respectively. Note that these values are non-dimensional. All the velocity values are non-dimensionalized using the reference inlet velocity value (see Chapter 7 for details). Similarly, the distances are scaled with respect to the diameter of the cylinder. These scalings result in a non-dimensional inlet velocity value of unity and a cylinder diameter of unity in the non-dimensional space. The initial values of pressure were assumed to be zero everywhere in the domain.

As mentioned previously, the solution to this problem is known to be periodic with respect to time. Once the solution reaches a steady periodic state, the periodic vortex shedding continues indefinitely. This process consists of vortex formation behind the cylinder and shedding.

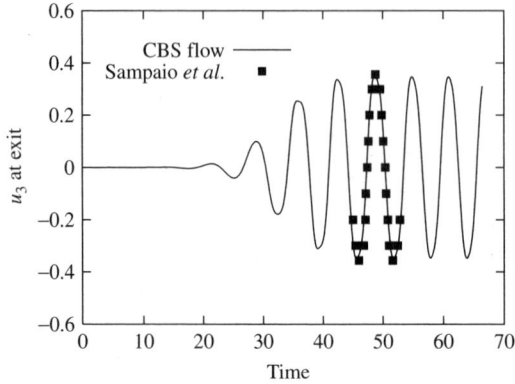

Figure 9.18   Isothermal flow past a circular cylinder. Comparison of u_3 velocity variation at an exit point, $Re = 100$

In Figure 9.17(b), we show only a 'snap shot' of the u_1 velocity distribution at a certain non-dimensional time. Several such 'snap shots' can be plotted but, for the sake of brevity, only one sample solution is given. Obviously, this restricts the discussion on the physical nature of the problem. Since this is an established test case, readers can find sufficient details from other works. We, however, provide the distribution of u_3 with respect to time at an exit point of the domain in Figure 9.18. The exit point is selected at the domain horizontal centre line on the exit plane. As anticipated, the velocity at the selected exit point undergoes a steady periodic change with respect to time after establishing a steady periodic pattern. The initial period of the solution process (up to a non-dimensional time of about 20) is marked with no sign of any periodic behaviour of the velocity at the exit. The periodic behaviour starts between non-dimensional times of 20 and 30 and establishes a steady periodic pattern between the non-dimensional time of 40 and 50. The peak values remain the same after establishing a steady pattern. The initial flow pattern depends heavily on the initial values of the variables, the time steps and the mesh used. It is therefore obvious that the results using different schemes do not match at all times from the beginning of the computation. However, once a steady periodic pattern is established the results should agree as shown in Figure 9.18. The solution used in the comparison was generated from an adaptive analysis in two dimensions by de Sampaio *et al.* (de Sampaio *et al.* 1993).

9.3   Non-isothermal Benchmark Flow Problem

Non-isothermal flow problems involve a solution for the energy equation in addition to the momentum and continuity equations. If the flow problem is a forced convection problem, the momentum and energy equations are uncoupled and should be solved as such. In other words, the momentum and continuity equations may be solved first to establish the velocity fields and then, using the established velocity field, the temperature field can be computed. However, in natural and mixed convection problems, coupling does exist between the momentum and the energy equations via a buoyancy term that is added to the momentum equations in the gravitational direction. In this section, we will consider a forced heat convection problem in the downstream portion of a backward-facing step. For coupled natural and mixed convection problems, the readers are referred to Chapter 7.

9.3.1 Backward-facing step

The problem definition is similar to the isothermal flow past a backward-facing step as discussed in the previous section, the difference being that additional boundary conditions are prescribed for the temperature field. The boundary conditions discussed in reference (Kondoh *et al.* 1993) will be adopted. The solid downstream bottom wall was assumed to be at a higher temperature than the fluid (results presented here are for air with $Pr = 0.71$) entering the channel. All other solid walls were assumed to be insulated. All other boundary conditions for the velocity and pressure values are the same as the ones discussed for the isothermal problem in the previous section and are repeated in Figure 9.19.

Three different meshes have been employed to make sure that the solutions presented are accurate. The first mesh used was mesh (a) in Figure 9.9. The second and third meshes are finer than the first mesh and are shown in Figure 9.20.

A maximum Reynolds number of 500 was studied. All three meshes were employed to study the heat transfer at this Reynolds number. The local Nusselt number distribution on the hot wall downstream of the step is shown in Figure 9.21. As seen, the Nusselt number

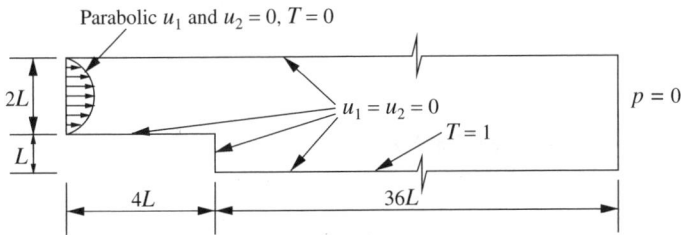

Figure 9.19 Forced convection heat transfer downstream of a backward-facing step. Geometry and boundary conditions

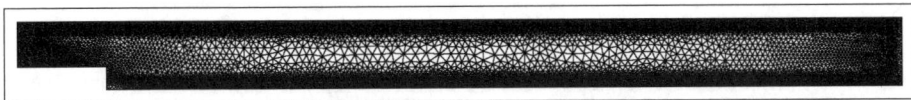

(a) Mesh2, nodes:8131, elements:15,410

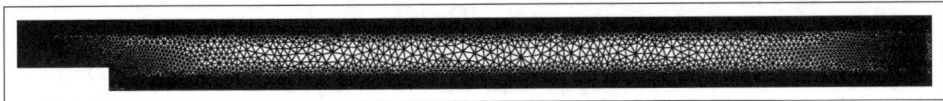

(b) Mesh3, nodes:11,659, elements:22,257

Figure 9.20 Forced convection heat transfer downstream of a backward-facing step. Unstructured meshes

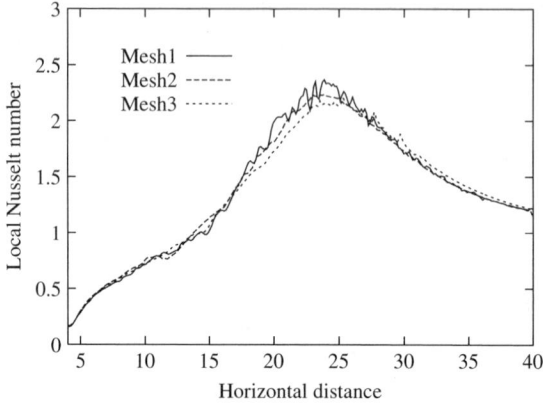

Figure 9.21   Forced convection heat transfer downstream of a backward-facing step. Local Nusselt number distribution on the hot wall for a Reynolds number of 500 on different meshes

difference between all the three meshes was very small. Therefore, the second mesh was used in all the calculations in order to save computational time, as the difference between the local Nusselt number distribution of the finest mesh (third mesh) and the second was very small. The small oscillations in the local Nusselt number distribution, especially on the first mesh, was generated by the coarseness of the unstructured meshes.

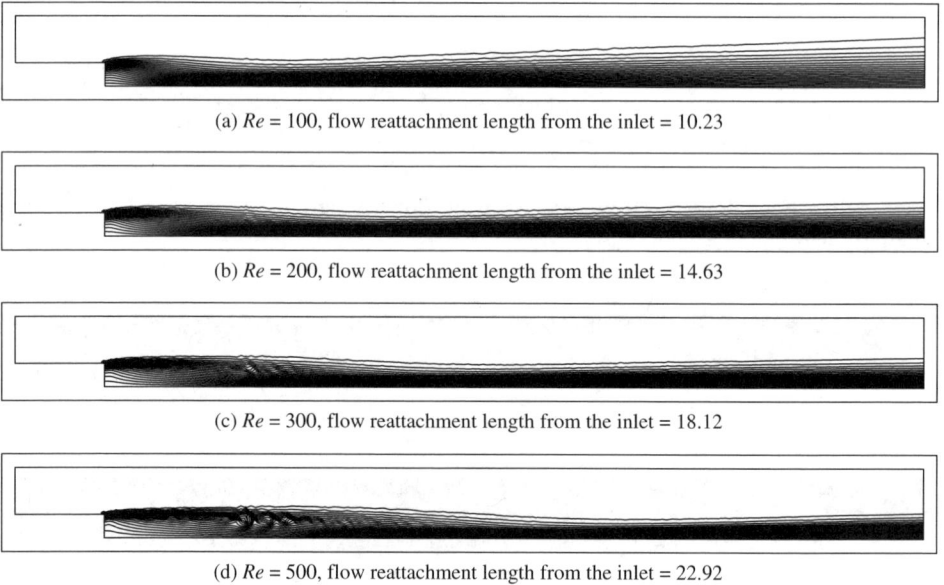

(a) $Re = 100$, flow reattachment length from the inlet = 10.23

(b) $Re = 200$, flow reattachment length from the inlet = 14.63

(c) $Re = 300$, flow reattachment length from the inlet = 18.12

(d) $Re = 500$, flow reattachment length from the inlet = 22.92

Figure 9.22   Forced convection heat transfer downstream of a backward-facing step. Temperature contours at different Reynolds numbers

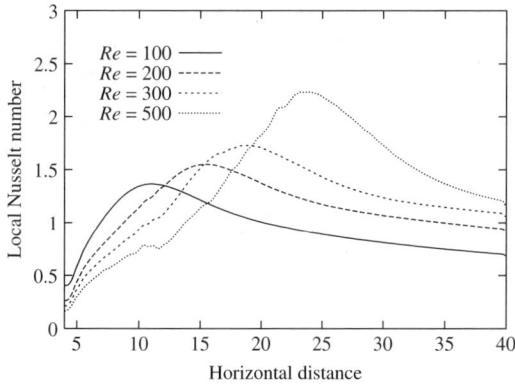

Figure 9.23   Forced convection heat transfer downstream of a backward-facing step. Local Nusselt number distribution on the hot wall for different Reynolds numbers

Figure 9.22 shows the temperature contours for all the different Reynolds numbers considered. Previous studies indicate that the maximum heat transfer occurred close to the reattachment length. The incompressible flow is attached to the wall from the inlet until it reaches the step. The flow is detached from the bottom wall and recirculation develops downstream of the step as shown previously for the non-isothermal case. The flow reattaches itself to the bottom wall after the recirculation in the downstream portion of the step. The location at which the reattachment takes place varies with the Reynolds number. The higher the Reynolds number, the farther will be the reattachment point from the step. The reattachment distances from the step are given in Figure 9.22. These values are in close agreement with reported results (Kondoh *et al.* 1993).

The thermal action predominantly takes place downstream of the step in the bottom portion of the channel. It may be observed that as the flow approaches the reattachment point, the thermal boundary layer shrinks indicating a stronger temperature gradient in the vicinity of the reattachment point and thus a higher heat transfer rate taking place close to this point. This is clearly demonstrated in Figure 9.23 in which the local Nusselt number is plotted along the hot wall downstream of the step. The local Nusselt number starts with an almost zero value at the corner close to the step and increases smoothly to a maximum value close to the reattachment point and then drops. It appears that the peak Nusselt number value is calculated close to, but just after, the reattachment point. After reaching the peak value, the local Nusselt number drops as the flow approaches the exit.

9.4   Thermal Conduction in an Electronic Package

Electronic packages (EP) are the integrated circuit (IC) carriers called *components* that are used in the boards of all electronic systems. EP protect IC chips from a hostile environment, communicate with other circuit boards and enhance the heat dissipation during operation.

In this section, an investigation has been carried out to find the thermal performance of an electronic package, which is represented normally by the thermal resistance between the chip (location of the maximum temperature) and the ambient, referred to as R_{ja} and defined as

$$R_{ja} = \frac{T_j - T_a}{P} \tag{9.1}$$

where T_j is the chip temperature, T_a is the ambient temperature and P is the power dissipated by the chip.

The analysis was carried out for a 106 Plastic Ball Grid Array (PBGA) package system using a 3-D analysis. Figure 9.24 shows a quarter model of a PBGA package, whereas Figure 9.25 shows the inside details of the same package. The amount of heat that can be dissipated within the package depends on the package attributes and also on the equipment operating conditions.

The analysis was carried out using the commercial package ANSYS. A quarter model of the PBGA was modelled because of the two axes of symmetry and was meshed using a free meshing technique. The mesh of the PBGA is shown in Figure 9.26. The boundary conditions created for the thermal analysis of the PBGA are as follows: (a) Chip power (0.75 Watt) was given as the volumetric heat source. (b) Convection from the outer surface of the package ($h = 10$ W/m^2 K, $T_a = 21°$C) (c) Temperature restraint on the bottom surfaces (board temperature assumed to be 53°C because several packages were mounted on the board).

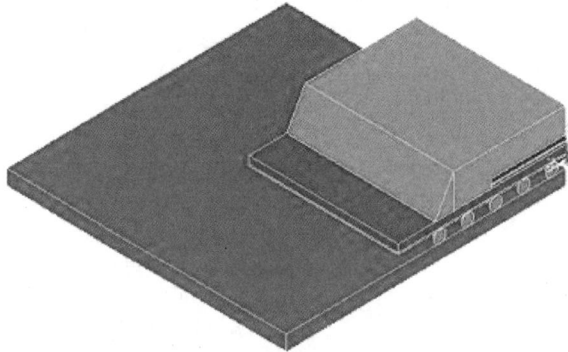

Figure 9.24   Quarter PBGA package model

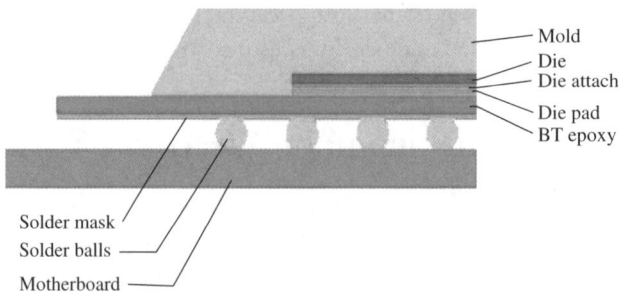

Figure 9.25   Detailed model of PBGA

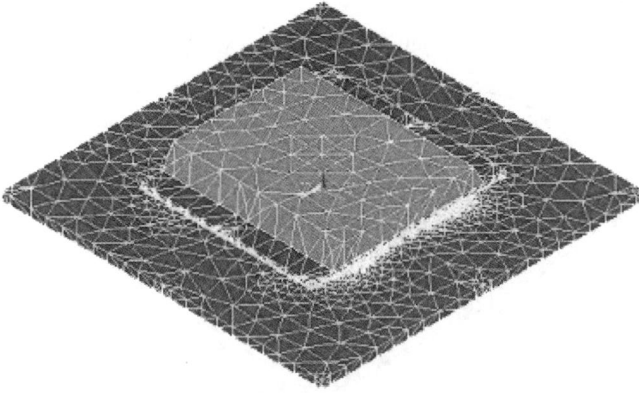

Figure 9.26   Element model of PBGA

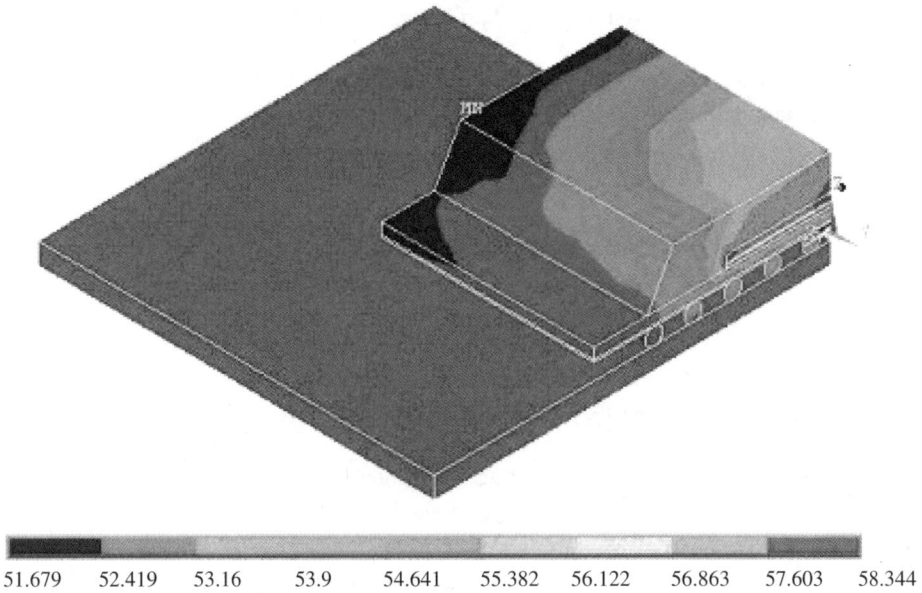

| 51.679 | 52.419 | 53.16 | 53.9 | 54.641 | 55.382 | 56.122 | 56.863 | 57.603 | 58.344 |

Figure 9.27   Temperature distribution of quarter PBGA model

The analysis was carried out for a free convection environment. The temperature distribution of the package can be obtained by plotting nodal solution contours. The results are shown in Figures 9.27 and 9.28 for a quarter model and an expanded full model and indicate that the maximum temperature occurs in the chip itself. Since the board temperature has been specified, the thermal resistance between the chip and the board R_{jb} is given by

$$R_{jb} = \frac{T_j - T_b}{P} = \frac{58.344 - 53}{0.75} = 7.125\,°C/W \qquad (9.2)$$

where $T_j = 58.334°C$ was obtained from the analysis.

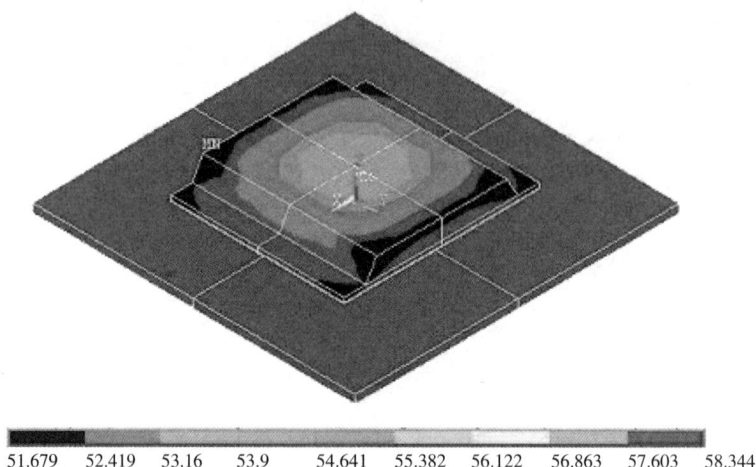

51.679   52.419   53.16   53.9   54.641   55.382   56.122   56.863   57.603   58.344

Figure 9.28   Temperature distribution of expanded full model

In a similar way, we can calculate the resistance between the board and the ambient, given by R_{ba} and defined as

$$R_{ba} = \frac{T_b - T_a}{P} = \frac{53.0 - 21}{0.75} = 42.67\,^{\circ}\text{C/W} \tag{9.3}$$

where T_b is the board temperature. The resistance between the chip and ambient, R_{ja}, is obtained by adding R_{jb} to R_{ba}, that is,

$$R_{ja} = R_{jb} + R_{ba} = 7.125 + 42.67 = 49.795\,^{\circ}\text{C/W} \tag{9.4}$$

9.5   Forced Convection Heat Transfer From Heat Sources

The modern design for the electronic cooling of a printed circuit board (PCB) utilizes numerical techniques in order to study varying situations (Bar-Cohen *et al.* 2001; Nakayama *et al.* 2001; Shidore *et al.* 2001; Watson *et al.* 2001). Most numerical simulations are performed using commercial codes; however, as the geometries involved in this type of application become increasingly more complicated, then commercial codes have deficiencies in both accuracy and speed. For this reason, simplified models have usually been employed, which are inadequate in predicting the heat transfer with sufficient accuracy. An alternative method of calculating the flow through an electronic device is to approximate the device as a porous device and to investigate the overall heat being transferred from the medium to the fluid (Heindel *et al.* 1996; Zhao and Lu 2002). However, this approach has not been characterized properly and more work is needed to understand the comparison between macroscopic and microscopic approaches to the solution of porous medium flows (Nakayama and Kuwahara 2000). In the meantime, the latest developments in numerical schemes for the solution of the complete Navier–Stokes equations can be employed in order to improve the thermal design of electronic packaging. Of all the numerical techniques, the finite element method seems to be the most flexible for the solution of complicated geometries (Zienkiewicz and Taylor 2000).

Recently, a fully explicit version of the CBS algorithm has been widely employed for both isothermal and non-isothermal flow problems (Nithiarasu 2003; Nithiarasu *et al.* 2004). In this form, the algorithm was proven to be both accurate and efficient when using unstructured meshes. In fact, for three-dimensional problems, such as those encountered in the present study, the unstructured mesh-based explicit CBS solver is an excellent choice. Although structured and semi-unstructured meshes are widely employed in the solution of incompressible flows, the use of unstructured meshes is inevitable if the geometry is really complex.

The problem considered in this section concerns the simulation of heat and fluid flow over an array of hot spherical solids resembling solder balls projecting out from a PCB (Nithiarasu and Massarotti 2004). Two different arrangements, 25 in-line (5×5 equally spaced) and 41 staggered partial spheres are analysed. The solder balls are considered to be partial spheres, whose centres lie on the same plane ($x - z$) as shown in Figure 9.29.

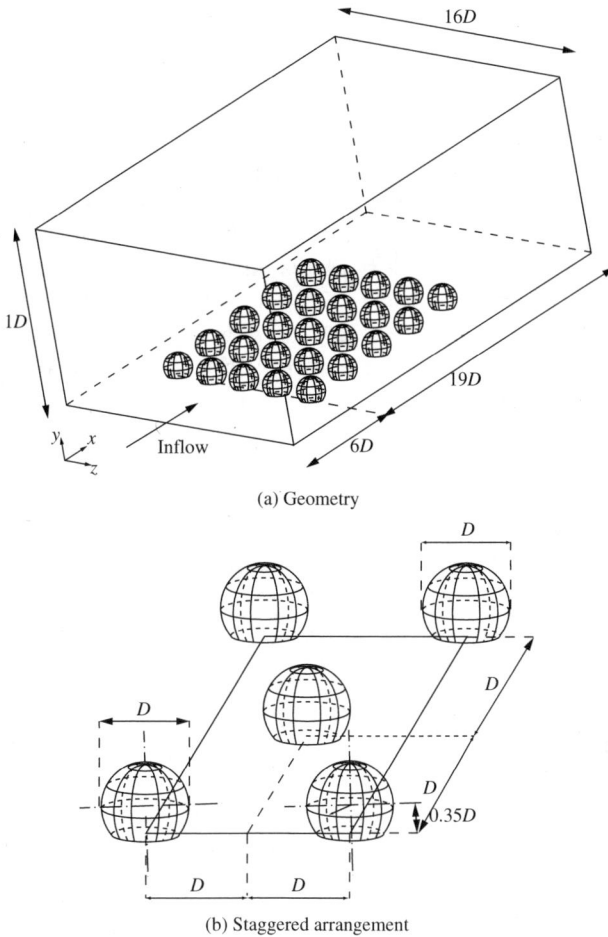

(a) Geometry

(b) Staggered arrangement

Figure 9.29   Forced convection heat transfer from spherical heat sources mounted on the wall

This arrangement is obtained by cutting the spheres with the horizontal wall (board) on which the balls are placed. The diameter of the spheres is considered to be equal to 1, and the distance between the ball centres and the plane that represents the circuit board is equal to 0.35, as can be seen from Figure 9.29(a). Figure 9.29 also shows the sketch of the staggered arrangement considered (Figure 9.29(b)). This is obtained by introducing another partial sphere at the centre of the space between the four in-line spheres.

The flow is assumed to enter the channel from a vertical section (plane $y - z$), which is placed at a distance of six diameters upstream of the centres of the first column of spheres (Figure 9.29(a)). The velocity at the inlet is assumed to be constant at a value of unity, but its direction (angle of attack) has been allowed to vary. The flow direction at the inlet section, although always parallel to the vertical sides of the domain ($x - y$ plane), has been varied with respect to the $x - z$ plane as shown in Figure 9.30. Three different inlet directions have been studied with $0°$, $10°$ and $20°$ angles of attack with respect to the $x - z$ plane.

In all the cases considered, no-slip velocity boundary conditions were assumed for the horizontal bottom wall and the solder ball surfaces. All the other surrounding boundaries were assumed to be far field (inlet and exit). In addition to the above flow conditions, varying thermal conditions were prescribed on the different boundaries. The solder ball surfaces were always assumed to be at a temperature higher ($T = 1$) than that of the incoming fluid ($T = 0$). All the side boundaries were assumed to be adiabatic and at the exit, free conditions were assumed (no temperature boundary conditions).

The domain presented in both the staggered and in-line configurations, has been subdivided into an unstructured mesh using a Delaunay mesh generator (Morgan *et al.* 1999; Weatherill *et al.* 2001). As may be seen, all meshes are refined near the solid walls where strong gradients exist. The meshes used contained 250,372 nodes and 1,398,845 elements for the in-line arrangement and 237,911 nodes and 1,309,963 elements for the staggered arrangement. These grids were found to be satisfactory from a computational point of view after an appropriate mesh sensitivity analysis. Figure 9.31 presents an example of the

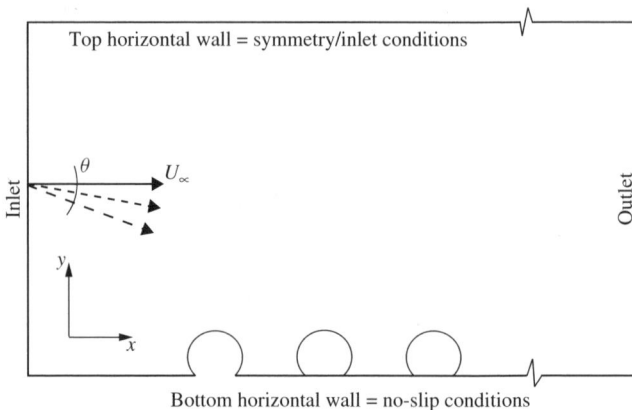

Figure 9.30   Forced convection heat transfer from spherical heat sources mounted on the wall. Angles of inclination

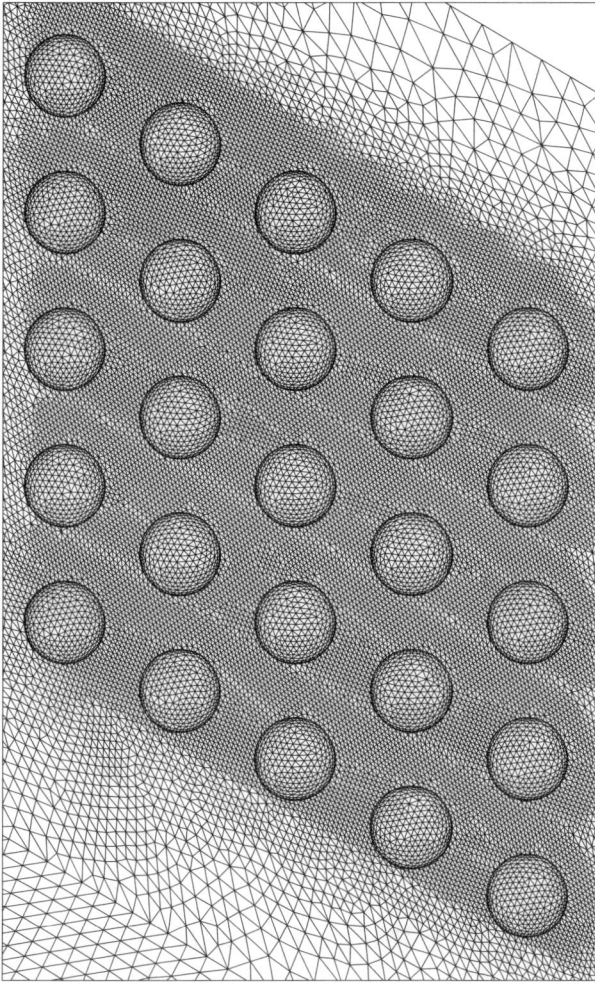

Figure 9.31   Forced convection heat transfer from spherical heat sources mounted on the wall. Surface mesh of an in-line arrangement

surface mesh used for the in-line arrangement. The bottom adiabatic wall, in which the no-slip boundary conditions are assumed, is refined near the spheres. For the staggered arrangement, the same density of nodes is assumed, and this results in a smaller number of nodes and elements.

The results are mainly presented in terms of the heat transfer and fluid flow quantities of interest. The non-dimensional heat transferred from the spheres to the fluid has been calculated from the computed temperature distribution. In particular, the average Nusselt number for each sphere, Nu_s, is obtained by using the following integral:

$$Nu_s = \frac{1}{A_s} \int_A (Nu_s)_p \, dA = \frac{1}{A_s} \int_A \nabla T \cdot \mathbf{n} \, dA = \frac{1}{A_s} \int_A \frac{\partial T}{\partial n} \, dA \qquad (9.5)$$

where A_s represents the surface area of each solder ball ($s = 1, \ldots, 25$ for in-line and $s = 1, \ldots, 41$ for staggered arrangements) and $\mathbf{n}$ represents the value of the outgoing normal at each triangular face on the surface of the spheres. The integral term written above has been calculated numerically by summing the constant (linear elements) values of the gradient at each surface element multiplied by its area. The values of the Nusselt number, Nu_s, have been calculated for each and every sphere, which are used in both the in-line and the staggered arrangements, and comparisons are made for different Re and θ.

The isotherms calculated on a horizontal plane surface on which the balls are placed are presented in Figure 9.32 for the in-line arrangement (top view). This diagram shows the isotherms for Reynolds numbers of 100 to 300 and for different flow angles imposed at the inlet of the computational domain. In this case, the value of the Reynolds number is based on the diameter of the spheres.

With a zero angle of attack, the isotherm distribution looks simple and uniform in the flow direction and convection from the ball cluster in the lateral direction is confined to a thermal boundary layer close to the cluster. However, as the angle of attack is increased, the isotherms spread to a wider area around the cluster and show a stronger convective mixing. At higher angles of attack, the isotherms spread out and reach the side boundaries. This behaviour is seen to enhance further as the Reynolds number is increased. It may be observed that the symmetry, with respect to the central row of spheres, is preserved for all the considered angles of attack and Reynolds numbers.

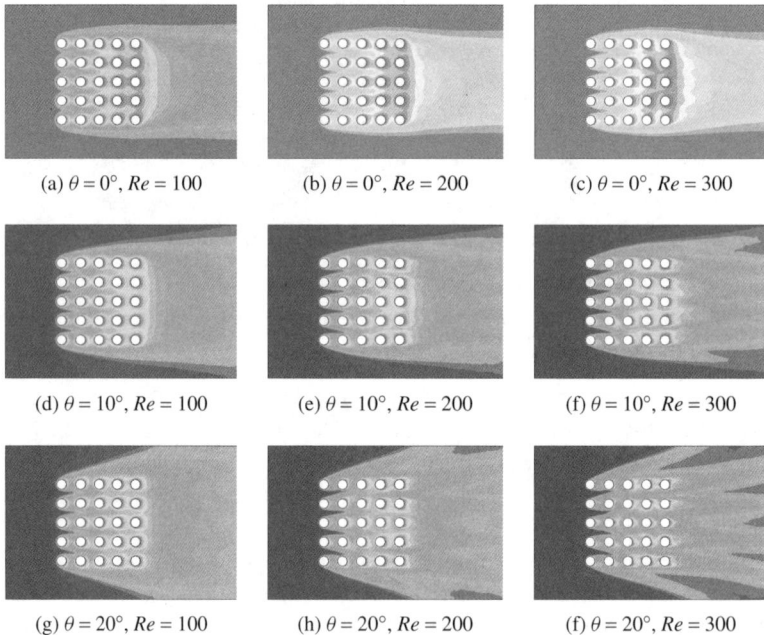

(a) $\theta = 0°$, $Re = 100$ (b) $\theta = 0°$, $Re = 200$ (c) $\theta = 0°$, $Re = 300$

(d) $\theta = 10°$, $Re = 100$ (e) $\theta = 10°$, $Re = 200$ (f) $\theta = 10°$, $Re = 300$

(g) $\theta = 20°$, $Re = 100$ (h) $\theta = 20°$, $Re = 200$ (f) $\theta = 20°$, $Re = 300$

Figure 9.32   Forced convection heat transfer from spherical heat sources mounted on the wall. Temperature contours from the in-line arrangement for different inclination angles and Reynolds numbers

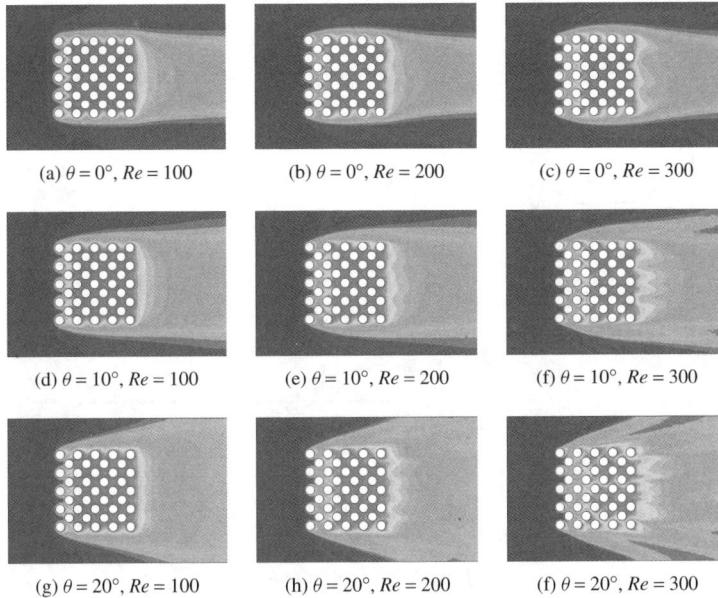

(a) $\theta = 0°$, $Re = 100$ (b) $\theta = 0°$, $Re = 200$ (c) $\theta = 0°$, $Re = 300$

(d) $\theta = 10°$, $Re = 100$ (e) $\theta = 10°$, $Re = 200$ (f) $\theta = 10°$, $Re = 300$

(g) $\theta = 20°$, $Re = 100$ (h) $\theta = 20°$, $Re = 200$ (f) $\theta = 20°$, $Re = 300$

Figure 9.33   Forced convection heat transfer from spherical heat sources mounted on the wall. Temperature contours from the staggered arrangement for different inclination angles and Reynolds numbers

Figure 9.33 shows the temperature contours for the staggered arrangement (top view) at different values of Re and angles θ of the inlet flow. It is seen that close packaging reduces the fluid penetration and thus the convection of the temperature in the vicinity of the cluster. In fact, the temperature gradients in the zone occupied by the balls are almost nil, and this is shown by the uniformity of the isothermal area at the centre of the packaging. The flow encounters several columns of balls in a staggered arrangement and therefore decelerates drastically after the first column. By increasing the velocity of the fluid (Reynolds number), it is obviously possible to increase the temperature gradients between the balls and the cooling fluid. As shown in Figure 9.33, for an angle of $0°$, the cooling fluid penetrates further into the packaging as the velocity increases. However, this is achieved at the cost of a large increase in the energy necessary to speed up the fluid. As for the case of the in-line arrangement, the fluid penetration increases with both Reynolds number and angle of attack. For the same intensity of fluid penetration into the cluster, the staggered arrangement needs a much higher Reynolds number and angle of attack than that of the in-line arrangement.

Before discussing the surface Nusselt number variation over the heat sources, it is useful to define some keywords in order to identify the heat sources. Figure 9.34 gives some definitions in order to explain the Nusselt numbers. These keywords will be referred to in the following paragraphs.

In Figure 9.35, the average Nusselt number is presented for the central and the lateral rows of balls for in-line arrangement (refer to Figure 9.34 for 'lateral' and 'central' rows).

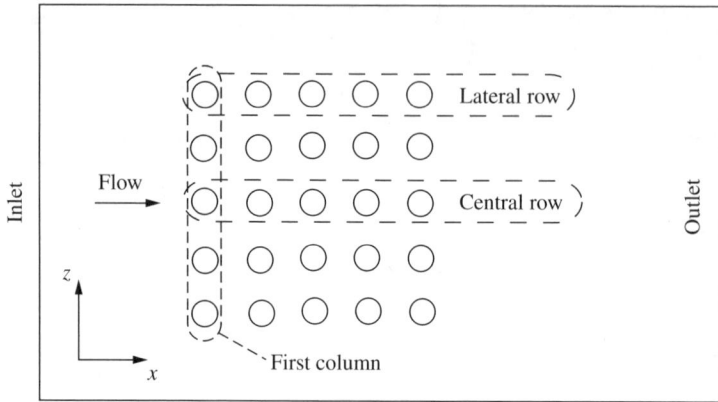

(a) Inline arrangement and rows and column names

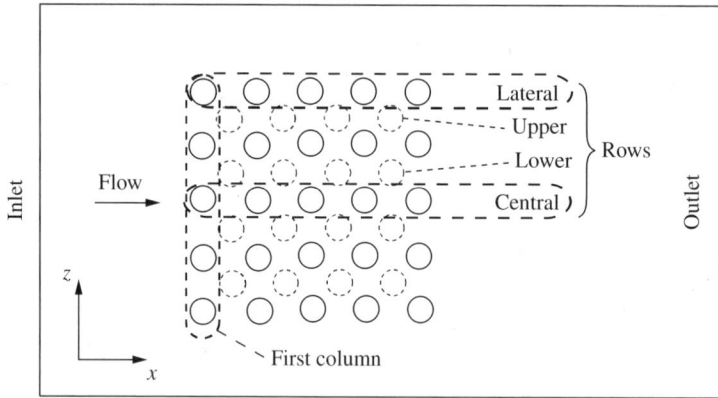

(b) Staggered arrangement and rows and column names

Figure 9.34   Forced convection heat transfer from spherical heat sources mounted on the wall

It should be noted here that the average Nusselt number for the spheres in the row between the 'central' and the 'lateral' rows is not presented in Figure 9.35 because it is practically the same as the Nusselt number values for the 'central' row. From Figure 9.35, it is clear that a significant drop in heat transfer from the solder balls occurs after the first column. A more uniform reduction in heat transfer occurs from the balls further towards downstream. This is obviously due to the flow obstruction caused by the columns of balls in the front region. However, this effect tends to decrease after the third column. In fact, the fourth and the fifth columns have practically the same values of Nu. As expected, the heat transfer rate from the lateral rows is much higher than that of the central rows. At lower Reynolds numbers and higher angles of attack, however, the difference between the Nusselt numbers for the 'central' and 'lateral' rows is very small. In general, an increase in the flow angle increases the heat transfer rate, which is due to the increase in participation of the balls at the middle of the cluster. This effect becomes more prominent, especially for higher values

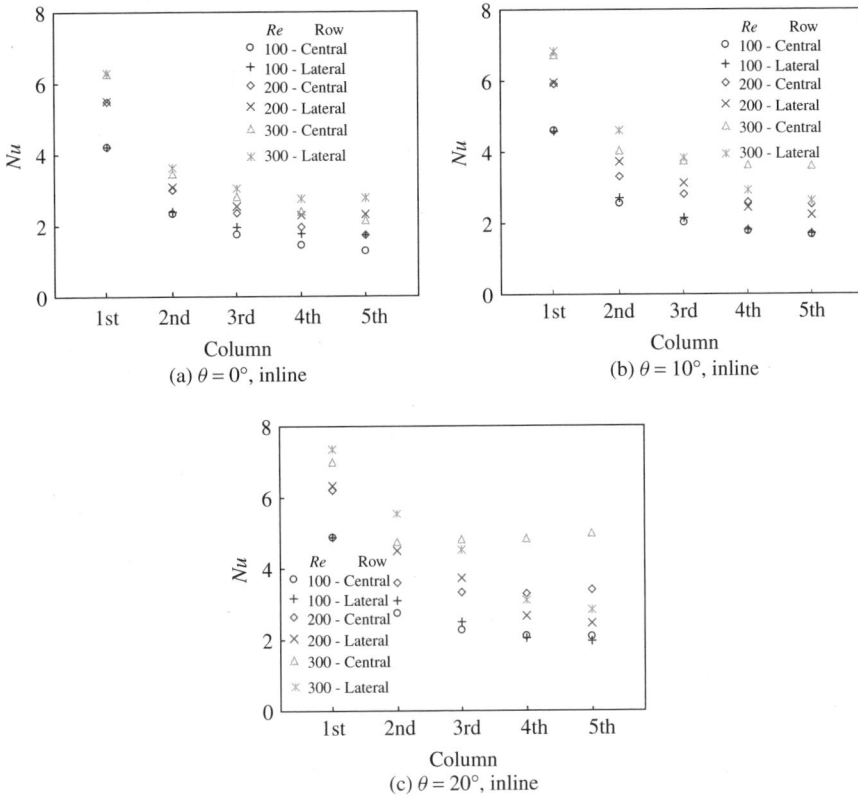

Figure 9.35   Forced convection heat transfer from spherical heat sources mounted on the wall. Average Nusselt number distribution for in-line arrangement at different inclination angles and Reynolds numbers

of Re. This information about the influence of the angle of attack can be very useful in this type of application, in which the central part of the electronic device tends to be the hottest.

The average Nusselt number variation for different Reynolds numbers and flow angles for the staggered arrangement of the solder balls is shown in Figure 9.36. In these figures, the x-axis represents the column numbers of the ball clusters. For all legend details, refer to Figure 9.34. The symbols used for the 'central' and the 'lower' rows are identical, as the balls from these rows do not fall onto the same column. For example, the 'central' row balls fall onto the columns with odd numbers but the 'lower' rows fall onto the columns with even numbers.

As for the in-line arrangement, the average Nusselt number obtained is smaller for the balls at the centre of the cluster. The front column, as expected, gives the highest heat transfer rate. As the angle of attack of the incoming flow is increased, the participation of the balls within the cluster increases, thus influencing the heat transfer. However, the Nusselt numbers calculated are much smaller than that of the in-line arrangement for the same Reynolds number and angle of attack.

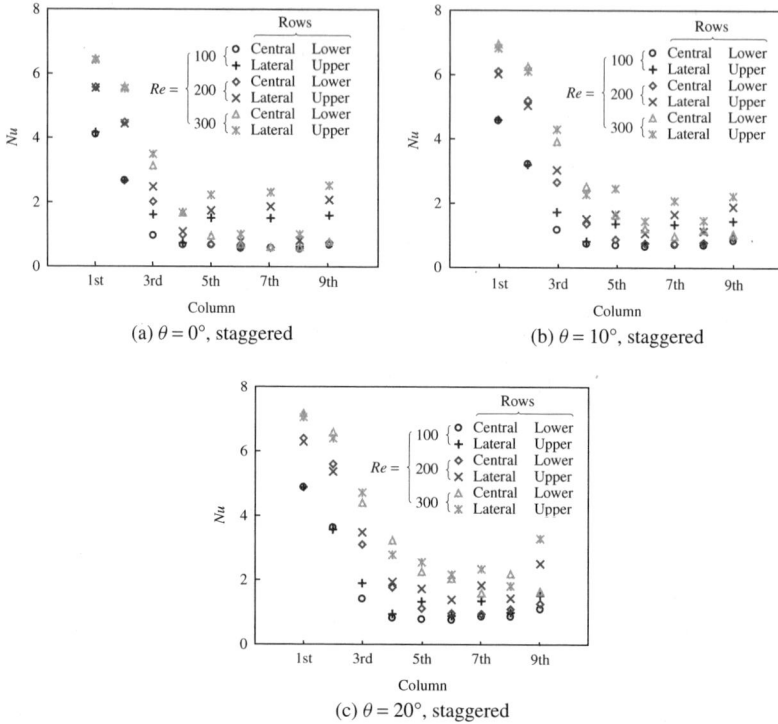

(a) $\theta = 0°$, staggered

(b) $\theta = 10°$, staggered

(c) $\theta = 20°$, staggered

Figure 9.36   Forced convection heat transfer from spherical heat sources mounted on the wall. Average Nusselt number distribution for staggered arrangement at different inclination angles and Reynolds numbers

9.6 Summary

In this chapter, the problem-solving capabilities of the finite element method have been demonstrated. The emphasis of the chapter has been on the use of unstructured meshes to prove the flexibility of the finite element method. Occasionally, structured meshes were used for the purposes of comparison. The readers should use this chapter as a starting point for problem-solving exercises, for which purpose several benchmark problems and a few applications have been given. The CBS flow code may be used to further enhance an understanding of the finite element method, heat transfer and fluid flow problems. This chapter should form a basis for researchers and students who want to further explore engineering heat transfer problems.

9.7 Exercise

Exercise 9.7.1 *In this exercise, you are asked to make appropriate assumptions and model flow past the heat exchanger tubes as shown in Figure 9.37.*

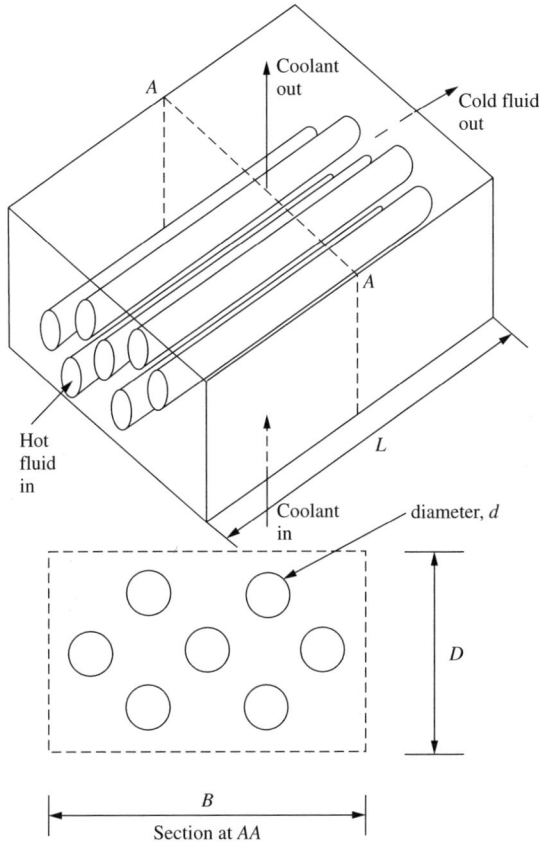

Figure 9.37 Schematic diagram of a cross flow heat exchanger, $d = 1$, $B = 8$, $D = 6$, pitch $= 3$, $L = 42$

A schematic diagram of a typical cross flow heat exchanger arrangement is shown in Figure 9.37. As seen, the hot working fluid from the industry is passed through tubes and the coolant is pumped from the bottom and used to cool the working fluid. In this particular heat exchanger, the tubes are arranged in a staggered style.

The flow and heat transfer analysis over these tubes is very important in determining an optimal tube arrangement. Neglecting the outer wall effects, carry out a heat transfer analysis at a Reynolds number of 300. Assume that the flow is laminar and the buoyancy effects are negligibly small.

Assume that the vortex-shedding effects can be neglected and simplify the three-dimensional problem to a two-dimensional problem. Set up the appropriate boundary conditions, generate the mesh and carry out the analysis either using the CBS flow code or any other available software.

Exercise 9.7.2 *In this exercise, you are asked to simulate the liquid flow through a liquid processing plant as shown in Figure 9.38.*

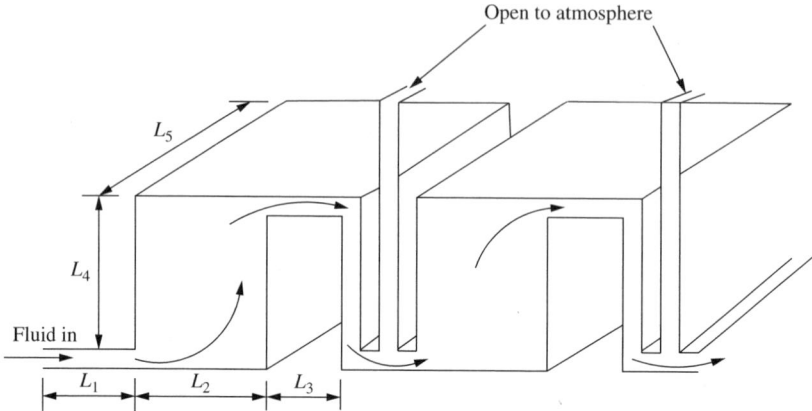

Figure 9.38   Schematic diagram of water processing plant, inlet/exit channel height $= 1$, $L_1 = 4$, $L_2 = 5$, $L_3 = 4$, $L_4 = 6$, $L_5 = 30$

In the liquid processing industry, liquid is passed through several tanks as shown in Figure 9.38. The diagram shows a simplified model of such a plant. With appropriate assumptions, simplify the problem further and determine the flow mechanism. The raw liquid is pumped into the plant from the left-hand side at a Reynolds number of 400, which is based on the width of the inlet channel and inlet velocity.

Include appropriate assumptions and formulate a simplified physical problem. The simplification should be in such a way that the model should not lose accuracy and at the same time should not be very expensive to solve. Discuss the project and design the boundary limits and conditions.

Once the problem has been simplified to two dimensions, generate a mesh and solve the problem using the CBS flow solver. Determine the temperature distribution if the bottom surface of the tank is hotter than the incoming fluid. Neglect the buoyancy effects and assume the liquid is water in the heat transport problem.

Exercise 9.7.3 *A two-dimensional square enclosure (all solid walls) filled with air is subjected to a linearly varying temperature on one of its vertical walls (say $T = (x_2/L)T_{max}$, where L is the characteristic dimension) and a constant temperature on the other vertical wall, which is less than that of T_{max}. If the horizontal walls are assumed to be adiabatic, obtain solutions for the flow and heat transfer inside the enclosure for different Rayleigh numbers. Refer to Chapter 7 for non-dimensional scales.*

Exercise 9.7.4 *In the above problem, if the linear variation of temperature is replaced with a constant heat flux, determine the temperature and flow patterns.*

Bibliography

Bar-Cohen A, Watwe A and Seetharamu KN 2001 Fundamentals of thermal management, *Chap. 6 of:* Tummala, R.R. (ed), *Fundamentals of Microsystem Packaging*, McGraw-Hill, New York.

Denham MK and Patrik MA 1974 Laminar flow over a downstream–facing step in a two-dimensional flow channel, *Transactions of the Institution of Chemical Engineers*, **52**, 361–367.

de Sampaio PAB, Lyra PRM, Morgan K and Weatherill NP 1993 Petrov-Galerkin solutions of the incompressible Navier-Stokes equations in primitive variables in with adaptive remeshing, *Computer Methods in Applied Mechanics and Engineering*, **106**, 143–178.

Donea A and Huerta A 2003 *Finite Element Method for Flow Problems*, John Wiley & Sons, Chichester.

Ghia U, Ghia KN and Shin CT 1982 High Re solutions for incompressible flow using the Navier-Stokes equations and multigrid method, *Journal of Computational Physics*, **48**, 387–411.

Gresho PM and Sani RL 2000 *Incompressible Flow and the Finite Element Method, Vol. 2, Isothermal Laminar Flow*, John Wiley & Sons, Chichester.

Heindel TJ, Incropera FP and Ramadhyami S 1996 Enhancement of natural convection heat transfer from an array of discrete heat sources, *International Journal of Heat Mass Transfer*, **39**, 479–490.

Kondoh T, Nagano Y and Tsuji T 1993 Computational study of laminar heat transfer downstream of a backward–facing step, *International Journal of Heat and Mass Transfer*, **36**, 577–591.

Lewis RW, Ravindran K and Usmani AS 1995 Finite element solution of incompressible flows using an explicit segregated approach, *Archives of Computational Methods in Engineering*, **2**, 69–93.

Löhner R 2001 *Applied CFD Techniques*, John Wiley & Sons, New York.

Malan AG, Lewis RW and Nithiarasu P 2002 An improved unsteady, unstructured, artificial compressibility, finite volume scheme for viscous incompressible flows. Part I: Theory and implementation, *International Journal for Numerical Methods in Engineering*, **54**, 695–714.

Malan AG, Lewis RW and Nithiarasu P 2002 An improved unsteady, unstructured, artificial compressibility, finite volume scheme for viscous incompressible flows. Part II: Application, *International Journal for Numerical Methods in Engineering*, **54**, 715–729.

Morgan K, Weatherill NP, Hassan O, Brookes PJ, Said R and Jones J 1999 A parallel framework for multidisciplinary aerospace engineering simulations using unstructured meshes, *International Journal for Numerical Methods in Fluids*, **31**, 159–173.

Nakayama W, Behnia M and Soodphakdee D 2001 Numerical modeling using microscopic structures, *IEEE Transactions of Computer Packaging Technology*, **24**, 199–206.

Nakayama A and Kuwahara F 2000 Numerical modeling using microscopic structures, *Chap. 10 of:* Vafai, K. (ed), *Handbook of Porous Media*, Marcel Dekker, New York.

Nithiarasu P 2003 An efficient artificial compressibility (AC) scheme based on the characteristic based split (CBS) method for incompressible flows, *International Journal for Numerical Methods in Engineering*, **56**, 1815–1845.

Nithiarasu P and Massarotti N 2004 Forced convection heat transfer from solder balls on a printed circuit board using the Characteristic Based Split (CBS) scheme, *International Journal of Numerical Methods in Heat and Fluid Flow* (in press).

Nithiarasu P, Mathur JS, Weatherill NP and Morgan K 2004. Three-dimensional incompressible flow calculations using the characteristic based split (CBS) scheme, *International Journal for Numerical Methods in Fluids* (in press).

Nithiarasu P and Zienkiewicz OC 2000 Adaptive mesh generation for fluid mechanics problems, *International Journal for Numerical Methods in Engineering*, **47**, 629–662.

Shidore S, Adams V and Lee Y-T 2001 A study of compact thermal model topologies in CFD for a flip chip plastic ball grid array package, *IEEE Transactions of Computer Packaging Technology*, **24**, 191–198.

Taylor C and Hughes TG 1981 *Finite Element Programming of the Navier-Stokes Equations*, Pineridge Press Ltd, Swansea.

Watson SP, Murray BT and Sammakia BG 2001 Computational parameter study of chip scale package array cooling, *IEEE Transactions of Computer Packaging Technology*, **24**, 184–190.

Weatherhill NP, Hassan O, Morgan K, Jones J and Larwood B 2001 A parallel framework for multidisciplinary aerospace engineering simulations using unstructured meshes, *Engineering Computations*, **18**, 347–375.

Zhao CY and Lu TJ 2002 Analysis of microchannel heat sinks for electronic cooling, *International Journal of Heat Mass Transfer*, **45**, 4857–4869.

Zhou YC, Patnaik BSV, Wan DC and Wei GW 2003 DSC solution for flow in a staggered double lid driven cavity, *International Journal for Numerical Methods in Engineering*, **57**, 211–234.

Zienkiewicz OC and Taylor RL 2000 *The Finite Element Method, Vol. 3, Fluid Dynamics*, Butterworth and Heinemann, Oxford, UK.

10

Implementation of Computer Code

10.1 Introduction

In this chapter, a brief introduction is given regarding the implementation of the computer code. It is assumed that the readers are familiar with Fortran programming (Smith and Griffiths 1998; Wille 1995). The whole chapter is based on the CBS scheme and the time-stepping algorithm discussed in the previous chapters. The discussion is limited to the essential aspects of the CBSflow code. However, the discussion on the pre- and postprocessing technique is common to many other schemes. Although CBSflow is a heat convection code, heat conduction may also be solved if the velocity calculations are suppressed.

The following discussion will be limited to linear triangular elements, which has already been covered in detail in Chapters 3 and 7. The CBS and conduction codes may be downloaded from the authors' web pages (email: P.Nithiarasu@swansea.ac.uk). The basic source codes for simple mesh generation and analysis are freely available for the readers to carry out two-dimensional studies[1].

In general, all the numerical programs contain three parts, that is, preprocessing, the main processing unit and postprocessing. The preprocessing part includes mesh generation, data structure and most of the element-related data, which are constant for an element. The main processing unit is responsible for the computational effort and often most of the computing (CPU) time during a calculation. Efficient programming can reduce the CPU time, which is especially important in three dimensions. The details of an efficient data structure are not discussed here, but readers may obtain information on such issues in various other relevant items of literature (Löhner 2001). In this chapter, the basic implementa-

---

[1] All the source codes available from the authors are copyrighted to the authors who developed the code. None of the material available within the code should be reproduced/copied in any form for commercial purposes without the written permission of the author of the source codes. Readers are expected to acknowledge by citing the book in their publications if the full/part of the code is used for producing results.

Fundamentals of the Finite Element Method for Heat and Fluid Flow   R. W. Lewis, P. Nithiarasu and K. N. Seetharamu
© 2004 John Wiley & Sons, Ltd   ISBNs: 0-470-84788-3 (HB); 0-470-84789-1 (PB)

tion procedures are given so that the readers can understand the basics of the computer implementation of the finite element method.

The final part of a finite element code is the postprocessing unit. This unit can either be a coupled postprocessor, which directly gives the solution in graphical form or may be linked to an external postprocessor via an interface. The latter option is chosen in this text and the readers can then prepare their own interface and link to a postprocessing unit. Often, it is necessary to extract data along a line within a domain. In such a situation, one can either use other available software or employ an interpolation routine to compute the data along an arbitrary line or at a point.

The CBSflow code has been used for various applications in the past (Nithiarasu 2000). The overall procedure of time-stepping the CBSflow code for thermal problems can be summarized as

```
call preprocessing    ! preprocessing
do itime = 1,ntime    ! time loop
   call timestep       ! time-step calculation
   call step1          ! intermediate momentum
   call step2          ! pressure calculation
   call step3          ! momentum(velocity) correction
   call step4          ! temperature calculation
   call check          ! check for steady state
enddo !
call postprocessing !postprocessing (output)
```

More details are given in the following sections.

10.2 Preprocessing

As mentioned previously, the preprocessing operation normally takes place before the main solution unit. Often, the mesh generation section is kept separate from the rest of the routines in order to simplify the data preparation. Such an approach is followed here and the mesh generation algorithm is kept separate from the rest of the program.

10.2.1 Mesh generation

As mentioned in previous chapters, there are two main types of meshes, namely, structured and unstructured meshes. Structured meshes are generally simple in form and follow a certain pattern, which may either be uniform or non-uniform. Alternatively, unstructured meshes follow no particular pattern and are generated by dividing a domain into an arbitrary number of triangles or other finite element shapes. Since unstructured meshes follow no fixed pattern, the control of the solution accuracy in those sections of the domain that are dominated by high gradients is difficult. Structured meshes, on the other hand, result in more accurate solutions. However, the generation of a structured mesh for a complex geometry, especially in three dimensions, is both time-consuming and difficult. Therefore, unstructured meshes, which are generated by a suitable unstructured mesh generator, will be used in this text.

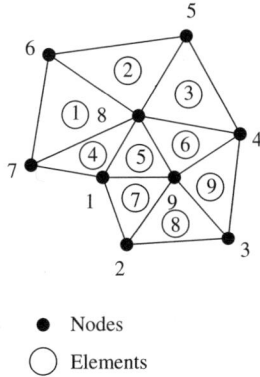

Figure 10.1 A typical unstructured mesh

There are several methods available for generating unstructured meshes. Two of the most prominent methods are the 'advancing front' (Löhner 2001; Löhner and Baum 1992; Peraire and Morgan 1997; Peraire *et al.* 1987) and 'Delaunay triangulation' (Kumar *et al.* 1997; Lewis *et al.* 1995; Thompson *et al.* 1999; Weatherill *et al.* 1994) techniques. Most of the unstructured meshes used in this book are generated by either one of these methods. Controlling the quality of elements for example the aspect ratio, is much easier in the Delaunay approach than in the advancing front method.

It is a common practice to store finite element data in terms of the nodal coordinates and element connectivity. In addition to these, some convenient form of boundary condition specification is also necessary. It is therefore important that a mesh generator enables the coordinates of discrete points, the nodal connectivity of the finite elements and some form of boundary node/side information. A typical mesh is shown in Figure 10.1 and the typical input from a mesh generator is given by

```
no of nodes, no elements and no of boundary sides
9    9    7
Element number and connectivity
1    7    8    6
2    6    8    5
3    8    4    5
4    1    8    7
5    1    9    8
6    9    4    8
7    2    9    1
8    2    3    9
9    9    3    4
Node number and xy-coordinates
1    1.1    1.2
2    1.6    0.0
3    3.3    0.1
4    3..4   1.9
5    2.1    3.3
6    0.4    3.0
```

```
7   0.0   1.0
8   1.8   2.1
9   2.3   1.1
Boundary side nodes and elements, boundary condition code
1   2   7   1
2   3   8   1
3   4   9   1
4   5   3   1
5   6   2   2
6   7   1   2
7   1   4   2
```

In the above mesh data, the total number of linear triangular elements is 9, the number of nodes is also 9 and the number of boundary sides is 7. The element connectivity of all the elements is numbered in an anticlockwise direction. The node numbering follows no particular pattern. For simply connected domains, the outer boundary sides are numbered in an anticlockwise direction, and in a multiple connected domain, the inner boundary is numbered in a clockwise direction.

The above-mentioned data structure of the element connectivity and the boundary side numbering are essential to make sure that the areas of the triangular elements are positive and that the appropriate boundary normals are determined from the boundary side data.

Note that the boundary condition code, that is, the last column in the boundary side data, is used to represent an appropriate boundary condition on a side. For example, 1 in the above data can be used to represent an inlet condition and 2 may be used to represent a solid wall condition (no-slip). The third column in the boundary side data is the element to which the corresponding side belongs. This information is useful in evaluating the boundary integral terms and helpful in applying Neumann boundary conditions. The above data are normally prepared by a mesh generator, and once available, these data may be read into the main analysis code by the following arrays:

```
intma(i,j) - Connectivity array. i = 1,2,3
  and j = 1,2...number of elements
coord(i,j) - Coordinates array. i = 1,2
  and j = 1,2 ... number of nodes.
isido(i,j) - Boundary side array. i=1,2,3,4
  and j = 1,2, ..number of boundary sides.
```

10.2.2   Linear triangular element data

As mentioned before, only linear triangular elements will be considered in this chapter. The essential data, including the mesh data and any other relevant data, are read from various input files at the preprocessing stage. Once all the external data are available, the remaining preprocessing procedure is carried out by the program. Some of the important preprocessing aspects of the finite element program are given in the following subsections.

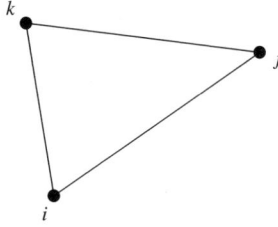

Figure 10.2   A triangular element

10.2.3   Element size calculation

The areas of the triangular elements are necessary for any finite element calculation, and these areas are constant if the mesh is unchanged throughout the analysis. With reference to Figure 10.2, the area of an element may be determined from the following expression:

$$A = \int dx_1 \, dx_2 = \frac{1}{2} \begin{vmatrix} 1 & x_{1i} & x_{2i} \\ 1 & x_{1j} & x_{2j} \\ 1 & x_{1k} & x_{2k} \end{vmatrix} \tag{10.1}$$

Note that i, j and k are the nodes and the subscripts 1 and 2 indicate the coordinate directions. A sample routine that calculates the area of the elements and the derivatives of the shape functions is given below.

```
c-------------------------------------------------------------------
      subroutine getgeo(mxpoi,mxele,npoin,nelem,coord,intma,geome)
c-------------------------------------------------------------------
c     Derivatives of shape functions and 2A are calculated and

c     stored in the array geome(7,mxele). First six entries are

c     derivatives of the shape functions and the last one

c     (seventh) is two times the area of an element

      implicit none

      integer   mxpoi, mxele, npoin, nelem,ielem, inode, in

      integer   intma(3,mxele)

      real*8    x21,x31,y21,y31,rj,rj1,xix,xiy,etx,ety
      real*8    rnxi,rnet

      real*8    geome(7,mxele),  coord(2,mxpoi)
      real*8    x(3),y(3),pnxi(3),pnet(3) !local arrays

      data pnxi/-1.0d00, 1.0d00, 0.0d00/
      data pnet/-1.0d00, 0.0d00, 1.0d00/
```

```
     do ielem      = 1,nelem !loop over number of elements
       do inode    = 1,3
         in        = intma(inode,ielem)
         x(inode)  = coord(1,in)
         y(inode)  = coord(2,in)
       enddo !inode
       x21         = x(2)-x(1)
       x31         = x(3)-x(1)
       y21         = y(2)-y(1)
       y31         = y(3)-y(1)
       rj          = x21*y31-x31*y21
       rj1         = 1.0d+00/rj
       xix         =  y31*rj1
       xiy         = -x31*rj1
       etx         = -y21*rj1
       ety         =  x21*rj1
       do in                 = 1,2
         rnxi                = pnxi(in)
         rnet                = pnet(in)
         geome(in,ielem)     = xix*rnxi + etx*rnet
         geome(in+3,ielem)   = xiy*rnxi + ety*rnet
       enddo !in
       geome(3,ielem)        = -( geome(1,ielem) + geome(2,ielem) )
       geome(6,ielem)        = -( geome(4,ielem) + geome(5,ielem) )
       geome(7,ielem)        = rj ! two times area

     enddo !ielem
     end
!-------------------------------------------------------------------
```

As stated previously, if the mesh is unchanged during the analysis, then the above calculation is carried out only once, and all the values are stored in the arrays for use in the main unit of the program.

10.2.4   Shape functions and their derivatives

For linear elements, an explicit calculation of the shape functions is not necessary as these may be integrated directly. However, it is necessary to calculate the derivatives of the shape functions, which are constant for a linear element. Therefore, these derivatives can be evaluated at the preprocessing stage and stored in an appropriate array. For a linear triangular element, we require six derivatives of the shape functions, that is,

$$\frac{\partial N_i}{\partial x_1}; \frac{\partial N_j}{\partial x_1}; \frac{\partial N_k}{\partial x_1}; \frac{\partial N_i}{\partial x_2}; \frac{\partial N_j}{\partial x_2} \text{ and } \frac{\partial N_k}{\partial x_2} \tag{10.2}$$

These derivatives are calculated and stored in the first six entries of an array

```
geome(7,mxele)
```

as mentioned in the previous subsection. Further details on the shape function derivatives are given in Chapter 3. Once the derivatives of the shape functions are stored, a calculation of the derivatives of any function/variable is straightforward. For example, the x_1 and x_2 derivatives of a nodal variable

```
unkno(2,ip)
```

within the elements are calculated as

```
do ie         = 1,nelem !loop over elements
   dpdx(ie)   = 0.0d00   !x_1 derivative
   dpdy(ie)   = 0.0d00   !x_2 derivative
   do i       = 1,3
      ip       = intma(i,ie)
     dpdx(ie) = dpdx(ie) + geome(i,ie)*unkno(2,ip)
     dpdy(ie) = dpdy(ie) + geome(i+3,ie)*unkno(2,ip)
   enddo !i
enddo !ie
```

These derivatives will be constant over an element for linear triangular elements.

10.2.5   Boundary normal calculation

The unit boundary outward normal, **n**, is shown in Figure 10.3. The components n_1 and n_2 are calculated and stored in an array at the preprocessing stage if the mesh is unchanged during the calculation. In addition to the normal components, the boundary side lengths are also computed and stored in the same array. The sample routine that calculates the normal components and the side lengths is given below.

```
c-------------------------------------------------------------------
      subroutine getnor(mxpoi,mxbou,npoin,nboun,coord,isido,rsido)
c-------------------------------------------------------------------
c       Boundary normal calculation

        implicit   none

        integer    mxpoi, mxbou, npoin, nboun,ib,ipoi0,ipoi1
        integer    isido(4,mxbou)
```

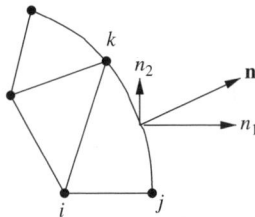

Figure 10.3   Outward normal from a boundary side

```
real*8      dx,dy,rl
real*8      rsido(3,mxbou), coord(2,mxpoi)

call rfillm(rsido,3,nboun,0.0d00) !fill with zeros
do ib           = 1, nboun !loop over boundary sides
   ipoi0        = isido(1,ib) !first node of a side
   ipoi1        = isido(2,ib) !second node of a side
   dx           = coord(1,ipoi1) - coord(1,ipoi0)
   dy           = coord(2,ipoi1) - coord(2,ipoi0)
   rl           = dsqrt(dx*dx+dy*dy) ! length of a side
   rsido(1,ib)  = dy/rl   ! cos(theta)
   rsido(2,ib)  = -dx/rl  ! sin(theta)
   rsido(3,ib)  = rl      ! side length
enddo !ib
end
c-------------------------------------------------------------------
```

Readers are reminded that the above routine will be applicable only if the outer boundary sides are numbered in an anticlockwise fashion for simply connected domains. For multiply connected domains, the inner boundary sides should be numbered in a clockwise direction in order to ensure that the normals point outwards in the analysis domain as shown in Figure 10.4.

In the routine considered above, the term

```
rsido(3,mxbou)
```

is the array used to store the normal components and the side lengths. The first two entries are the x_1 and x_2 components of the normals and the third entry is the side length.

10.2.6   Mass matrix and mass lumping

The calculation of the mass matrices is required at many stages during the solution of a heat transfer problem. For example, all the transient terms, if solved in an explicit mode, lead to mass matrices after spatial and temporal discretizations. These mass matrices can

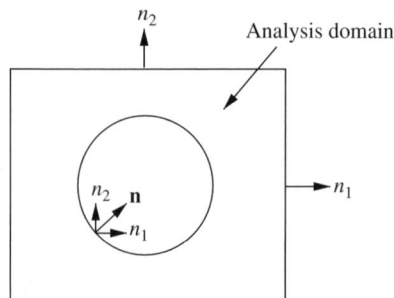

Figure 10.4   Multiply connected domain. Outward normal

be 'lumped' using a standard row-summing approach if the steady state solution is the only interest. In such situations, the mass matrix is lumped, inverted and stored in an array during the preprocessing stage if the mesh is unchanged during the calculation. For details of mass matrices and the lumping procedure, refer to Chapter 7. The following Fortran routine gives the details of how the inverse of the mass matrix is calculated and then stored into an array.

```
!-------------------------------------------------------------------
      subroutine getmat(mxpoi,mxele,npoin,nelem,intma,geome,dmmat)
!-------------------------------------------------------------------
c     This routine calculates inverse lumped mass matrix

c     and stores in an array dmmat(mxpoi)

      implicit    none

      integer     mxpoi, mxele, npoin, nelem,ielem,inode,i,in
      integer     intma(3,mxele)

      real*8      rj,rj6
      real*8      geome(7,mxele), dmmat(mxpoi)

      call rfillv(dmmat, npoin, 0.0d00) !fill with zeros

      do ielem = 1, nelem
        rj          = geome(7,ielem) ! 2A
        rj6         = rj/6.0d+00      ! A/3
        do inode = 1, 3
          in        = intma(inode,ielem)
          dmmat(in) = dmmat(in) + rj6 ! assembly
        enddo !inode
      enddo !ielem
      do i = 1, npoin
        dmmat(i)    = 1.0d+00/dmmat(i) ! inverse
      enddo !i
      end
c-------------------------------------------------------------------
```

Note that

```
dmmat(mxpoi)
```

is the lumped and inverted mass matrix. Once stored, this may be used during the solution update of an explicit solution procedure in the main program unit.

10.2.7   Implicit pressure or heat conduction matrix

Often, the pressure calculation in fluid dynamics or pure heat conduction calculations is carried out using implicit procedures. For instance, the pressure Poisson equation of an incompressible flow calculation may have the following form:

$$-\frac{\partial^2 p}{\partial x_1^2} - \frac{\partial^2 p}{\partial x_2^2} = \frac{1}{\Delta t}\left(\frac{\partial u_1^*}{\partial x_1} + \frac{\partial u_2^*}{\partial x_2}\right) \tag{10.3}$$

If a standard Galerkin weighting procedure and linear triangular elements are used, then this will lead to the following discrete form of the LHS of the above equation (integration by parts) for a triangular element.

$$\frac{1}{4A}\begin{bmatrix} b_i^2 & b_i b_j & b_i b_k \\ b_j b_i & b_j^2 & b_j b_k \\ b_k b_i & b_k b_j & b_k^2 \end{bmatrix}\begin{Bmatrix} p_i \\ p_j \\ p_k \end{Bmatrix} + \frac{1}{4A}\begin{bmatrix} c_i^2 & c_i c_j & c_i c_k \\ c_j c_i & c_j^2 & c_j c_k \\ c_k c_i & c_k c_j & c_k^2 \end{bmatrix}\begin{Bmatrix} p_i \\ p_j \\ p_k \end{Bmatrix} \tag{10.4}$$

where i, j and k are the three nodes of a triangle. The terms b_i, b_j and b_k are the x_1 derivatives of the shape functions and c_i, c_j and c_k are the x_2 derivatives of the shape functions (see Chapters 3 and 7). The above equation needs to be assembled in order to obtain a global LHS matrix. As mentioned previously, the derivatives of the shape functions are constants and do not change if the mesh is fixed during the calculation. It is therefore convenient to calculate the matrices of the above equation at the preprocessing stage, so that they may be used whenever necessary in the main unit of the code. A sample calculation of the pressure matrix for a banded (direct) matrix solver is given below.

```
c-------------------------------------------------------------------
      subroutine pstiff(mxpoi,mxele,mbw,npoin,nelem,nbw,intma,
     &                  geome,theta,gsm)
c-------------------------------------------------------------------

c *** calculates global LHS matrix for pressure

      implicit    none

      integer     mxpoi,mxele,mbw,npoin,nelem,nbw,i

      integer     ie,ip1,ip2,ip3,j,ielem,i3,j3,ii,i1,jj,i2,j1,j2

      integer     intma(3,mxele)

      real*8      area,thett

      real*8      geome(7,mxele), theta(2), gsm(mbw,mxpoi)
      real*8      s(3,3) !local

      do i = 1, npoin
        do j = 1, nbw
          gsm(j,i) = 0.0d00 !initialise
        enddo !j
      enddo !j
```

```
        do ielem = 1, nelem
          area    = geome(7,ielem)*0.5d00 ! area of an element
          thett   = theta(1)*theta(2) ! theta parameters (see
                                      ! Chapter 7 for details)
          do i    = 1, 3
            i3    = i + 3
            do j     = 1, 3
              j3     = j + 3
c     Element by element calculation of the shape function

c     derivatives and summation
              s(i,j) = thett*area*(geome(i,ielem)*geome(j,ielem)
      &                          + geome(i3,ielem)*geome(j3,ielem))
            enddo !j
          enddo !i
          do ii = 1, 3
            i1 = intma(ii,ielem)
            do jj = ii, 3
              i2 = intma(jj,ielem)
              if(i2.lt.i1) then !banded arrangement
                j1 = i2
                j2 = i1
                j2 = j2 - j1 +1
                gsm(j2,j1) = gsm(j2,j1) + s(jj,ii)!assembly
              else
                i2 = i2 - i1 + 1 !banded arrangement
                gsm(i2,i1) = gsm(i2,i1) + s(jj,ii)!assembly
              endif
            enddo !jj
          enddo !ii
        enddo !ielem
      end
c-------------------------------------------------------------------
```

In this case, the term

```
gsm(mbw,mxpoi)
```

is the global LHS matrix, which is unchanged during the calculation if the mesh is unaltered.

10.3   Main Unit

The following important list of parameters and quantities are normally available from the preprocessing unit.

```
intma(3,mxele) - connectivity; coord(2,mxpoi) - nodal coordinates;
isido(4,mxbou) - boundary side information; geome(7,mxele) -
derivatives of shape functions and element area; rsido(3,mxbou) -
boundary side normals and its length; dmmat(mxpoi) - lumped and
```

inversed mass matrix; gsm(mbw,mxpoi) - LHS matrix (only for
implicit solution); nelem - number of elements; npoin - number of
nodes, nboun - number of boundary sides

In addition to the above, several other quantities and parameters need to be either
read from an input file or developed within the preprocessing unit. Readers are asked to
consult the source codes and manuals, which are available to download, to understand these
additional auxiliary parameters.

The discussion on the main unit of the program is provided here by assuming that a
time-stepping approach is adopted for the solution of heat transfer problems and that the
above-listed parameters are available from the preprocessing unit.

10.3.1   Time-step calculation

As stated previously, if a steady state solution is obtained, via a time-stepping approach,
an appropriate stable time step should be employed in the calculations. The time-step
magnitude for a convection heat transfer problem may be stated as

$$\Delta t = \min \left(\frac{h}{|u|}, \frac{h^2}{2v}, \frac{h^2}{2\alpha} \right) \tag{10.5}$$

where h is the element size, u is the velocity, v is the kinematic viscosity of the fluid and
α is the thermal diffusivity. For Prandtl numbers of unity, the time-step values due to the
kinematic viscosity and thermal diffusivity are equal. If the Prandtl number is greater than
unity, then the time step calculated using the thermal diffusivity is greater than that of the
one due to the kinematic viscosity. Assuming that the magnitude of the thermal time step,
that is, $h^2/2\alpha$ is greater than that of the viscous time step, then the following routine may
be utilized to calculate the value.

```
c----------------------------------------------------------------
      subroutine alotim( mxpoi, mxele, npoin, nelem, intma, geome,
     &             unkno, number, dtfix, ilots, csafm, ani, deltp,
     &             delte )
c----------------------------------------------------------------

c      calculates the critical time step for all the elements

c      and nodes. iopt = -1 - fixed user specified global time step

c      (dtfix). iopt = 0 - global time step calculated as minimum

c      from all nodal values. iopt = 1 - local time step nodally

c      varies

       implicit  none

       integer   mxpoi,mxele,npoin,nelem,ilots,ip,ie,ip1,ip2,ip3
```

```
      integer    intma(3,mxele), number(mxpoi)

      real*8     u1,u2,u3,v1,v2,v3,vn1,vn2,vn3,veln,anx,any
      real*8     alen1,alen2,alen3,alen,dm,dtfix,csafm
      real*8     ani,aloti1,aloti2,tiny

      real*8     geome(7,mxele), unkno(4,mxpoi), deltp(mxpoi)
      real*8     delte(mxele)

c     global user specified fixed time step

      if(ilots.le.-1) then
        call rfillv(deltp, npoin, dtfix) !fill with fixed value
        call rfillv(delte, nelem, dtfix) !fill with fixed value
        return
      endif

      tiny = 0.1d-05
      do ip = 1, npoin
        deltp(ip) = 1.0d06 !nodal value initialise
      enddo !ip
      do ie   = 1, nelem !loop over elements
        ip1   = intma(1,ie) !node1
        ip2   = intma(2,ie) !node1
        ip3   = intma(3,ie) !node3
        u1    = unkno(2,ip1) !u1 node1
        u2    = unkno(2,ip2) !u1 node2
        u3    = unkno(2,ip3) !u1 node3
        v1    = unkno(3,ip1) !u2 node1
        v2    = unkno(3,ip2) !u2 node2
        v3    = unkno(3,ip3) !u2 node3
        vn1   = dsqrt(u1**2 + v1**2) ! |V| node1
        vn2   = dsqrt(u2**2 + v2**2) ! |V| node2
        vn3   = dsqrt(u3**2 + v3**2) ! |V| node3
        veln  = max(vn1,vn2,vn3)        ! Maximum |V|
        anx   = geome(1,ie)
        any   = geome(4,ie)
        alen1 = 1.0d+00/dsqrt(anx**2 + any**2) !element size (h1)
        anx   = geome(2,ie)
        any   = geome(5,ie)
        alen2 = 1.0d+00/dsqrt(anx**2 + any**2) !element size (h2)
        anx   = geome(3,ie)
        any   = geome(6,ie)
        alen3 = 1.0d+00/dsqrt(anx**2 + any**2) !element size (h3)
        alen  = min(alen1,alen2,alen3) !minimum h

c     local time step

        aloti1    = alen/(veln+tiny) ! convection limit
        aloti2    = 0.5*alen**2/ani  ! viscous limit
```

```
        deltp(ip1) = min(deltp(ip1), aloti1,aloti2) !nodes
        deltp(ip2) = min(deltp(ip2), aloti1,aloti2) !nodes
        deltp(ip3) = min(deltp(ip3), aloti1,aloti2) !nodes
        delte(ie)  = min(deltp(ip3), aloti1,aloti2) !elements
      enddo !ie
      do ip = 1,npoin
        deltp(ip) = csafm*deltp(ip) !multiply by safety factor
      enddo !ip
      do ie = 1,nelem
        delte(ie) = csafm*delte(ie) !multiply by safety factor
      enddo !ie

c     global minimum time step

      if(ilots.eq.0)then
      dm = 5.0d03
      do ip = 1,npoin
        dm = min(deltp(ip),dm)
      enddo !ip
      do ip = 1, npoin
        deltp(ip) = dm
      enddo !ip
      do ie = 1, nelem
        delte(ie) = dm
      enddo!ie
      endif
      end
c-----------------------------------------------------------------
```

The element size at a node is calculated in the routine using the sizes represented by Figure 10.5 as

$$h_i = \min(h_1, h_2, h_3, h_4, h_5) \qquad (10.6)$$

Again, the above element size will be unchanged if the mesh is unaltered during a calculation. It is therefore possible to calculate and store the element sizes into an array at the preprocessing stage. A more accurate representation of an element size is possible by determining the element size in the streamline direction. However, such a calculation

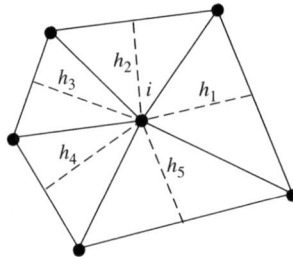

Figure 10.5   Element size calculation

will lead to a variation in the element size at each time step, if a time-stepping scheme is employed, or it will vary at each iteration if a steady state equation system with an iterative procedure is employed.

10.3.2 Element loop and assembly

A loop over the number of elements is the commonly employed form of LHS matrix/RHS vector construction in finite element codes. The assembly process is normally associated with the element loop. An example of such a loop, when assembling the full viscous terms of the momentum equations, is

```
do ia = 1, nelem !loop over number of elements
  do lok       = 1, 3!loop over three nodes of an element
    in         = intma(lok,ia) !nodes of an element
    lok1       = lok + 3
    velo1      = unkno(2,in) ! velocity component1
    velo2      = unkno(3,in) ! velocity component2
    sigxx(ia) = sigxx(ia) + ( ani )*
&                 ( geome(lok,ia)*2.0*velo1 ) !stress 11
    sigyy(ia) = sigyy(ia) + ( ani )*
&                 ( geome(lok1,ia)*2.0*velo2 )!stress 22
    sigxy(ia) = sigxy(ia) + ( ani )*
&                 ( geome(lok,ia)*velo2
&                 + geome(lok1,ia)*velo1 )    !stress 12
  enddo !lok
  do lok        = 1, 3
    lok1        = lok + 3
    rh1p(1,lok) = -geome(7,ia)*( sigxx(ia)*geome(lok,ia)
&                 + sigxy(ia)*geome(lok1,ia) )*0.5d00
    rh1p(2,lok) = -geome(7,ia)*( sigxy(ia)*geome(lok,ia)
&                 + sigyy(ia)*geome(lok1,ia) )*0.5d00
  enddo !lok
  do lok         = 1, 3
    in           = intma(lok,ia)
    do ja        = 1, 2
      ja1        = ja + 1
      rhs0(ja1,in) = rhs0(ja1,in) + rh1p(ja,lok) !assembly
    enddo !ja
  enddo !lok
enddo !ia
```

The stress components, τ_{11}, τ_{22} and τ_{12} are determined element by element and assembled into the RHS vector

```
rhs0(4,mxpoi)
```

Both the stress arrays

```
sigxx(mxele); sigyy(mxele); sigxy(mxele)
```

and the RHS vector array have to be initialized to a value of zero at every time step of the
calculation.

10.3.3   Updating solution

Two types of solution updating are possible when a time-stepping procedure is employed.
In the first type, a solution is updated after solving a simultaneous system of equations.
In the second type, the solution is updated by multiplying a lumped and inverted mass
matrix. In the latter procedure, the lumped mass matrix is a diagonal matrix and requires
no simultaneous solution, as shown in the following portion of the code for the momentum
equations.

```
c      add advection and diffusion RHS and multiply

c      by inversed mass

       do ip        = 1, npoin ! nodal loop
          dt        = dmmat(ip)
          rhs2(2,ip) = ( rhs2(2,ip) + rhs0(2,ip) )*dt
          rhs2(3,ip) = ( rhs2(3,ip) + rhs0(3,ip) )*dt
       enddo !ip

c      update the solution.

       do ip        = 1, npoin
          unkno(2,ip) = unkno(2,ip) + deltp(ip)*rhs2(2,ip) !update u_1
          unkno(3,ip) = unkno(3,ip) + deltp(ip)*rhs2(3,ip) !update u_2
       enddo !ip
```

Note that the time step is multiplied only at the end. The solution in the above part of
the routine is updated as follows:

$$u_1^{n+1} = u_1^n + \Delta t * \mathrm{RHS} * dmmat \tag{10.7}$$

The matrix solution procedures for updating the analysis is carried out by either a
direct or an iterative solver. Direct solvers, such as the Gaussian elimination technique are
employed when the simultaneous system is small and structured. However, for unstructured
meshes and large systems, it is difficult to employ such direct solvers. It is therefore
necessary to employ iterative solvers, for example, a conjugate gradient solver, in such
situations. A typical LHS matrix is discussed in Section 10.2.7 for a banded direct solver.
An RHS vector needs to be constructed before the solver can be used to obtain a solution.
The RHS vector is constructed at each time step and is subjected to boundary conditions
during the simultaneous solution procedure (see Chapter 3). The complete details of the
solvers used are available, along with the source codes, from the authors' web sites.

10.3.4   Boundary conditions

The boundary conditions are imposed after each time step by allotting an appropriate boundary condition code to a side (see mesh data). For instance, the no velocity flux condition, or normal velocity zero condition, is imposed using the following routine during an explicit calculation. Note that the boundary code for such a condition is assumed to be 4.

```
c-------------------------------------------------------------
      subroutine corsym( mxpoi, mxbou, npoin, nboun, unkno,
     &                     isido, rsido )
c-------------------------------------------------------------

c *** Applies the zero velocity flux boundary conditions

      implicit    none

      integer     mxpoi,mxbou,npoin,nboun,is,in,ip

      integer     isido(4,mxbou)

      real*8      anx,any,us

      real*8      unkno(4,mxpoi), rsido(3,mxbou)

      do is = 1, nboun
        if(isido(4,is).eq.4) then
          anx = rsido(1,is) !boundary normal
          any = rsido(2,is) !boundary normal
          do in = 1, 2
          ip = isido(in,is)
          us = -unkno(2,ip)*any + unkno(3,ip)*anx
          unkno(2,ip) = - us*any
          unkno(3,ip) =   us*anx
        enddo !in
      endif
    enddo !is
    end
c-------------------------------------------------------------
```

Note that

```
unkno(4,mxpoi)
```

is the unknown array. The first entry is the temperature, the second is the velocity component u_1, the third is the velocity component u_2 and the fourth is the pressure. As seen in the above routine, the 'no mass flux' condition is applied only to the velocity components.

10.3.5 Monitoring steady state

The steady state may be monitored via a fixed prescribed tolerance of the difference in a variable between two consecutive time steps. For example,

$$\max(\phi_i^{n+1} - \phi_i^n) \leq 10^{-10} \tag{10.8}$$

where ϕ is any variable such as velocity components, temperature etc. and the subscript i varies from 1 to the total number of nodes. Other ways of monitoring whether the steady state has been reached are discussed in Chapter 7. The following portion of the code explains how such a steady state check is carried out between two consecutive time steps. In addition to screening the maximum difference, the following section of code stores the node at which such a maximum occurs.

```
do ip            = 1, npoin
   adel1         = unkno(1,ip) - unkn1(1,ip) !temperature
   adel2         = unkno(2,ip) - unkn1(2,ip) !u_1
   adel3         = unkno(3,ip) - unkn1(3,ip) !u_2
   adel4         = pres1(ip) - pres(ip)      !pressure
   cder          = dabs(adel1)
   if(cder.gt.ha(1)) then
      icount(1) = ip                !node
      ha(1)     = cder              !maximum value
   endif
   cder          = dabs(adel2)
   if(cder.gt.ha(2)) then
      icount(2) = ip                !node
      ha(2)     = cder              !maximum value
   endif
   cder          = dabs(adel3)
   if(cder.gt.ha(3)) then
      icount(3) = ip                !node
      ha(3)     = cder              !maximum value
   endif
   cder          = dabs(adel4)
   if(cder.gt.ha(4)) then
      icount(4) = ip                !node
      ha(4)     = cder              !maximum value
   endif
enddo !ip
print*, (ha(ia),ia = 1,4)        !printing on screen max value
print*, (icount(ia),ia = 1,4) !printing on screen the node
```

Note that the array

```
unkn1(4,mxpoi)
```

stores the variables at the previous time step n. The array

```
unkno(4,mxpoi)
```

stores the variable values at the current time step of $n + 1$. The maximum difference between these two time levels forms the criterion for the steady state condition.

10.4 Postprocessing

The postprocessing unit is mainly employed after a solution to a problem has been achieved. An interface to another graphical package may be linked to the main program unit so that the output from the main unit can be directly loaded into a postprocessor to visualize the data. For beginners, it is important to assess the accuracy of the calculations by investigating the qualitative distribution of any quantity. The choice of the graphical package is left to the user. The source code available on the web includes interfaces to standard packages.

10.4.1 Interpolation of data

It is often necessary to plot the quantities along a straight line within a domain or at an arbitrary point within a domain. If the nodes are not placed along the line of interest, or no node coincides with the point of interest, the variable required has to be interpolated using the shape functions. Such an interpolation routine may be used either as part of the main program unit or may be employed externally.

Once the data is obtained via interpolation, the plots may be generated using any standard package. Plots of interest can be of a spatial variation and/or a temporal variation of the fluid flow and heat transfer variables.

10.5 Summary

In this chapter, we have provided the readers with a brief introduction to the computer implementation of the finite element method for heat and fluid flow applications. Several advanced issues, such as the edge-based data structure, parallel implementation and multi-grid acceleration procedure have not been discussed in this chapter. However, some appropriate references are provided for those who would like to read about such advanced topics. Further details on the programming and how to use the source codes are available from the authors' web sites.

Bibliography

Kumar KVS, Babu AVR, Seetharamu KN, Sundararajan T and Narayana PAA 1997 A generalised Delaunay triangulation algorithm with adaptive grid size control, *Communications in Numerical Methods in Engineering*, **13**, 941–948.

Lewis RW, Zhang Y and Usmani AS 1995 Aspects of adaptive mesh generation based on domain decomposition and Delaunay triangulation, *Finite Elements in Analysis and Design*, **20**, 47–70.

Löhner R 2001 *Applied CFD Techniques*, John Wiley & Sons, New York.

Löhner R and Baum JD 1992 Adaptive h-refinement on 3D unstructured grid for transient problems, *International Journal for Numerical Methods in Fluids*, **14**, 1407–1419.

Nithiarasu P 2000 Computer implementation of the CBS algorithm, Chapter 9, *The Finite Element Method, Vol. 3, Fluid Dynamics*, O.C. Zienkiewicz and R.L. Taylor (eds), Fifth Edition, Butterworth and Heinemann, Oxford, 274–290.

Peraire J and Morgan K 1997 Unstructured mesh generation including directional refinement for aerodynamic flow simulation, *Finite Elements in Analysis and Design*, **25**, 343–356.

Peraire J, Vahdati M, Morgan K and Zienkiewicz OC 1987 Adaptive remeshing for compressible flow computations, *Journal of Computational Physics*, **72**, 449–466.

Smith I and Griffiths DV 1998 *Programming the Finite Element Method*, Third Edition, Wiley, Chichester.

Thompson JF, Soni BK and Weatherill NP 1999 *Handbook of Grid Generation*, CRC Press, Boca Raton.

Weatherill NP, Eiseman PR, Hause J and Thompson JF 1994 *Numerical Grid Generation in Computational Fluid Dynamics and Related Fields*, Pinridge Press, Swansea.

Wille DR 1995 *Advanced Scientific Fortran*, Wiley, Chichester.

Appendix A

Green's Lemma

Green's lemma states that for differentiable functions α_1 and α_2, we can write (for a two-dimensional problem)

$$\int_\Omega \alpha_1 \frac{\partial \alpha_2}{\partial x_1} \, d\Omega = -\int_\Omega \frac{\partial \alpha_1}{\partial x_1} \alpha_2 \, d\Omega + \int_\Gamma \alpha_1 \alpha_2 n_1 \, d\Gamma \qquad (A.1)$$

Similarly

$$\int_\Omega \alpha_1 \frac{\partial \alpha_2}{\partial x_2} \, d\Omega = -\int_\Omega \frac{\partial \alpha_1}{\partial x_2} \alpha_2 \, d\Omega + \int_\Gamma \alpha_1 \alpha_2 n_2 \, d\Gamma \qquad (A.2)$$

where n_1 and n_2 are the components of the outward normals on the enclosed curve Γ (see Figure A.1) and Ω is the two-dimensional domain. Let us consider the integration of a second-order term weighted by the shape function. The following form is common in finite element formulations:

$$\int_\Omega N_k \frac{\partial^2 T}{\partial x_1^2} \, d\Omega \qquad (A.3)$$

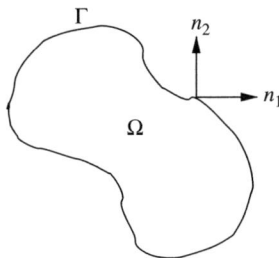

Figure A.1 Domain, boundary and outward normals

Fundamentals of the Finite Element Method for Heat and Fluid Flow   R. W. Lewis, P. Nithiarasu and K. N. Seetharamu
© 2004 John Wiley & Sons, Ltd   ISBNs: 0-470-84788-3 (HB); 0-470-84789-1 (PB)

Applying Green's lemma, the above equation becomes

$$-\int_{\Omega} \frac{\partial N_k}{\partial x_1} \frac{\partial T}{\partial x_1} \, d\Omega + \int_{\Gamma} N_k \frac{\partial T}{\partial x_1} n_1 \, d\Gamma \tag{A.4}$$

In a similar fashion, the x_2 direction can also be simplified using Green's lemma.

Appendix B

Integration Formulae

B.1 Linear Triangles

Let i, j and k be the nodes of a triangular element. Integrating over the triangular area gives

$$A = \int dx_1\, dx_2 = \frac{1}{2} \begin{vmatrix} 1 & x_{1i} & x_{2i} \\ 1 & x_{1j} & x_{2j} \\ 1 & x_{1k} & x_{2k} \end{vmatrix} \tag{B.1}$$

where A is the area of the triangle. For a linear triangular element (shape functions are same as local coordinates), the integration of the shape functions can be written as

$$\int_\Omega N_i^a N_j^b N_k^c\, d\Omega = \frac{a!\,b!\,c!\,2A}{(a+b+c+2)!} \tag{B.2}$$

On the boundaries

$$\int_\Gamma N_i^a N_j^b\, d\Gamma = \frac{a!\,b!\,l}{(a+b+1)!} \tag{B.3}$$

Note that $i-j$ is assumed to be the boundary side. The above equation is identical to the integration formula of a one-dimensional linear element. In the above equation, l is the length of a boundary side.

B.2 Linear Tetrahedron

Let i, j, k and m be the nodes of a linear tetrahedron element. Integrating over the volume gives

Fundamentals of the Finite Element Method for Heat and Fluid Flow   R. W. Lewis, P. Nithiarasu and K. N. Seetharamu
© 2004 John Wiley & Sons, Ltd   ISBNs: 0-470-84788-3 (HB); 0-470-84789-1 (PB)

$$V = \int dx_1\, dx_2\, dx_3 = \frac{1}{6} \begin{vmatrix} 1 & x_{1i} & x_{2i} & x_{3i} \\ 1 & x_{1j} & x_{2j} & x_{3j} \\ 1 & x_{1k} & x_{2k} & x_{3k} \\ 1 & x_{1m} & x_{2m} & x_{3m} \end{vmatrix} \tag{B.4}$$

where V is the volume of a tetrahedron. For linear shape functions, the integration formula can be written as

$$\int_{\Omega} N_i^a N_j^b N_k^c N_m^d \, d\Omega = \frac{a!\,b!\,c!\,d!\,6V}{(a+b+c+3)!} \tag{B.5}$$

On the boundaries

$$\int_{\Gamma} N_i^a N_j^b N_k^c \, d\Gamma = \frac{a!\,b!\,c!\,2A}{(a+b+c+2)!} \tag{B.6}$$

Note that the above formula is identical to the integration formula of triangular elements within the domain. In the above equation, A is the area of a triangular face.

Appendix C

Finite Element Assembly Procedure

Consider the two-dimensional linear triangular elements shown in Figure C.1. Let us assume the following elemental LHS matrix for the variable ϕ

For element 1,

$$\mathbf{K_1} = \begin{bmatrix} a_{11} & a_{12} & a_{13} \\ a_{21} & a_{22} & a_{23} \\ a_{31} & a_{32} & a_{33} \end{bmatrix} \tag{C.1}$$

and for element 2,

$$\mathbf{K_2} = \begin{bmatrix} b_{22} & b_{23} & b_{24} \\ b_{32} & b_{33} & b_{34} \\ b_{42} & b_{43} & b_{44} \end{bmatrix} \tag{C.2}$$

The elemental RHS vectors are the following:
For element 1,

$$\mathbf{f_1} = \begin{Bmatrix} c_1 \\ c_2 \\ c_3 \end{Bmatrix} \tag{C.3}$$

and for element 2,

$$\mathbf{f_2} = \begin{Bmatrix} d_2 \\ d_3 \\ d_4 \end{Bmatrix} \tag{C.4}$$

Fundamentals of the Finite Element Method for Heat and Fluid Flow   R. W. Lewis, P. Nithiarasu and K. N. Seetharamu
© 2004 John Wiley & Sons, Ltd   ISBNs: 0-470-84788-3 (HB); 0-470-84789-1 (PB)

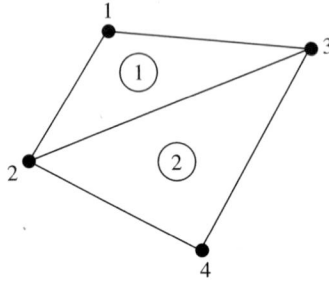

Figure C.1   A domain with two linear triangular elements

Assembling the above elemental contributions gives the following global equation:

$$[\mathbf{K}]\{\boldsymbol{\phi}\} = \{\mathbf{f}\} \tag{C.5}$$

where $[\mathbf{K}]$ and $\{\mathbf{f}\}$ are the global LHS matrix and RHS vector respectively and $\{\boldsymbol{\phi}\}$ is the unknown vector for the system shown in Figure C.1 as follows:

$$\{\boldsymbol{\phi}\} = \begin{Bmatrix} \phi_1 \\ \phi_2 \\ \phi_3 \\ \phi_4 \end{Bmatrix} \tag{C.6}$$

The global LHS matrix is assembled as follows. The entries with the same subscripts in Equations C.1 and C.2 are added together to form an assembled global LHS matrix, that is,

$$[\mathbf{K}] = \begin{bmatrix} a_{11} & a_{12} & a_{13} & 0 \\ a_{21} & a_{22} + b_{22} & a_{23} + b_{23} & b_{24} \\ a_{31} & a_{32} + b_{32} & a_{33} + b_{33} & b_{34} \\ 0 & b_{42} & b_{43} & b_{44} \end{bmatrix} \tag{C.7}$$

In a similar fashion, the RHS vector is assembled as

$$\{\mathbf{f}\} = \begin{Bmatrix} c_1 \\ c_2 + d_2 \\ c_3 + d_3 \\ d_4 \end{Bmatrix} \tag{C.8}$$

The global system of equations is written as follows:

$$\begin{bmatrix} a_{11} & a_{12} & a_{13} & 0 \\ a_{21} & a_{22} + b_{22} & a_{23} + b_{23} & b_{24} \\ a_{31} & a_{32} + b_{32} & a_{33} + b_{33} & b_{34} \\ 0 & b_{42} & b_{43} & b_{44} \end{bmatrix} \begin{Bmatrix} \phi_1 \\ \phi_2 \\ \phi_3 \\ \phi_4 \end{Bmatrix} = \begin{Bmatrix} c_1 \\ c_2 + d_2 \\ c_3 + d_3 \\ d_4 \end{Bmatrix} \tag{C.9}$$

As seen, there are four simultaneous equations, each of them associated with a node. The first equation, which is associated with node 1, is

$$a_{11}\phi_1 + a_{12}\phi_2 + a_{13}\phi_3 = c_1 \tag{C.10}$$

In the above equation, the contributions are from node 1 and the nodes connected to node 1. As seen, node 1 receives contributions from 2 and 3. Similarly, the second nodal equation receives contributions from all other nodes, which is obvious from Equation C.9.

Appendix D

Simplified Form of the Navier–Stokes Equations

To derive the Navier–Stokes equations in their non-conservative form, we start with the conservative form.

Conservation of mass:

$$\frac{\partial \rho}{\partial t} + \frac{\partial (\rho u_i)}{\partial x_i} = \frac{\partial \rho}{\partial t} + \rho \frac{\partial u_i}{\partial x_i} + u_i \frac{\partial \rho}{\partial x_i} = 0 \tag{D.1}$$

Conservation of momentum:

$$\frac{\partial (\rho u_i)}{\partial t} + \frac{\partial (u_j \rho u_i)}{\partial x_j} - \frac{\partial \tau_{ij}}{\partial x_j} + \frac{\partial p}{\partial x_i} = 0 \tag{D.2}$$

Conservation of energy:

$$\frac{\partial (\rho E)}{\partial t} + \frac{\partial (u_j \rho E)}{\partial x_j} - \frac{\partial}{\partial x_i} \left(k \frac{\partial T}{\partial x_i} \right) + \frac{\partial (u_j p)}{\partial x_j} - \frac{\partial (\tau_{ij} u_j)}{\partial x_j} = 0 \tag{D.3}$$

Rewriting the momentum equation with terms differentiated as

$$\rho \frac{\partial u_i}{\partial t} + u_i \left(\frac{\partial \rho}{\partial t} + \rho \frac{\partial u_j}{\partial x_j} + u_j \frac{\partial \rho}{\partial x_j} \right) + \rho u_j \frac{\partial u_i}{\partial x_j} - \frac{\partial \tau_{ij}}{\partial x_j} + \frac{\partial p}{\partial x_i} = 0 \tag{D.4}$$

and substituting the equation of mass conservation (Equation D.1) into the above equation gives the reduced momentum equation, that is,

$$\frac{\partial u_i}{\partial t} + u_j \frac{\partial u_i}{\partial x_j} - \frac{1}{\rho} \frac{\partial \tau_{ij}}{\partial x_j} + \frac{1}{\rho} \frac{\partial p}{\partial x_i} = 0 \tag{D.5}$$

The above momentum equation can be further simplified if the fluid is incompressible. For an incompressible fluid, the conservation of mass equation becomes

$$\frac{\partial u_i}{\partial x_i} = 0 \tag{D.6}$$

Fundamentals of the Finite Element Method for Heat and Fluid Flow   R. W. Lewis, P. Nithiarasu and K. N. Seetharamu
© 2004 John Wiley & Sons, Ltd   ISBNs: 0-470-84788-3 (HB); 0-470-84789-1 (PB)

The deviatoric stresses in Equation D.5 are written as

$$\tau_{ij} = \mu \left(\frac{\partial u_i}{\partial x_j} + \frac{\partial u_j}{\partial x_i} - \frac{2}{3} \frac{\partial u_k}{\partial x_k} \delta_{ij} \right) \tag{D.7}$$

Note that the last term in the above equation is zero from the continuity equation for incompressible flows. The deviatoric stresses become

$$\tau_{ij} = \mu \left(\frac{\partial u_i}{\partial x_j} + \frac{\partial u_j}{\partial x_i} \right) \tag{D.8}$$

Substituting the above equation into Equation D.5, we have (assuming μ is a constant)

$$\frac{\partial u_i}{\partial t} + u_j \frac{\partial u_i}{\partial x_j} - \frac{\mu}{\rho} \frac{\partial}{\partial x_j} \left(\frac{\partial u_i}{\partial x_j} + \frac{\partial u_j}{\partial x_i} \right) + \frac{1}{\rho} \frac{\partial p}{\partial x_i} = 0 \tag{D.9}$$

If we substitute $i = 1$ and $j = 1, 2$, we get the x_1 component of the momentum equation as (in two dimensions)

$$\frac{\partial u_1}{\partial t} + u_1 \frac{\partial u_1}{\partial x_1} + u_2 \frac{\partial u_1}{\partial x_2} = -\frac{1}{\rho} \frac{\partial p}{\partial x_1} + 2\nu \frac{\partial^2 u_1}{\partial x_1^2} + \nu \frac{\partial^2 u_1}{\partial x_2^2} + \nu \frac{\partial}{\partial x_2} \left(\frac{\partial u_2}{\partial x_1} \right) \tag{D.10}$$

Rewriting the above equation as

$$\frac{\partial u_1}{\partial t} + u_1 \frac{\partial u_1}{\partial x_1} + u_2 \frac{\partial u_1}{\partial x_2} = -\frac{1}{\rho} \frac{\partial p}{\partial x_1} + \nu \frac{\partial^2 u_1}{\partial x_1^2} + \nu \frac{\partial^2 u_1}{\partial x_2^2} + \nu \frac{\partial}{\partial x_1} \left(\frac{\partial u_1}{\partial x_1} + \frac{\partial u_2}{\partial x_2} \right) \tag{D.11}$$

Applying the conservation of mass, we get

$$\frac{\partial u_1}{\partial t} + u_1 \frac{\partial u_1}{\partial x_1} + u_2 \frac{\partial u_1}{\partial x_2} = -\frac{1}{\rho} \frac{\partial p}{\partial x_1} + \nu \frac{\partial^2 u_1}{\partial x_1^2} + \nu \frac{\partial^2 u_1}{\partial x_2^2} \tag{D.12}$$

In a similar fashion, the other components of the momentum and energy equations can be simplified.

Index

Note: Figures and Tables are indicated by *italic page numbers*

advancing front method for generation
of unstructured meshes 301
air, dry, thermal conductivity *4*
aircraft structures, heat transfer in 126
aluminium alloy(s), thermal
conductivity *4*
analytical solution(s)
compared with FEM
plane homogeneous wall *112*
two-dimensional square plate
131–2
mixed convection heat transfer 228,
230
procedure 112n(1)
in transient heat conduction
analysis 159
anisotropic materials, heat conduction
equation(s) 11–12
annular enclosure, natural convection in
fluid-saturated porous media
261–2
area coordinates, for triangular element
52–4
artificial compressibility-based CBS
scheme 205, 213
assembly of finite element equations 41
for one-dimensional problems 86,
107
procedure 323–5

axisymmetric problems
convection heat transfer in 234–5
Galerkin method 145–6
example calculations 146–7
steady-state heat conduction in
126–7, 142–7
exercises on 148

Babuska–Brezzi condition 202
backward Euler scheme 161
backward-facing step
forced convection heat transfer
after 281–3
isothermal steady-state flow over
270, 272–4
non-isothermal flow over 281–3
basis functions 41
see also shape functions
benchmark problems
natural convection in square cavity
224–6
with porous media 256–62
non-isothermal flow problem
280–3
steady-state isothermal flow
backward-facing step 270, 272–4
in double-driven cavity 274–6,
277, 278
in lid-driven cavity 266–70, *271*

Fundamentals of the Finite Element Method for Heat and Fluid Flow   R. W. Lewis, P. Nithiarasu and K. N. Seetharamu
© 2004 John Wiley & Sons, Ltd   ISBNs: 0-470-84788-3 (HB); 0-470-84789-1 (PB)

benchmark problems (*continued*)
  transient isothermal flow past
    cylinder 276–80
Berenati–Brosilow correlation 255
Bernard convection, transient solution
    for convection heat transfer
    212
Biot number 152
boundary conditions
  application of
    in one-dimensional problems
      19–20
    in two-dimensional problems 136
  in CBS scheme 211
    computer code for 315
    conduction equation 13–14
    convection heat transfer 211, *212*
Boussinesq approximation 185, 247, 257
Boussinesq hypothesis 232
brick *see* hexahedron element
Brinkman extension to Darcy's law 242
  forced convection in porous media
    257
buoyancy-driven convection 2, 174, 185,
    223–4
  examples 224
  heat transfer 224–6
    non-dimensional form of
      governing equations 185–7
    in two-dimensional square
      enclosure 224–6
    with porous media 258–62

C^0 elements 47
C^1 elements 47
CBS scheme *see* characteristic based
    split scheme
CBSflow code
  interface(s) to graphical package(s)
    317
  main unit 309–16
    boundary conditions 315
    element loop and assembly
      313–14

monitoring of steady state 316
solution updating 314
time-step calculation 310–13
overall procedure 300
postprocessing unit 317
preprocessing unit 300–9
  boundary normal calculation
    305–6
  element size calculation 303–4
  heat conduction calculations
    307–9
  linear triangular element data
    302
  mass lumping 307
  mass matrix calculation 306–7
  mesh generation subsection
    300–2
  pressure calculations 307–9
  shape functions and derivatives,
    calculations 304–5
central difference scheme 162
central heating system, pipe network,
    exercise on 31, *33*
CG scheme *see* characteristic Galerkin
    scheme
characteristic based split (CBS) scheme
    201–12
  advantages over CG procedure
    201–2
  artificial compressibility form 205,
    213, 230
  axisymmetric convection heat
    transfer problems 235
  boundary conditions 211, *212*
  implementation steps
    for convection in porous media
      250
    intermediate velocity calculation
      202–3, 205–6, 250
    pressure calculation 203–5, 206,
      250
    temperature calculation 205, 206
    velocity/momentum correction
      205, 206, 250

initial conditions 212
isothermal flow problems 218–20,
    265–80
laminar non-isothermal flow
    problems, mixed convection
    226–30
non-isothermal flow problems
    220–30, 280–3
  buoyancy-driven/natural
    convection 223–6
  forced convection 220–3, 281–3
porous medium flow equations
    solved using 247–53
quasi-implicit form 253
semi-implicit form 252–3, 266
spatial discretization 206–10
  for convection in porous media
    249–52
steady-state solution method 212
temporal discretization, for
    convection in porous media
    247–9
time-step calculation 210–11
transient solution method 212
characteristic Galerkin (CG) scheme
    188–95
  extension to multi-dimensions
    195–200
combined conduction–convection,
    steady-state problem, discrete
    system 25–7
composite slab
  heat flow in 19–21
    exercise(s) 31, 32, 34
composite wall
  steady-state heat conduction in
    103–4
  exercises on 123, 124
computational fluid dynamics (CFD) 173
  books on 173
  examples of applications 173
computer code implementation 299–319
  see also CBSflow code
conduction–convection systems 120–3

conduction heat transfer 2
conduction heat transfer equation(s)
    11–12
  boundary conditions 13–14
  for composite slab 20–1
  initial conditions 13
conduction heat transfer problems
  examples 5–10
  methodology 14–15
    analytical solutions 14
    numerical methods 14–15
conduction resistance, ratio to
    convection resistance 152
conservation of energy equation see
    energy-conservation equation
conservation of mass equation see
    continuity equation;
    mass-conservation equation
conservation of momentum equation see
    momentum-conservation
    equation
continuity equation 177–8, 183, 245
  non-dimensional form
    convection in porous media 245
    forced convection 184
    natural convection 186, 246
continuous/continuum system 18
convection–diffusion equation(s)
    187–8
  characteristic Galerkin (CG)
    approach 188–95
    extension to multi-dimensions
      195–200
  finite element solutions 188–200
  one-dimensional problems 189–95
  stability conditions 200–1
  time-step restrictions 200
  two-dimensional problems
    195–200
convection heat transfer 2–3, 173–239
  axisymmetric problems 234–5
  boundary condition 13
  characteristic-based split (CBS)
    scheme 201–12

convection heat transfer (*continued*)
    coefficient 3
    exercises on 236
    Navier–Stokes equations 175–83
    non-dimensional form of governing
        equations 183–7, 218
    in porous media 240–64
    stability conditions 200–1
    see also buoyancy-driven
        convection; forced convection;
        mixed convection; natural
        convection
coordinate transformation 63
    Jacobian(s) of 64, 66, 68
counterflow heat exchanger, exercise 32,
    33
Crank–Nicolson method 162
    application 157
cross-flow heat exchanger, exercise on
    294–5
crystal growth, phase changes during
    164
cubic triangular element, shape
        functions for 56–7
cylinders
    isothermal flow past, with vortex
        shedding 276–80
    radial heat flow in 115–20
        example calculations 117,
        118–20
    with heat source 117–20
cylindrical coordinate system
    axisymmetric convection heat
        transfer 2305
    heat conduction equation 12, 115,
        144

Darcy's law 240–1
    Brinkman's extension 242, *257*
    Ergun's correlation 242, 244
    Forchheimer's extension 241,
        257
Darcy number 246

Darcy–Rayleigh number 247
Darcy–Weisbach formula 24
Delaunay mesh generator 288, 301
direct current circuit, exercise 35
Direct Numerical Simulation (DNS)
        turbulence modelling approach
        230–1
Dirichlet (boundary) conditions 13, 211,
        220
discrete systems 18–37
    meaning of term 18
    steady-state problems 19–29
        fluid flow network 22–5
        heat exchangers 27–9
        heat flow in composite slab
            19–21
        heat sinks (combined
            conduction–convection) 25–7
    steps in analysis 19
    transient/propagation heat transfer
        problem 29–31
double-driven cavity, isothermal flow
        past 274–6, *277*, *278*
double-glazed window, exercise on
        33–4
drag calculation 215–16
drag coefficient 215
    values, for forced convection flow
        past a sphere *223*
drag force 215
    Forchheimer relationship 241
    on porous medium particle 241
drawing of wires, fibres, etc 8–10,
        14

edges, in finite element method *40*
effective heat capacity method
    phase change problems 166
        example calculations 166–7
electronic packages
    thermal conduction in 283–6
    see also plastic ball grid array
        packages

electroslag melting, phase changes
during 164
elements (in finite element method) *40*,
41–74
meaning of term *40*, 41
see also one-dimensional elements;
three-dimensional elements;
two-dimensional elements
emissivity 4
energy-conservation equation
moving bodies/systems 9
in Navier–Stokes equations 181–3,
184
non-dimensional form
convection in porous media 246
forced convection 184
natural convection 186, 247
phase change problems 164–5
enthalpy method, phase change
problems 165–7
Ergun's correlation for Darcy's law 242,
244
Euler–Lagrange equation 78
explicit time-stepping scheme *157*, 161
extrusion of plastics, metals, etc 8–10,
14

fin
array, in heat sink 25
one-dimensional 75–6
rectangular
example calculations 93–8
exercise on 100
tapered 120–2
example calculations 122–3
types *120*
finite difference method (FDM) 38–9
compared with FEM, for
two-dimensional plane
problem 132
time discretization in transient heat
conduction analysis 156–60
finite element discretization 39–40
composite wall 106–7

homogeneous wall 105–6, *110*,
114
with convection *111*
one-dimensional problems 85,
105–7
tapered fin *122*
two-dimensional plane problems
130, *135*
finite element method (FEM) 38–102
elements 41–74
isoparametric elements 62–70
one-dimensional linear element
42–5
one-dimensional quadratic
element *42*, 45–8
three-dimensional elements
70–4
two-dimensional linear triangular
element 48–52
two-dimensional quadratic
triangular element 54–7
two-dimensional quadrilateral
elements 57–62
example calculations, for
rectangular fin 93–8
steps in solution of continuum
problem 39–41
assembly of element equations
41, 86, 323–5
calculation of secondary
quantities 41
discretization of continuum
39–40, 85
formulation of element equations
41, 86
selection of interpolation or
shape functions 40, 41–74
solving system of equations 41
time discretization in transient heat
conduction analysis 160–1
finite volume method 39
first law of thermodynamics, in heat
transfer terms 5

fluid dynamics 173
  computer-based analysis 173
  Navier–Stokes equations 175–83
  time-step restrictions 200–1
fluid flow, benchmark problems 265–80
fluid flow network
  discrete system, steady-state
    problem 22–5
  exercise 31, *33*
fluid resistance 22
fluid-motion-assisted heat transport,
    types 2–3, 174
forced convection 2–3, 174
  heat transfer 220–3
    backward-facing step 281–3
    from heat sources 286–94
    non-dimensional form of
      governing equations 184–5
    three-dimensional flow over
      sphere 221–3
    two-dimensional channel
      problem 220–1
  in porous media 255–6
Forchheimer extension to Darcy's law
    241
  forced convection in porous media
    257
forcing vector(s)
  convection heat transfer 194, 209
    in porous media 251–2
  elemental 41
  for plane composite wall 106
  for plane homogeneous wall, with
    internal heat source 110, 113
  for rectangular fin 95
  for tapered fin 122
  transient heat transfer 158
  for two-dimensional square plate
    138–9
forward Euler scheme 161
Fourier analysis 161
Fourier's law of heat conduction 3
  heat flux calculated by 10, 182
  spatial variation of temperature 7

free convection 2, 174
  see also natural convection

Galerkin method 83, 85–7, 91–2
  axisymmetric problems 145–6
    example calculations 146–7
  compared with exact solution *84,
    87*
  transient heat conduction analysis
    153–4, 161
generalized porous medium flow
    approach 243–7
  see also porous medium flow
    equations
Goodman's method 76–7
gradient matrix
  after spatial discretization of CBS
    steps 208
  one-dimensional elements 44, 47,
    94
  two-dimensional elements 50, 60,
    128, 137
Grashof number 187, 246
Green's lemma 319–20
  applications 91, 191, 208
grid of nodal points 14–15

heat balance integral method,
    Goodman's method 76–7
heat conduction analysis 10–12
  differential control volume for
    10
heat conduction equation(s) 11–12
  boundary conditions 13–14
  for composite slab 20–1
  formulation of finite element
    equations for 87–92
    by Galerkin method 91–2
    by variational approach 88–91
  initial conditions 13
heat convection 2–3, 173
  types 2–3, 174
  see also convection heat transfer
heat exchangers
  calculation of effectiveness 27–9

exercises on 32, *33*, 35–6, 100,
    294–5
heat sinks
    exercise 35, *36*
    heat transfer in 25–7
heat transfer
    benchmark problems 280–3
    coefficient, typical values *4*
    importance 1–2
    laws 3–5
    modes 2–3
    problems 5–10, 283–94
        incandescent lamp 7–8
        moving systems 6–10
        plate exposed to solar heat flux
        5–7
heat treatment chamber, heat transfer
        processes associated 29–31
Hermite polynomials 47
hexahedron element *70*, 73–4
    linear 73
    quadratic (20-node) 73–4
human body, exercise on 34

implicit pressure calculations
    in CBS scheme 203–5, 206,
    250
        computer code for 307–9
implicit time-stepping scheme(s) *157*,
    161, 162
incandescent lamp, energy balance in
    7–8
insulating material, heat transfer
        through, exercise 31, *32*
integrated circuit (IC) carriers, thermal
        conduction in 283–6
integration formulae 321–2
    linear tetrahedron 321–2
    linear triangle 321
internal heat source, plane wall with,
        one-dimensional steady-state
        heat conduction 108–15
interpolation functions 41
    requirements for 92–3
    see also shape functions

inverse heat conduction problems
    168–70
    one-dimensional problem 168–70
inverse modelling 168
isoparametric elements 62–70
isothermal flow
    problems 218–20, 265–80
        steady-state flow 265–76
        transient flow 276–80
isotherm(s)
    linear triangular element 51–2
    quadrilateral elements 61–2
isotropic materials, heat conduction
        equation(s) 12

Jacobian matrix 64

kinematic viscosity 184
Kroneker delta 180

Lagrangian interpolation 47
laminar flow
    in pipe network 22–4
    Reynolds number criterion 174
laminar isothermal flow 218–20
    boundary conditions 218–19
    geometry of example 218
    initial conditions 219
    solution 219–20
laminar non-isothermal flow 220–30
    buoyancy-driven convection heat
        transfer 223–6
    forced convection heat transfer
        220–3
    mixed convection heat transfer
        227–30
    natural/free convection heat transfer
        223–6
Large Eddy Simulation (LES) turbulence
        modelling approach 230, 231
lid-driven cavity, isothermal flow past
    266–70
linear element 42–5, *42*
    in convection–diffusion problems
    190

linear element (*continued*)
    example calculations 45
    exercises on 98–9
    shape functions 43–4, 155
    in solution for plane wall with
        internal heat source 108–12
    in transient heat conduction
        analysis 155
linear tetrahedron element 70–2
    application in three-dimensional
        problems 141
    integration formulae for 321–2
linear triangular element 48–52
    in computer code implementation
        302, *303*
    in convection heat transfer *201*
    example calculations 50–2
    exercise on 99
    integration formulae for 321
    shape functions for 50, 304
    in transient heat conduction
        analysis 159
    in two-dimensional heat conduction
        problems 127–36
load vector, elemental 41
local coordinates
    linear elements 53
    for triangular element 52–4
lumped heat capacity method 150–2

macro-segregation 164
marginally stable scheme 162
mass conservation equation 175–8
    in cylindrical coordinates 234
    turbulent flow 232
mass lumping procedure (in CBS
        scheme) 210, 253
    computer code for 307
mass matrix (in CBS scheme) 210
    in artificial compressibility scheme
        213
    computer code for 306–7
melting *see* phase change problems
mesh convergence 217–18

mesh of nodal points 14–15
    computer code for generation of
        300–2
    see also unstructured meshes
metal casting
    heat transfer processes associated,
        exercise on 32–3, *34*
    phase changes during 164
metal heat treatment, heat transfer
        processes associated 29–31
metals, thermal conductivity listed *4*
mixed convection 3, 174
    analytical solution 228, 230
    flow reversal in *227, 229*
    heat transfer 227–30
    non-dimensional form of governing
        equations 187
    in vertical channel 227–30
momentum-conservation equation(s)
        178–81, 183
    non-dimensional form
        convection in porous media 246
        forced convection 184
        natural convection 186, 246
    turbulent flow 232
Moody friction factor 25
moving bodies/systems
    energy balance 8–10
    heat conduction equation 14
multi-dimensional steady-state heat
        conduction 126–49
multi-dimensional transient heat
        conduction 162–4
mushy zone (during solidification of
        alloy) 164

natural convection 2, 174, 185, 223–4
    examples 224
    heat transfer 224–6
        non-dimensional form of
            governing equations 185–7
    in porous media 256–62
        constant-porosity medium
            258–62

in two-dimensional square
enclosure 224–6
with porous media 258–62
Navier–Stokes equations 175–83
conservation of energy equation
181–3
conservation of mass equation
175–7
conservation of momentum
equation 177–81
simplified form 326–7
Neumann (boundary) conditions 13, 211
Newton's law of cooling 3, 214
nodal points 14
nodes, meaning of term in finite element
method 39, *40*
non-isothermal flow 220–30
forced convection heat transfer
220–3
mixed convection heat transfer
227–30
in porous media 254–62
numerical solution
transient heat conduction problem
152–4
boundary conditions 153
Galerkin method 153–4
governing equations 152–3
initial condition 153
Nusselt number 214–15
calculation of average 215
for forced convection flow
past a backward-facing step *283*
past a sphere *223*
for spherical heat sources on wall
289–90, 291–3, *293*, *294*
for natural convection in square
enclosure *225*
with porous media *259*
relation for forced convection in
porous media 257

one-dimensional convection–diffusion
equations 188–95

one-dimensional finite elements
linear element 42–5, *42*
in convection–diffusion
problems 190
example calculations 45
exercises on 98–9
shape functions 43–4, 155
in solution for plane wall with
internal heat source 108–12
in transient heat conduction
analysis 155
quadratic element *42*, 45–8
exercises on 98, 99
shape functions 47–8
one-dimensional heat conduction,
inverse problem 168–70
one-dimensional steady-state heat
conduction 102–25
examples 102
plane walls 102–15
composite wall 103–4
exercises on 123–4
finite element discretization
105–7
with heat source, solution by
linear elements 108–12
with heat source, solution by
modified quadratic equations
114–15
with heat source, solution by
quadratic elements 112–14
homogeneous wall 102–3
with varying cross-sectional area
107–8
radial heat flow in cylinders
115–20
exercises on 125
one-dimensional transient heat
conduction 154–60

packed beds, flow through 255
Peclet number 185, 195
pentahedron element, linear *70*, 74
phase change problems 164–7
enthalpy formulation 165–7

phase change problems (*continued*)
  example calculations 166–7
  exercise on 172
  governing equations 164–5
pipe network
  example fluid flow calculations 24
  exercise(s) 31, *33*, 34–5
  laminar flow in 22–4
  turbulent flow in 24–5
plastic ball grid array (PBGA) package
      systems, thermal analysis of
      284–6
plastics, thermal conductivity *4*
polynomial type functions 41–2
polynomials, geometric isotropy
      93
porosity, definition 244
porous media
  convection in 240–64
    forced convection 255–6
    natural convection 256–62
  fluid flow in 240–3
    generalized approach 243–7
porous medium flow equations 243–7
  CBS scheme used to solve 247–53
  discretization procedure 247–53
    spatial discretization 249–52
    temporal discretization 247–9
  limiting cases 247
  non-dimensional scaling 245–7
  non-isothermal flow 254
Prandtl mixing length 233
Prandtl number 185, 246
  turbulent 233
printed circuit boards
  cooling of 286–94
  exercise on 36
prism *see* pentahedron element

quadratic element *42*, 45–8
  exercises on 98, 99
  shape functions 47–8
  solution using, for plane wall with
      internal heat source 112–14
quadratic hexahedral element 73–4

quadratic tetrahedral element 72–3
  shape functions 72–3
quadratic triangular element 54–7
  shape functions 55–6
quadrilateral elements 57–62
  example calculations 60–2
  isoparametric mapping from *62*
  shape functions 58–9
quasi-implicit (QI) time-stepping
      scheme(s) 253

radiation heat transfer 3
  in transient heat transfer problem
      29, 30–1
Rayleigh number 187, 224, 246
Rayleigh–Ritz method 78–80
rectangular finite element 57–62
  example calculations 60–2
  exercise on 99
  non-dimensional coordinates 59
  shape functions 58–9, 137
  two-dimensional heat conduction
      problems 136–9
Reynolds Averaged Navier–Stokes
      (RANS) turbulence modelling
      approach 230, 231–2
Reynolds number 174, 185, 246
Reynolds stress 232
Reynolds Transport Theorem 175
Richardson number 187
Ritz method 76–7
  compared with exact solution *78*

semi-implicit time-stepping scheme *157*,
      162, 252–3
shape function derivatives 59, 63, 70, 71
  computer code for 304–5
shape function matrix 43
shape functions
  isoparametric elements 63–4, 67–8
    example calculations 66–7, 69
  one-dimensional finite elements
    line element 43–4
    quadratic element 47–8

three-dimensional elements 72–3, 73–4
two-dimensional finite elements
  cubic (10-node) triangular element 56–7
  linear triangular element 50
  quadratic triangular element 55–6
  quadrilateral elements 58–9
  rectangular elements 58–9
shell-and-tube heat exchanger 27–9
Silvester's triple-index numbering scheme 55
simplex element 48
  see also two-dimensional finite elements, linear triangular element
solar applications 5–7
solidification see phase change problems
space vehicle heat shields 126
sphere, forced convection flow past 221–3
spherical coordinate system, heat conduction equation 12
spherical heat sources on wall, forced convection heat transfer 287–94
square enclosure
  natural convection in 224–6
    fluid-saturated constant-porosity medium 258–61
    fluid-saturated variable-porosity medium 256–8
stainless steel, thermal conductivity 4
static condensation procedure 114–15
steady-state flow problems 265–76
steady-state heat conduction
  axisymmetric 142–7
  multi-dimensional 12, 126–49
  one-dimensional 12, 102–25
  three-dimensional 141–2
  two-dimensional 127–41
Stefan–Boltzmann constant 3, 30
Stefan–Boltzmann Law 3–4

stiffness matrix
  elemental 41
    composite wall 105
    rectangular fin 95
    tapered fin 122
    two-dimensional plane problems 129, 131, 134–5
  global 41
    tapered fin 121
    two-dimensional plane problems 137, 138
stream function 216–17
streamlines 216
  natural convection in square enclosure 226

Taylor–Galerkin (TG) scheme 188
Taylor series expansion 156, 169, 175, 178, 182
tetrahedron elements 70–3, 70
  linear 70–2
    applications 141, 222
    integration formulae for 321
  quadratic 72–3
shape functions 71
  volume coordinate system for 72
thermal conductivity
  as tensor 11
  values listed for various materials 4
thermal diffusivity 12, 183
thermal potential difference 104
thermal resistance(s)
  in composite wall 104
  in PBGA electronic package 285
thermodynamics, first law 5
three-dimensional finite elements 70–4
  hexahedral element 73–4
  tetrahedral element 70–3
    applications 141, 222
    integration formulae for 321–2
three-dimensional meshes, generation of 222
three-dimensional steady-state heat conduction problems 141–2
  examples 126

time-step calculation in CBS scheme
     210–11
  computer code for 310–13
time-stepping schemes *157*
  stability 161–2
  see also characteristic based split
     (CBS) scheme
transient convection–diffusion problem
     187–200
transient flow, isothermal flow 276–80
transient heat conduction analysis
     150–72
  exercises on 170–1
  lumped heat capacity method
     150–2
  multi-dimensional problems 162–4
  numerical solution 152–4
  one-dimensional problems 154–61
transient heat transfer problem
     29–31
trial functions 76
triangular elements
  area coordinates for 52–4
  coordinate transformation of 67–8
  isoparametric mapping from *62*
  linear 48–52
     in computer code implementation
        302, *303*
     in convection heat transfer *201*
     example calculations 50–2
     exercise on 99
     integration formulae for 321
     shape functions 50
     in transient heat conduction
        analysis 159
     in two-dimensional heat
        conduction problems 127–36
  quadratic 54–7
     coordinate transformation of
        67–8
     shape functions 55–6
turbulent eddy viscosity 232
turbulent flow
  convection heat transfer 230–4

  result for two-dimensional
     rectangular channel 233–4
  solution procedure 233
  models 230–2
  in pipe network 24–5
  Reynolds number criterion 174
two-dimensional convection–diffusion
     equations 195–200
two-dimensional finite elements
  cubic (10-node) triangular element
     56–7
     shape functions 56–7
  linear triangular element 48–52
     in convection heat transfer
        201
     example calculations 50–2
     exercise on 99
     integration formulae for 321
     shape functions 50
     in transient heat conduction
        analysis 159
     in two-dimensional heat
        conduction problems 127–36
  quadratic triangular element 54–7
     shape functions 55–6
  quadrilateral elements 57–62
     example calculations 60–2
     exercises on 99
     shape functions 58–9
  rectangular element 57–62
     example calculations 60–2
     exercise on 99
     non-dimensional coordinates 59
     shape functions 58–9
two-dimensional plane steady-state heat
     conduction problems 127–39
  examples 126
  exercises on 147–8
  plate with linearly varying
     thickness 139–41
  exercise on 148
  with rectangular elements 136–9
     example calculations 138–9
     exercises on 147

with triangular elements
127–36
example calculations 130–6
exercises on 147

unstructured meshes 127
application(s) in examples 132,
167, 266, 267
computer code for generation of
301–2
upwinding schemes 188

variational method 78–80
compared with exact solution 80,
87
for three-dimensional steady-state
heat conduction 88–91
viscous drag force 216
vortex shedding past cylinder 212,
277–80

water, thermal conductivity 4
water-processing plant, fluid flow in,
exercise on 295–6

weak formulation, as variational
formulation as 80
weighted residuals method(s) 80–4
collocation method 81–2
compared with exact solution 84,
87
compared with exact solution 84,
87
Galerkin method 83, 85–7
compared with exact solution 84,
87
in transient heat conduction
analysis 153–4, 161
least-squares method 83–4
compared with exact solution 84,
87
sub-domain method 82–3
compared with exact solution 84,
87
welding, phase changes during 164
wood, thermal conductivity 4

zone melting, phase changes during
164

Index compiled by Paul Nash

University of Plymouth
Charles Seale-Hayne Library

Customer ID: *****10593

Title: Fundamentals of the finite
element method for heat and fluid
flow /
ID: 9006321666
Due: 12/05/2015 23:59:00 BST

Total items: 1
31 Mar 2015
Checked out: 1
Overdue: 0
Hold requests: 0

Thank you for using the
3M SelfCheck™ System.